A Level
Mathematics
for Edexcel

Core

Peter Hind

OXFORD
UNIVERSITY PRESS

OXFORD
UNIVERSITY PRESS

Great Clarendon Street, Oxford OX2 6DP

Oxford University Press is a department of the University of Oxford.
It furthers the University's objective of excellence in research, scholarship,
and education by publishing worldwide in

Oxford   New York

Auckland   Cape Town   Dar es Salaam   Hong Kong   Karachi
Kuala Lumpur   Madrid   Melbourne   Mexico City   Nairobi
New Delhi   Shanghai   Taipei   Toronto

With offices in

Argentina   Austria   Brazil   Chile   Czech Republic   France   Greece
Guatemala   Hungary   Italy   Japan   Poland   Portugal   Singapore
South Korea   Switzerland   Thailand   Turkey   Ukraine   Vietnam

British Library Cataloguing in Publication Data

Data available

ISBN-13: 9780-19-911779 6

3 5 7 9 10 8 6 4 2

Printed in Great Britain by Ashford Colour Press, Ltd, Gosport.

Paper used in the production of this book is a natural, recyclable product made from
wood grown in sustainable forests. The manufacturing process conforms to the
environmental regulations of the country of origin.

Acknowledgements

The Publisher would like to thank the following for permission to reproduce
photographs:
P18 Ingram; **p32** Janne Ahvo/iStockphoto; **p47** Photodisc; **p50** Scott
Leigh/iStockphoto; **p60** Photodisc; **p110** Mark Strevens/iStockphoto; **p138** Stephen
Sweet/iStockphoto; **p156** Corel; **p174** Photodisc; **p190** Alex Slobodkin/iStockphoto;
p212 Grazyna Niedzieska/iStockphoto; **p260** Ginevre Marlow/iStockphoto; **p286**
Christine Balderas/iStockphoto; p306Photodisc; p317 Vasiliki Varvaki/iStockphoto.
Cover image: jscalev/Fotolia

The publishers would also like to thank David Bones, John Rayneau and Mike Lynn for
their expert help in compiling this book.

About this book

Endorsed by Edexcel, this book is designed to help you achieve your best possible grade in Edexcel GCE Mathematics Core 1 and Core 2 units. The material is separated into the two units, C1 and C2. You can use the tabs at the edge of the pages for quick reference.

Each chapter starts with a list of objectives and a 'Before you start' section to check that you are fully prepared. Chapters are structured into manageable sections, and there are certain features to look out for within each section:

Key points are highlighted in a blue panel.

Key words are highlighted in bold blue type.

Worked examples demonstrate the key skills and techniques you need to develop. These are shown in boxes and include prompts to guide you through the solutions.

> EXAMPLE 2
>
> Complete the square for the expression $x^2 + 8x$
>
> Try $(x + 4)^2$:
> $$(x + 4)^2 = x^2 + 8x + 16$$
> This is close, however you want $x^2 + 8x$
> Subtract 16: $\qquad x^2 + 8x = (x + 4)^2 - 16$

Derivations and additional information are shown in a panel.

Helpful hints are included as blue margin notes and sometimes as blue type within the main text.

Misconceptions are shown in the right margin to help you avoid making common mistakes.

Investigational hints prompt you to explore a concept further.

Each section includes an exercise with progressive questions, starting with basic practice and developing in difficulty. Some exercises also include

'stretch and challenge' questions marked with a stretch symbol

and investigations to apply your knowledge in a variety of situations.

> INVESTIGATION
>
> 6   Which four of these six lines would describe a square?
> $y = x + 1$ $y = -x + 2$ $y = x - 1$
> $y = x - 2$ $y = -x - 2$ $y = -x + 4$
> Is it possible to find the area of the square?

At the end of each chapter there is 'Review' section which includes exam style questions as well as past exam paper questions. There are also two 'Revision' sections per unit which contain questions spanning a range of topics to give you plenty of realistic exam practice.

The final page of each chapter gives a summary of the key points, fully cross-referenced to aid revision. Also, a 'Links' feature provides an engaging insight into how the mathematics you are studying is relevant to real life.

At the end of the book you will find full solutions, a key word glossary, a list of essential formulae and an index.

Contents

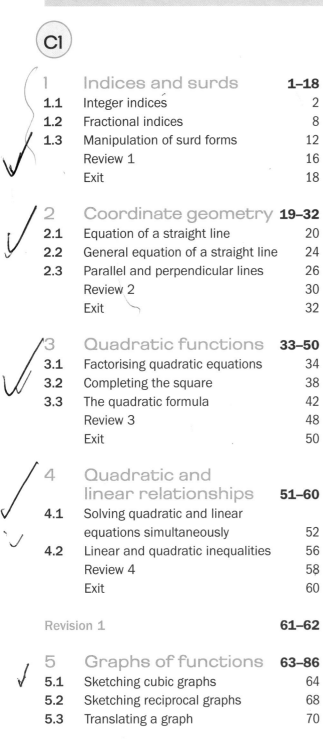

1

Indices and surds

This chapter will show you how to
- understand and use index notation
- recall and apply the laws of indices
- simplify expressions containing surd forms.

Before you start

You should know how to:

1 Recognise perfect squares and square roots
e.g. $1^2 = 1 \times 1 = 1$ and $2^2 = 2 \times 2 = 4$
and cubes and cube roots
e.g. $1^3 = 1$, $2^3 = 8$ and $3^3 = 27$
and evaluate 2^n.
e.g. $2^6 = 2 \times 2 \times 2 \times 2 \times 2 \times 2 = 64$

2 Perform operations in the correct order.
e.g. $5 + 3 \times 2 - 4 \div 2$
divide: $= 5 + 3 \times 2 - 2$
multiply: $= 5 + 6 - 2$
add: $= 11 - 2$
subtract: $= 9$

3 Apply the difference of two squares.
DOTS:
$a^2 - b^2 = (a + b)(a - b)$
e.g. Evaluate $17^2 - 3^2$
$(17)^2 - (3)^2 = (17 + 3)(17 - 3)$
$\qquad\qquad = 20 \times 14$
$\qquad\qquad = 280$

Check in:

1 Evaluate the following.
a The square of each integer from 1 to 20
b **i** 3^3 **ii** 4^3 **iii** 5^3
c The cube root of
  i 125 **ii** 216
d 2^n for each integer from $n = 1$ to $n = 10$

2 Perform these operations correctly.
a $6 \div 2 + 3 \times 2$ BIDMAS:
b $8 + 4 \times 5 - 1$ Brackets
c $3 + 5 \div 2 - 2$ Indices
d $1 \times 6 \div 3 + 3$ Division
e $12 \div 4 + 2$ Multiplication
f $(2 + 8) \times 2 \div 5$ Addition
                       Subtraction

3 Use the difference of two squares to evaluate these expressions.
a $19^2 - 9^2$
b $23^2 - 3^2$
c $18^2 - 12^2$
d $27^2 - 13^2$

In the quantity 2^3, the base is 2 and the index is 3.

2^3 is evaluated as $2^3 = 2 \times 2 \times 2 = 8$

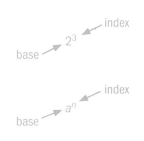

Generally, for any number a, the quantity a^n
has base a and index n.

a^n is evaluated as $a^n = \underbrace{a \times a \times \ldots \times a}_{n \text{ times}}$

There are rules to help you perform arithmetic using indices.

Indices is the plural of index.

Consider	$2^3 \times 2^2$	$= (2 \times 2 \times 2) \times (2 \times 2)$	$= 2^5$
	3×3^3	$= 3 \times (3 \times 3 \times 3)$	$= 3^4$
	$5 \times 5^3 \times 5^2$	$= 5 \times (5 \times 5 \times 5) \times (5 \times 5)$	$= 5^6$

$5 = 3 + 2$
$4 = 1 + 3$
$6 = 1 + 3 + 2$

Generally, for any number a, $a^m \times a^n = a^{m+n}$

This result is true for any numbers m and n.

Consider $2^5 \div 2^2 = \dfrac{2^5}{2^2} = \dfrac{2 \times 2 \times 2 \times 2 \times 2}{2 \times 2} = 2 \times 2 \times 2 = 2^3$

$3 = 5 - 2$

$5^4 \div 2^2 = \dfrac{5^4}{5^2} = \dfrac{5 \times 5 \times 5 \times 5}{5 \times 5} = 5 \times 5 = 5^2$

$2 = 4 - 2$

Generally, for any number a, $a^m \div a^n = a^{m-n}$

This result is true for any numbers m and n.

Some important results follow from these two index laws.

Consider $2^3 \div 2^3 = \dfrac{2^3}{2^3} = \dfrac{2 \times 2 \times 2}{2 \times 2 \times 2} = 1$

From the general rule for dividing indices you know that

$2^3 \div 2^3 = 2^{3-3} = 2^0$

Using $a^m \div a^n = a^{m-n}$
with $a = 2$, $m = 3$ and $n = 3$.

Hence it follows that $2^0 = 1$

Generally, for any number a, $a^0 = 1$

Test this rule for yourself by using different values of a.

Consider $3^3 \div 3^5 = \dfrac{3^3}{3^5} = \dfrac{3 \times 3 \times 3}{3 \times 3 \times 3 \times 3 \times 3} = \dfrac{1}{3 \times 3} = \dfrac{1}{3^2}$

From the general rule for dividing indices you know that

$3^3 \div 3^5 = 3^{3-5} = 3^{-2}$

Hence it follows that $3^{-2} = \dfrac{1}{3^2}$

Generally, for any number a, $a^{-n} = \dfrac{1}{a^n}$

A negative index is equivalent to a positive reciprocal index.

Consider
$$(3^2)^3 = (3^2) \times (3^2) \times (3^2)$$
$$= (3 \times 3) \times (3 \times 3) \times (3 \times 3)$$
$$= 3^6$$

$6 = 2 \times 3$

Generally, for any number a, $(a^m)^n = a^{m \times n}$

Test this rule for yourself by using different values of a, m and n.

You can use the laws of indices to evaluate numerical quantities.

EXAMPLE 1

Simplify

a $3^2 \times 3^3$

b $2^7 \div 2^4$

---

a Use $a^m \times a^n = a^{m+n}$: $\quad 3^2 \times 3^3 = 3^{2+3}$
$$= 3^5$$

$a = 3$, $m = 2$ and $n = 3$

b Use $a^m \div a^n = a^{m-n}$: $\quad 2^7 \div 2^4 = 2^{7-4}$
$$= 2^3$$

$a = 2$, $m = 7$ and $n = 4$

EXAMPLE 2

Evaluate

a $(0.2)^3$

b $\left(\dfrac{3}{2}\right)^{-2}$

---

a $(0.2)^3 = (0.2 \times 0.2) \times 0.2$
$\qquad\quad = 0.04 \times 0.2$
$\qquad\quad = 0.008$

Breaking down the calculation makes the multiplication easier to do without a calculator.

b $\left(\dfrac{3}{2}\right)^{-2}$

Use $a^{-n} = \dfrac{1}{a^n}$: $\left(\dfrac{3}{2}\right)^{-2} = \dfrac{1}{\left(\dfrac{3}{2}\right)^2}$

$a = \dfrac{3}{2}$ and $n = 2$

$\qquad\qquad\qquad\qquad = \dfrac{1}{\left(\dfrac{9}{4}\right)}$

Remember that $\dfrac{1}{\left(\dfrac{a}{b}\right)} = \dfrac{b}{a}$

$\qquad\qquad\qquad\qquad = \dfrac{4}{9}$

You can also use the laws of indices to simplify algebraic expressions.

EXAMPLE 3

Simplify

a $p^2 \times p^3$

b $t^5 \div t^3$

---

a Use $a^m \times a^n = a^{m+n}$: $p^2 \times p^3 = p^{2+3}$
$\qquad\qquad\qquad\qquad\qquad\qquad = p^5$

b Use $a^m \div a^n = a^{m-n}$: $t^5 \div t^3 = t^{5-3}$
$\qquad\qquad\qquad\qquad\qquad\qquad = t^2$

You can apply the index laws to simplify expressions which contain numbers and variables.

EXAMPLE 4

Simplify

a $(3a^2)^3$

b $(2a^3)^{-2}$

a Use the rule $(a^m)^n = a^{m \times n}$ on both terms:

$$(3a^2)^3 = (3)^3 \times (a^2)^3 = 27 \times a^{2 \times 3}$$
$$= 27 \times a^6$$
$$= 27a^6$$

Splitting the 3 and the a^2 may help you to simplify the problem.

Remember that both the 3 and the a^2 need to be cubed.

b Use the rule $a^{-n} = \frac{1}{a^n}$:

$$(2a^3)^{-2} = \frac{1}{(2a^3)^2}$$

Now use the rule $(a^m)^n = a^{m \times n}$ in the denominator:

$$\frac{1}{(2a^3)^2} = \frac{1}{2^2 \times (a^3)^2}$$
$$= \frac{1}{2^2 \times a^{3 \times 2}}$$
$$= \frac{1}{4 \times a^6}$$
$$= \frac{1}{4a^6}$$

Remember that both the 2 and the a^3 need to be squared.

C1

EXAMPLE 5

Simplify each expression giving the final answer in the form kx^n where k is a constant and n an integer.

a $3a^3 \times (4a)^2$

b $\left(\dfrac{3}{x^2}\right)^{-3}$

a $3a^3 \times (4a)^2 = 3a^3 \times 16a^2$

$$= 3 \times 16 \times a^3 \times a^2$$
$$= 48a^5$$

Using the rule $(a^m)^n = a^{m \times n}$
Using the rule $a^m \times a^n = a^{m+n}$

b $\left(\dfrac{3}{x^2}\right)^{-3}$ $= \dfrac{1}{\left(\dfrac{3}{x^2}\right)^3}$

$$= \dfrac{1}{\left(\dfrac{27}{x^6}\right)}$$
$$= \dfrac{x^6}{27}$$

Using the rule $a^{-n} = \dfrac{1}{a^n}$

Using the rule $(a^m)^n = a^{m \times n}$ to simplify the denominator.

Since $\dfrac{1}{\left(\dfrac{a}{b}\right)} = \dfrac{b}{a}$

Exercise 1.1

1 Evaluate the following quantities.

  a 2^7 **b** 3^5

  c 13^2 **d** $2^3 + 4^2$

  e $2^5 + 5^2$ **f** $9^2 - 3^4$

  g $(2^2)^3$ **h** $\left(\dfrac{4}{3}\right)^3$

  i $(0.4)^3$ **j** $(1.01)^2 - (0.99)^2$

  k $(98)^2 - (2)^2$ **l** $(0.4)^2 - (9.6)^2$

2 Write each of the following quantities in an index form.

  a 32 **b** 81 **c** 125

  d 0.001 **e** $\dfrac{25}{64}$ **f** 0.04

  g $\dfrac{1}{10\,000}$ **h** $\dfrac{441}{400}$ **i** $\dfrac{128}{243}$

3 Evaluate these quantities.

  a 4^{-1} **b** 6^{-2}

  c 7^0 **d** $\left(\dfrac{1}{2}\right)^{-3}$

  e $\left(\dfrac{2}{3}\right)^{-3}$ **f** $(0.5)^{-2}$

  g $\left(\dfrac{1}{3}\right)^{-4}$ **h** $\left(\dfrac{1}{2}\right)^{-8}$

4 Simplify each expression.

  a $p \times p^3$ **b** $3a \times 4a^2 \times 5a^3$

  c $12b \div 3b^4$ **d** $(3y^2)^2$

  e $7p^2 + 9p^2$ **f** $(5a)^2 \div 5a^3$

  g $(-4b^3)^2 \times 5b^2$ **h** $(3a^3)^2 \div (3a^2)^3$

  i $4p^3(3p^3 \div 2p^3)$ **j** $(-3y)^3 \times (-2y)^2$

5 Simplify these expressions.

a $\left(\dfrac{5a}{b^2}\right)^2$

b $(-2a^2b)^4$

c $(5t^2)^3 - (5y^2)^3$

d $(2y)^3 \times (3z)^3$

e $(3a)^{-2}$

f $\left(\dfrac{2}{r^2}\right)^{-3}$

g $\left(\dfrac{2z^2}{3y}\right)^{-1}$

h $(4b)^{-3} \times \left(\dfrac{1}{3b}\right)^{-2}$

i $4(y^2)^{-3} \div (2y)^{-2}$

j $(3y^2t)^2 \div (3yt^2)^{-2}$

6 Simplify each of the following expressions where possible.

a $4a^2 + 9a^2$

b $9a^2 + 4a^3$

c $4a^2 \times 9a^3$

d $4a^2 \div 9a^3$

e $9a^2 - 4a^3$

f $9a^2 \div 4a^3$

g $9 \div 4a^2$

h $4a - 9a$

i $9a^2 \times 4a - 9a^2$

j $4a^2 \div 9a - 4a$

INVESTIGATIONS

7 Which of these numbers can be expressed either as a power of 3 or as a power of 4?

$\dfrac{1}{9}$ $\dfrac{1}{24}$ 64 12 $\dfrac{1}{16}$ $\dfrac{1}{27}$ 24 81 36

8 Which of these expressions simplify to give the answer, a?

$\dfrac{5a^3}{a^2}$ $\dfrac{4a^3}{(2a)^2}$ $\dfrac{2a}{2a^2}$ $\dfrac{3a^{-1}}{3a^{-2}}$ $\dfrac{4a^3}{2a^2}$ $\dfrac{\left(\dfrac{a^{-1}}{25}\right)}{(5a)^{-2}}$

9 A saver deposits £80 with a bank giving an interest rate of 5%. Use your knowledge of indices to express as $a \times b^n$ the value of the investment

a after five years

b after n years.

After how many years and months will the investment reach £100?

The index laws also apply to fractional indices.

Consider $\qquad \sqrt{3} \times \sqrt{3} = 3$

You know that $\quad 3^{\frac{1}{2}} \times 3^{\frac{1}{2}} = 3^{\frac{1}{2}+\frac{1}{2}}$

Using $a^m \times a^n = a^{m+n}$

$$= 3^1$$
$$= 3$$

You can deduce that $\sqrt{3}$ is written as $3^{\frac{1}{2}}$ in index notation.

Similarly $\sqrt{4} = 4^{\frac{1}{2}}$ and $\sqrt{5} = 5^{\frac{1}{2}}$

You can follow the steps above to show this for yourself.

Now consider $\qquad \sqrt[3]{2} \times \sqrt[3]{2} \times \sqrt[3]{2} = 2$

$\sqrt[3]{2}$ is the cube root of 2.

You know that $\qquad 2^{\frac{1}{3}} \times 2^{\frac{1}{3}} \times 2^{\frac{1}{3}} = 2^{\frac{1}{3}+\frac{1}{3}+\frac{1}{3}}$

You can deduce this for yourself by considering $a^m \times a^n \times a^p$ and using the index laws.

$$= 2^1$$
$$= 2$$

You can deduce that $\sqrt[3]{2}$ is written as $2^{\frac{1}{3}}$ in index notation.

Similarly $\sqrt[3]{5} = 5^{\frac{1}{3}}$ and $\sqrt[3]{7} = 7^{\frac{1}{3}}$

Generally, for any number a, $\quad \sqrt[n]{a} = a^{\frac{1}{n}}$

This is the nth root of a.

The other index laws also apply to fractional indices.

Consider $\qquad (\sqrt[3]{8})^2$

This can be rewritten as $\quad \left(8^{\frac{1}{3}}\right)^2$

Using $(a^m)^n = a^{m \times n}$

$$= 8^{\frac{1}{3} \times 2}$$

$$= 8^{\frac{2}{3}}$$

Similarly $\qquad (8^2)^{\frac{1}{3}} = 8^{\frac{2}{3}}$

Using $(a^m)^n = a^{m \times n}$

Hence $\qquad \left(8^{\frac{1}{3}}\right)^2 = (8^2)^{\frac{1}{3}} = 8^{\frac{2}{3}}$

Generally, for any number a, $\left(a^{\frac{1}{n}}\right)^m = \left(a^m\right)^{\frac{1}{n}} = a^{\frac{m}{n}}$

$\left(\sqrt[n]{a}\right)^m = \sqrt[n]{a^m} = a^{\frac{m}{n}}$

You can use the index laws to evaluate expressions involving fractional indices.

EXAMPLE 1

Evaluate   **a** $(27)^{\frac{2}{3}}$ **b** $(9)^{-0.5}$

a   Rewrite the expression: $(27^2)^{\frac{1}{3}}$ or $\left(27^{\frac{1}{3}}\right)^2$

   You know that $27^{\frac{1}{3}} = \sqrt[3]{27} = 3$

   Hence $(27)^{\frac{2}{3}} = \left(27^{\frac{1}{3}}\right)^2 = (3)^2 = 9$

b $(9)^{-0.5} = \dfrac{1}{(9)^{\frac{1}{2}}}$

           $= \dfrac{1}{3}$

Choose $\left(27^{\frac{1}{3}}\right)^2$ as this is simpler to work with.

You should recognise that
$27^{\frac{1}{3}} = \sqrt[3]{27} = 3$

$9^{\frac{1}{2}} = \sqrt{9} = 3$

Sometimes the expression will involve a fraction as the base number.

EXAMPLE 2

Evaluate

a $\left(\dfrac{125}{8}\right)^{\frac{2}{3}}$ **b** $\left(\dfrac{256}{81}\right)^{-\frac{3}{4}}$

a $\left(\dfrac{125}{8}\right)^{\frac{2}{3}} = \left[\left(\dfrac{125}{8}\right)^{\frac{1}{3}}\right]^2$

         $= \left(\dfrac{5}{2}\right)^2$

         $= \dfrac{25}{4}$

b $\left(\dfrac{256}{81}\right)^{-\frac{3}{4}} = \left(\dfrac{81}{256}\right)^{\frac{3}{4}}$

         $= \left[\left(\dfrac{81}{256}\right)^{\frac{1}{4}}\right]^3$

         $= \left(\dfrac{3}{4}\right)^3$

         $= \dfrac{27}{64}$

Using $a^{\frac{m}{n}} = \left(a^{\frac{1}{n}}\right)^m$

Since $\sqrt[3]{125} = 5$ and $\sqrt[3]{8} = 2$

Remember to square both the top and bottom numbers.

Using the rule $a^{-n} = \dfrac{1}{a^n}$

Using $a^{\frac{m}{n}} = \left(a^{\frac{1}{n}}\right)^m = \sqrt[n]{a^m}$

Remember to cube both the top and bottom numbers.

You can also apply the laws of indices in algebra questions.

EXAMPLE 3

Simplify

a $(4a)^2 \times 4a^3$ 　　　　　**b** $\left(27p^6\right)^{\frac{2}{3}}$

---

a $(4a)^2 \times 4a^3 = 16a^2 \times 4a^3$

$\qquad\qquad = 16 \times 4 \times a^2 \times a^3$

$\qquad\qquad = 64a^5$

Remember to square both the 4 and the a in the bracket.

b $\left(27p^6\right)^{\frac{2}{3}} = \left[\left(27p^6\right)^{\frac{1}{3}}\right]^2$

$\qquad\qquad = (3p^2)^2$

$\qquad\qquad = 9p^4$

Using $a^{\frac{m}{n}} = \left(a^{\frac{1}{n}}\right)^m$

Remember to cube root both the 27 and the p^6 inside the inner bracket.

You can solve equations containing indices.

EXAMPLE 4

Solve 　$3^x = 9^{x-1}$

$\qquad 3^x = (3^2)^{x-1}$

$\qquad 3^x = 3^{2(x-1)}$

$\qquad 3^x = 3^{2x-2}$

So $\qquad x = 2x - 2$

$\qquad\quad x = 2$

Using $(a^m)^n = a^{mn}$

Check: $3^2 = 9^{2-1} = 9^1$

Exercise 1.2

1 Evaluate these quantities.

　a $8^{\frac{1}{3}}$ 　　　　**b** $16^{\frac{1}{4}}$ 　　　　**c** $625^{0.25}$ 　　　　**d** $243^{\frac{1}{5}}$

　e $\left(\frac{12}{27}\right)^{\frac{1}{2}}$ 　　**f** $\left(\frac{1}{125}\right)^{\frac{1}{3}}$ 　　**g** $\left(5\frac{1}{16}\right)^{\frac{1}{2}}$ 　　**h** $(0.04)^{\frac{1}{2}}$

2 Evaluate each quantity.

　a $27^{-\frac{1}{3}}$ 　　　**b** $\left(\frac{9}{4}\right)^{-0.5}$ 　　　**c** $\dfrac{1}{36^{-\frac{1}{2}}}$

　d $\left(\frac{5}{7}\right)^0$ 　　　**e** $\left(\frac{125}{216}\right)^{-\frac{1}{3}}$ 　　**f** $\left(\frac{25}{9}\right)^{-\frac{1}{2}}$

C1

3 Simplify these quantities.

a $\left(\dfrac{8}{27}\right)^{\frac{2}{3}}$

b $\left(1\dfrac{9}{16}\right)^{\frac{3}{2}}$

c $\left(3\dfrac{3}{8}\right)^{\frac{2}{3}}$

d $\left(\dfrac{16}{81}\right)^{0.75}$

e $(1000)^{\frac{2}{3}}$

f $\left(\dfrac{4}{9}\right)^{-\frac{3}{2}}$

g $\left(\dfrac{81}{16}\right)^{-\frac{3}{4}}$

h $\left[(49)^{-\frac{1}{2}}\right]^{2}$

i $8^{-\frac{5}{3}}$

4 Simplify each expression.

a $(y^2)^{-\frac{1}{2}}$

b $(4a^6)^{\frac{1}{2}}$

c $\left(\dfrac{4}{9}a^4\right)^{\frac{3}{2}}$

d $\left(\dfrac{8}{b^3}\right)^{\frac{5}{3}}$

e $\left(y^{\frac{2}{3}}\right)^{-\frac{9}{4}}$

5 Simplify these expressions.

a $a^{\frac{1}{2}} \times 4a^{\frac{3}{2}}$

b $5t^{0.5} \times 2t^{-1.5}$

c $9p^2 \div (9p^2)^{\frac{1}{2}}$

d $4(49t^2)^{\frac{1}{2}}$

e $(3t \times 9t^2)^{\frac{1}{3}}$

f $(16a \div 4a^3)^{-\frac{1}{2}}$

6 Simplify

a $\left(\dfrac{1}{4t^2}\right)^{-\frac{5}{2}}$

b $\left(\dfrac{0.0001}{t^8}\right)^{-\frac{3}{4}}$

7 Solve $4^x = 16^{2x+1}$

C1

The square root is referred to as a **surd** form.

Surds can be used to accurately represent solutions.

> A surd is a quantity that cannot be expressed as a rational number. It consists of the root of a number. e.g. $\sqrt{2}$ and $\sqrt{5}$ are surds.

Surds occur naturally in mathematics.

Consider the square with sides of unit length.

By applying the theorem of Pythagoras to the right-angled triangle ABC

you can show that

$$AC = \sqrt{2}$$

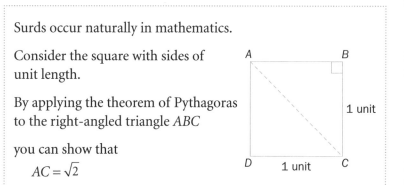

> Unit length means 1 cm, 1 m etc.

> By convention $\sqrt{}$ is the positive square root.

There are rules that you can use to manipulate surds.

Generally, $\sqrt{(a \times b)} = \sqrt{a} \times \sqrt{b}$

There is a similar rule for division.

Generally, $\sqrt{\dfrac{a}{b}} = \dfrac{\sqrt{a}}{\sqrt{b}}$

You can use these results to simplify expressions.

EXAMPLE 1

Simplify

a $\sqrt{90}$

b $\sqrt{\dfrac{5}{9}}$

---

a $\sqrt{90} = \sqrt{9} \times \sqrt{10}$

$\qquad = 3 \times \sqrt{10}$

$\qquad = 3\sqrt{10}$

b $\sqrt{\dfrac{5}{9}} = \dfrac{\sqrt{5}}{\sqrt{9}}$

$\qquad = \dfrac{\sqrt{5}}{3}$

Sometimes you will need to use a combination of rules to simplify an expression.

EXAMPLE 2

Simplify   **a** $\sqrt{18} + \sqrt{98}$ **b** $(5 - \sqrt{5})^2$

a $\sqrt{18} + \sqrt{98} = \sqrt{9} \times \sqrt{2} + \sqrt{49} \times \sqrt{2}$

               $= 3\sqrt{2} + 7\sqrt{2}$

               $= 10\sqrt{2}$

b $(5 - \sqrt{5})^2 = (5 - \sqrt{5})(5 - \sqrt{5})$

               $= 25 - 5\sqrt{5} - 5\sqrt{5} + \sqrt{5} \times \sqrt{5}$

               $= 25 - 10\sqrt{5} + 5$

               $= 30 - 10\sqrt{5}$

Using $\sqrt{(a \times b)} = \sqrt{a} \times \sqrt{b}$ in both terms.

Since
$3\sqrt{2} + 7\sqrt{2} = (3 + 7)\sqrt{2} = 10\sqrt{2}$

Make sure you multiply each term in the first bracket by each term in the second bracket.
$\sqrt{5} \times \sqrt{5} = 5$

Without a calculator a seemingly simple calculation can be tedious to perform.

e.g. Evaluating $\dfrac{1}{\sqrt{2}}$ given that $\sqrt{2} = 1.4142$

It is challenging to calculate $1 \div 1.4142$ using long division. You can overcome this by multiplying both the numerator and denominator by $\sqrt{2}$.

$$\frac{1}{\sqrt{2}} = \frac{1}{\sqrt{2}} \times \frac{\sqrt{2}}{\sqrt{2}} = \frac{\sqrt{2}}{2} \quad \text{and} \quad \frac{\sqrt{2}}{2} = \frac{1.4142}{2} = 0.7071$$

So $\dfrac{1}{\sqrt{2}} = 0.7071$

Notice that $\dfrac{\sqrt{2}}{\sqrt{2}} = 1$ so

multiplying by $\dfrac{\sqrt{2}}{\sqrt{2}}$ does not change the value of the expression.

Multiplying by $\dfrac{\sqrt{2}}{\sqrt{2}}$ has eliminated the surd from the denominator.

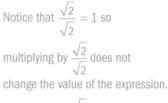

Generally, since $\sqrt{a} \times \sqrt{a} = a$ $\dfrac{b}{\sqrt{a}} = \dfrac{b}{\sqrt{a}} \times \dfrac{\sqrt{a}}{\sqrt{a}} = \dfrac{b\sqrt{a}}{a}$

This method of eliminating a surd from the denominator to simplify a fraction is known as **rationalising the denominator**.

To rationalise the denominator of a fraction $\dfrac{b}{\sqrt{a}}$ you multiply both top and bottom by $\sqrt{a}$.

EXAMPLE 3

Rationalise the denominator in each expression.

a $\dfrac{5}{\sqrt{3}}$ **b** $\dfrac{2}{\sqrt{5}}$

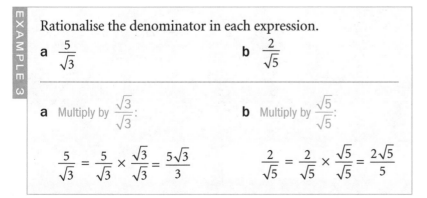

a Multiply by $\dfrac{\sqrt{3}}{\sqrt{3}}$:   **b** Multiply by $\dfrac{\sqrt{5}}{\sqrt{5}}$:

$$\frac{5}{\sqrt{3}} = \frac{5}{\sqrt{3}} \times \frac{\sqrt{3}}{\sqrt{3}} = \frac{5\sqrt{3}}{3} \qquad\qquad \frac{2}{\sqrt{5}} = \frac{2}{\sqrt{5}} \times \frac{\sqrt{5}}{\sqrt{5}} = \frac{2\sqrt{5}}{5}$$

Always multiply the numerator and denominator by the same number so that the value is not changed.

You can rationalise the denominator in expressions

of the type $\dfrac{5}{2-\sqrt{3}}$.

$$(2-\sqrt{3})(2+\sqrt{3}) = 2^2 - (\sqrt{3})^2 = 4 - 3 = 1$$

Multiplying both numerator and denominator by $(2+\sqrt{3})$ eliminates the surd from the denominator.

Hence $\dfrac{5}{2-\sqrt{3}} = \dfrac{5}{(2-\sqrt{3})} \times \dfrac{(2+\sqrt{3})}{(2+\sqrt{3})}$

$$= \dfrac{5 \times (2+\sqrt{3})}{2^2 - (\sqrt{3})^2}$$

$$= \dfrac{5 \times (2+\sqrt{3})}{4-3}$$

$$= 5(2+\sqrt{3})$$

You can show this yourself using the method of the difference of two squares (DOTS) seen in Chapter 0 ◯.

C1

To rationalise the denominator of a fraction of the form

- $\dfrac{c}{a+b\sqrt{n}}$ you multiply top and bottom by $a - b\sqrt{n}$
- $\dfrac{c}{a-b\sqrt{n}}$ you multiply top and bottom by $a + b\sqrt{n}$.

You can use the method of rationalising the denominator to simplify expressions containing fractions.

EXAMPLE 4

Rationalise the denominator in $\dfrac{\sqrt{3}}{3+\sqrt{2}}$

Multiply top and bottom by $3-\sqrt{2}$:

$$\dfrac{\sqrt{3}}{3+\sqrt{2}} = \dfrac{\sqrt{3}}{3+\sqrt{2}} \times \dfrac{(3-\sqrt{2})}{(3-\sqrt{2})}$$

$$= \dfrac{\sqrt{3} \times (3-\sqrt{2})}{9-2}$$

$$= \dfrac{\sqrt{3}(3-\sqrt{2})}{7}$$

$(3+\sqrt{2})(3-\sqrt{2}) = 3^2 - 2$

Exercise 1.3

1 Write each expression in the simplified form $a\sqrt{n}$.

   a $\sqrt{8}$ **b** $\sqrt{32}$ **c** $\sqrt{24}$ **d** $\sqrt{50}$

   e $\sqrt{48}$ **f** $\sqrt{\dfrac{18}{25}}$ **g** $\sqrt{\dfrac{98}{121}}$ **h** $\sqrt{\dfrac{245}{100}}$

2 Simplify each of the following.

   a $3\sqrt{2}+\sqrt{18}$ **b** $2\sqrt{3}(\sqrt{3}-2\sqrt{3})$

   c $\sqrt{20}-2\times\sqrt{45}$ **d** $4\sqrt{2}\div\sqrt{2}+3$

   e $\dfrac{5\sqrt{7}}{3}-\sqrt{28}$ **f** $(1+\sqrt{5})(1-\sqrt{5})$

   g $(1+\sqrt{3})^2$ **h** $\dfrac{\sqrt{72}}{4}\div\dfrac{\sqrt{24}}{3}$

   i $(3-\sqrt{3})(2+\sqrt{3})$ **j** $\sqrt{20}\times\sqrt{45}-\sqrt{80}\div\sqrt{20}$

3 Rationalise the denominator in each fraction.

   a $\dfrac{1}{\sqrt{7}}$ **b** $\dfrac{4}{\sqrt{13}}$ **c** $\dfrac{7}{\sqrt{8}}$ **d** $\dfrac{2\sqrt{3}}{\sqrt{7}}$

   e $\dfrac{3\sqrt{5}}{\sqrt{75}}$ **f** $\dfrac{\sqrt{28}}{\sqrt{18}}$ **g** $\dfrac{4}{3\sqrt{6}}$ **h** $\dfrac{2}{\sqrt{3}}(\sqrt{45}+\sqrt{5})$

4 Rationalise the denominator in each fraction.
Write the result in the simplest form.

   a $\dfrac{1}{1+\sqrt{2}}$ **b** $\dfrac{3}{1-\sqrt{3}}$ **c** $\dfrac{4}{2+\sqrt{2}}$ **d** $\dfrac{11}{5-\sqrt{3}}$ **e** $\dfrac{\sqrt{2}}{2+\sqrt{2}}$

   f $\dfrac{\sqrt{3}}{1-\sqrt{3}}$ **g** $\dfrac{1+\sqrt{2}}{1-\sqrt{2}}$ **h** $\dfrac{3-\sqrt{3}}{3+\sqrt{3}}$ **i** $\dfrac{5-\sqrt{6}}{3-\sqrt{5}}$ **j** $\dfrac{4}{\sqrt{3}-\sqrt{2}}$

5 Express $\dfrac{2\sqrt{2}}{\sqrt{3}-1}-\dfrac{2\sqrt{3}}{\sqrt{2}+1}$, in the form $p\sqrt{6}+q\sqrt{3}+r\sqrt{2}$,
where the integers p, q and r are to be found.

INVESTIGATION

6 A triangle has base length as given. The area is $6\,\text{m}^2$.

Find the height giving your answer in the form $a+b\sqrt{5}$
where a and b are integers.

$1+\sqrt{5}$

1 Evaluate

   a 4^3 **b** $3^2 - 2^3$ **c** $\left(1\frac{1}{4}\right)^2$ **d** $(-3)^3$

   e 3^{-2} **f** $\left(1\frac{1}{2}\right)^{-6}$ **g** $(0.1)^{-2}$ **h** $\left(\frac{15}{7}\right)^0$

2 Write in simplified index form.

   a 625 **b** $\frac{25}{16}$ **c** 0.125 **d** $\frac{196}{169}$

3 Simplify

   a $3p \times (3p)^2$ **b** $(5y^3)^2$ **c** $(-2y^2) \times (3y)^2$

   d $(-3a^2)^4$ **e** $\left(\frac{3t^2}{2}\right)^{-2}$ **f** $\left(-\frac{4t}{5}\right)^{-3}$

4 Evaluate

   a $\left(\frac{9}{25}\right)^{\frac{1}{2}}$ **b** $\left(1\frac{7}{9}\right)^{\frac{1}{2}}$ **c** $(27)^{-\frac{2}{3}}$ **d** $\left(\frac{25}{4}\right)^{1.5}$

   e $(49)^{\frac{3}{2}}$ **f** $(100)^{\frac{5}{2}}$ **g** $(8)^{-\frac{7}{3}}$ **h** $\dfrac{1}{(0.001)^{-\frac{2}{3}}}$

5 Simplify

   a $(9a^4)^{\frac{1}{2}}$ **b** $\left(\frac{4}{t}\right)^{-\frac{1}{2}}$ **c** $(18t^6 \div 8t^4)^{-\frac{1}{2}}$

   d $\left(y^{\frac{1}{4}}\right)^{-8}$ **e** $(64t^6)^{\frac{5}{6}}$ **f** $(125p^6q^3)^{\frac{4}{3}}$

6 Simplify

   a $\sqrt{200}$ **b** $\sqrt{128}$ **c** $\sqrt{\frac{400}{98}}$

7 Rationalise the denominator and simplify

   a $\dfrac{4}{\sqrt{2}}$ **b** $\dfrac{2\sqrt{3}}{\sqrt{6}}$ **c** $\dfrac{5}{\sqrt{5}}$ **d** $\dfrac{4\sqrt{7}}{\sqrt{8}}$

8 Simplify

   a $3\sqrt{2} + 4\sqrt{2} \times 3$ **b** $(2+\sqrt{3})(2-\sqrt{3})$

   c $(1+\sqrt{5})^2$ **d** $\dfrac{4\sqrt{3}}{3} - \dfrac{3\sqrt{3}}{8}$

C1

9 Rationalise the denominator and give each answer in its simplest form.

a $\dfrac{1}{\sqrt{3}+2}$ b $\dfrac{3}{5-\sqrt{3}}$ c $\dfrac{1+\sqrt{2}}{2-\sqrt{2}}$ d $\dfrac{2}{\sqrt{5}-\sqrt{2}}$

10 a Write the expression $(2-\sqrt{3})^2$ in the form $a+b\sqrt{n}$ where a, b and n are integers.

b Given that $\dfrac{1}{3-\sqrt{5}}=a+b\sqrt{5}$, find the values of a and b.

c Simplify $(3-2\sqrt{7})(4-\sqrt{7})$.

d Simplify $3\sqrt{2}+4\times2\sqrt{2}$.

11 One side of a rectangle is of length $(3+\sqrt{3})$ cm and another side is $(2+2\sqrt{3})$ cm.
Find   a   the perimeter   b   the area of the rectangle.

12 Simplify

a $\sqrt{(\sqrt{144})}$

b $\sqrt{(\sqrt{9}\sqrt{27})}$

c $\sqrt{(\sqrt{a^4}\sqrt{b^8}\sqrt{c^6})}$

13 a Express $\sqrt{45}$ in the form $a\sqrt{5}$, where a is an integer.

b Express $(2-\sqrt{5})^2$ in the form $b+c\sqrt{5}$, where b and c are integers.

14 a Write $\sqrt{80}$ in the form $a\sqrt{5}$, where a is an integer.

b Express $\dfrac{4(3+\sqrt{5})}{(3-\sqrt{5})}$ in the form $b + c\sqrt{5}$, where b and c are integers.

15 a Expand and simplify $(3 + \sqrt{3})(3 - \sqrt{3})$.

b Express $\dfrac{24}{3+\sqrt{3}}$ in the form $a + b\sqrt{3}$, where a and b are integers.

16 Find the value of

a $81^{\frac{1}{2}}$ b $81^{\frac{3}{4}}$ c $81^{-\frac{3}{4}}$ [(c) Edexcel Limited 2002]

17

C1

Summary

Refer to

○ The general laws of indices are 1.1 and 1.2

- ○ $a^m \times a^n = a^{m+n}$

- ○ $a^m \div a^n = a^{m-n}$

- ○ $a^{-m} = \dfrac{1}{a^m}$

- ○ $(a^m)^n = a^{mn}$

- ○ $a^{\frac{1}{m}} = \sqrt[m]{a}$

- ○ $\left(\sqrt[n]{a}\right)^m = a^{\frac{m}{n}} = \sqrt[n]{a^m}$

- ○ $a^0 = 1$

○ You can multiply and divide surds using the rules 1.3

- ○ $\sqrt{a \times b} = \sqrt{a} \times \sqrt{b}$

- ○ $\sqrt{\dfrac{a}{b}} = \dfrac{\sqrt{a}}{\sqrt{b}}$

○ To rationalise the denominator of a fraction of the form 1.3

- ○ $\dfrac{c}{a + b\sqrt{n}}$ you multiply top and bottom by $a - b\sqrt{n}$

- ○ $\dfrac{c}{a - b\sqrt{n}}$ you multiply top and bottom by $a + b\sqrt{n}$

Links

Standard index form, which you will have met at GCSE,
is a good example of indices having a practical use.
In physics very large numbers such as 1.2×10^{14}
can be used to describe the distance
between two planets in our solar system.

In biology very small numbers such as 4.1×10^{-9}
can be used to describe measurements relating
to cells.

The rules of indices can be used when multiplying together
numbers in standard form helping to simplify such calculations.

eg. $1.1 \times 10^6 \times 5 \times 10^9 = 5.5 \times 10^{15}$ which is a very large number.

2

Coordinate geometry

This chapter will show you how to
- find the equation of a straight line from geometrical information
- find the general equation of a straight line
- determine if two lines are parallel or perpendicular.

Before you start

You should know how to:

1 Recognise a linear equation.

e.g. $3x + 2y = 4$

is a linear equation (no powers higher than 1)
e.g. $x^2 + 3y - 2 = 0$

is not a linear equation as it has an x^2-term.

2 Plot a straight line graph.

e.g. $y = 2x - 4$

Make a table of values:

x	0	2	4
y	-4	0	4

(choose three values)
Plot the graph:

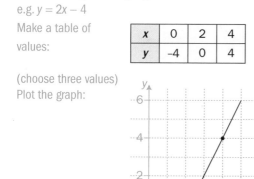

$y = 2x - 4$

3 Identify the gradient and y-intercept of a straight line graph from its equation.

e.g. $y = 2x - 1$

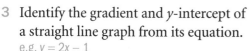

gradient = 2 y-intercept = -1

Check in:

1 Identify which of these equations are linear.
   a $4x = 3y + 1$
   b $x^2 + y^2 = 1$
   c $3(x - 1) = 4(y + 2)$
   d $\dfrac{x - 6}{2y - 7} = 4$
   e $xy = 3$
   f $x^2 = 1$

2 Plot these straight line graphs taking values of x in the range $0 \leqslant x \leqslant 4$.
   Comment on any similarities or differences.
   a $y = 2x + 1$
   b $y = 2x + 3$
   c $y = 2x - 1$
   d $y = x + 1$

3 Find the gradient and y-intercept of the graph described by each equation.
   a $y = 3x + 2$
   b $y - 1 = 2x$
   c $y = 1 - x$
   d $3y = 2x + 3$

2

The diagram shows a straight line graph with two points marked.
(x_1, y_1) is a known point on the line.
(x, y) is a general point (it can be anywhere on the line).

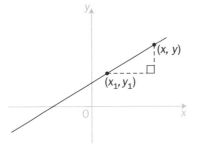

The gradient $m = \dfrac{y - y_1}{x - x_1}$

Rearrange: $y - y_1 = m(x - x_1)$

- The equation of a straight line with gradient m that passes through the point (x_1, y_1) is given by

$$y - y_1 = m(x - x_1)$$

You should already know the general equation of a straight line $y = mx + c$

You can find the equation of a straight line if you know
- a point on the line   and   - the gradient of the line.

Find the equation of the straight line which passes through the point $(1, 3)$ and has gradient 2.

Write the straight line equation:
$$y - y_1 = m(x - x_1)$$

In this case $m = 2$ and $(x_1, y_1) = (1, 3)$

Substitute the values for m, x_1 and y_1: $y - 3 = 2(x - 1)$
Rearrange: $y - 3 = 2x - 2$
$$y = 2x + 1$$

Hence the equation of the line is $y = 2x + 1$

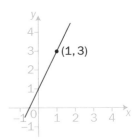

It often helps to sketch the graph with the facts that you know.

From its equation you can find where a line cuts the axes.

A line cuts the x-axis when $y = 0$.
A line cuts the y-axis when $x = 0$.

EXAMPLE 2

A straight line passes through the point $P(-2, 4)$, and has gradient $-\frac{2}{3}$. Find the equation of the line and the point where it cuts the x-axis.

$m = -\frac{2}{3}$ and $(x_1, y_1) = (-2, 4)$

Hence $y - 4 = -\frac{2}{3}(x - (-2))$

$$y - 4 = -\frac{2}{3}x - \frac{4}{3}$$

$$y = -\frac{2}{3}x - \frac{4}{3} + 4$$

$$= -\frac{2}{3}x + \frac{8}{3}$$

Hence the equation of the line is $\qquad y = -\frac{2x}{3} + \frac{8}{3}$

The line cuts the x-axis when $y = 0$ giving $0 = -\frac{2x}{3} + \frac{8}{3}$

Rearrange: $\qquad\qquad\qquad\qquad \frac{2x}{3} = \frac{8}{3}$

$$x = 4$$

So the line cuts the x-axis at $(4, 0)$.

> Be careful with the negatives in this example.

You can also find the equation of the line if you know two points on it.

The diagram shows a straight line graph.
(x_1, y_1) and (x_2, y_2) are known points on the line.

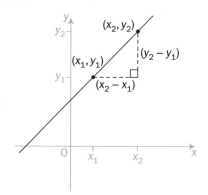

The gradient of the line, $m = \dfrac{y_2 - y_1}{x_2 - x_1}$

○ If you know two points, (x_1, y_1) and (x_2, y_2), on a straight line then the gradient of the line is given by

$$m = \frac{y_2 - y_1}{x_2 - x_1}$$

> It doesn't matter which of the two points you choose to be (x_1, y_1) and which you choose to be (x_2, y_2).

EXAMPLE 3

Find the gradient of the straight line which passes through the points $A(1, 4)$ and $B(-3, 2)$.
Hence find the equation of the line.

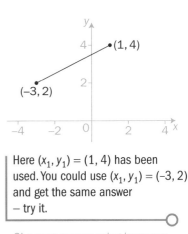

Use the x- and y-values of points A and B to find the gradient:

$$(x_1, y_1) = (1, 4) \qquad (x_2, y_2) = (-3, 2)$$

$$m = \frac{y_2 - y_1}{x_2 - x_1} = \frac{2 - 4}{-3 - 1} = \frac{-2}{-4} = \frac{1}{2}$$

Now use $y - y_1 = m(x - x_1)$: $y - 4 = \frac{1}{2}(x - 1)$

Expand: $y - 4 = \frac{1}{2}x - \frac{1}{2}$

Rearrange: $y = \frac{1}{2}x + \frac{7}{2}$

Here $(x_1, y_1) = (1, 4)$ has been used. You could use $(x_1, y_1) = (-3, 2)$ and get the same answer – try it.

Give your answer using improper fractions not mixed numbers.

Exercise 2.1

1 Find the equation of the straight line passing through the given point with the given gradient.

  a $(4, 2)$; gradient -1

  b $(2, 0)$; gradient 3

  c $(-1, 3)$; gradient -2

  d $(3, 4)$; gradient $\frac{1}{2}$

  e $(-1, 5)$; gradient $-\frac{2}{3}$

  f $\left(\frac{1}{2}, 1\frac{1}{2}\right)$; gradient -1

2 Find the equation of the straight line, AB, joining each pair of points.

  a $A(0, 2)$, $B(3, 6)$

  b $A(1, 0)$, $B(3, -2)$

  c $A(1, -3)$, $B(2, -4)$

  d $A(-4, 2)$, $B(3, 5)$

  e $A\left(1, \frac{1}{2}\right)$, $B(5, -2)$

  f $A(-7, -3)$, $B(-2, -6)$

3 a The line $y = mx + 3$ passes through the point $(3, -2)$.
     What is the gradient of the line?

  b Find the equation of the line which passes through the origin, $(0, 0)$, and has a gradient $-\frac{2}{3}$.

  c Write down the equation of the straight line which has a gradient of 2 and cuts the y-axis at $(0, 3)$.

  d Find the gradient of the line joining $(3, -2)$ and $(5, 3)$.
     What is the equation of this line?

C1

4 **a** The points $P(a, 3)$ and $Q(4, 5)$ lie on the line with gradient 2.
What is the value of a?

b The two points $P(k, 3)$ and $Q(3, k)$ lie on the line with gradient 4.
Find the value of k and comment on your result.

c The points $A(3, 4)$ and $B(5, 10)$ lie on the straight line AB
Show that $C(6, 13)$ also lies on the line AB produced.

Find the equation of AB.
Produced means extended.

5 **a** The gradient of a straight line is –2 and it intersects the
x-axis at $(3, 0)$ What is the equation of the line?

b If the gradient of a straight line is –3 and the intercept on the
y-axis is $\frac{1}{2}$, write the equation of the line in the form $y = mx + c$.

c The straight line $y = ax - 3$, where a is a constant, passes through
the point $(4, -1)$. Find the gradient of the line.

d The straight line $y = mx + c$ passes through the points
$(1, -1)$ and $(3, 3)$.
What is the equation of the line?

e The line with equation $2y = 3x - 1$ intersects the line $x = 0$
at P and the line $y = 0$ at Q.
Write down the coordinates of P and Q.
State the gradient of the line joining P and Q.

f The two lines, $y = 2x - 1$ and $2y = x + 4$, intersect at $P(x, y)$.
A third line, $y = mx + c$, also passes through P and has a
gradient of 4. What is the equation of this third line?

See Chapter 0 for revision on
solving simultaneous equations.

INVESTIGATION

6 Which four of these six lines would describe a square?

$y = x + 1$ $y = -x + 2$ $y = x - 1$

$y = x - 2$ $y = -x - 2$ $y = -x + 4$

Is it possible to find the area of the square?

General equation of a straight line

○ You can express the equation of a straight line in the **general form**

$ax + by + c = 0$ where a, b and c are constants.

EXAMPLE 1

Write the straight line equation $y = 3 - x$ in the form $ax + by + c = 0$

$$y = 3 - x$$

Rearrange: $\quad y - 3 + x = 0$

Hence $\quad\quad x + y - 3 = 0$

Take all the terms to one side of the equation.

You can also rearrange equations containing fractions.

EXAMPLE 2

Write the following equation in the form $ax + by + c = 0$

$$\frac{1}{1+x} = \frac{3}{1-2y}$$

$$\frac{1}{1+x} = \frac{3}{1-2y}$$

Eliminate the fractions: $\quad\quad (1 - 2y) \times 1 = 3(1 + x)$

$$1 - 2y = 3 + 3x$$

Multiply each term by $(1 + x)$ and $(1 - 2y)$.

Collect all the terms on the left-hand side:

$$1 - 2y - 3 - 3x = 0$$

Rearrange and simplify: $\quad\quad -3x - 2y - 2 = 0$

Multiply through by (-1): $\quad\quad 3x + 2y + 2 = 0$

You should give the equation in its simplest form.

Exercise 2.2

1 Rearrange these straight line equations into the form $ax + by + c = 0$, where a, b and c are integers.

a $\quad y = x - 3$

b $\quad 4 - x = 0$

c $\quad y = \frac{1}{3}(x - 3)$

d $\quad \frac{x}{y} = 5$

e $\quad y = 7$

f $\quad \frac{y}{2} + \frac{x}{3} = 1$

g $\quad \frac{4}{x} = \frac{3}{y}$

h $\quad \frac{1+x}{2} - \frac{1-y}{3} = 0$

i $\quad \frac{1}{x+1} = \frac{3}{y-1}$

j $\quad 2(x - 2) = 5(3 - y)$

2　**a**　Find the points where the line $2y + 3x - 1 = 0$
　　　cuts the x- and y-axes.

　b　Find the equation of the line whose gradient is $-\dfrac{1}{2}$
　　　and whose y-intercept is $\dfrac{3}{4}$.
　　　Give your answer in its general form, $ax + by + c = 0$.

　c　The point $(2, 3)$ lies on the line $ax + by = 4$
　　　which has a gradient of 2.
　　　Find the values of the constants a and b and hence,
　　　in its general form, the equation of the straight line.

　d　The lines $2y = 3x - 2$ and $3y + 2x = 1$
　　　intersect each other at the point P.

　　　i　Find the coordinates of P.
　　　ii　Sketch the two lines.
　　　　What do you notice?

See Chapter 0 for revision on
simultaneous equations.

INVESTIGATION

3　The equations of two straight lines are

$$ax + by + c = 0$$
and　　$$dx + ey + f = 0$$

　a　Given that the lines do not intersect, write down
　　　an equation connecting a, b, d and e.

　b　Given that the lines have the same y-intercept,
　　　write down another equation.

　c　Given that the first line has identical x- and
　　　y-intercepts, write down a third equation.

Parallel and perpendicular lines

○ **Parallel** lines have the same gradient.

The lines $y = 3x + 2$ and $y = 3x - 4$ both have gradient 3.

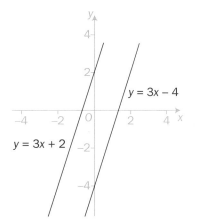

The two lines are parallel.

○ **Perpendicular** lines are at right angles to each other.

The lines $y = 2x + 3$ and $y = -\frac{1}{2}x - 7$ have gradients 2 and $-\frac{1}{2}$.

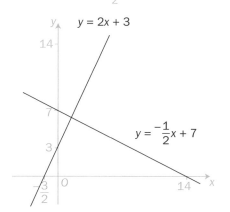

The two lines are perpendicular.

○ Two lines $y = m_1x + c_1$ and $y = m_2x + c_2$ are **parallel** $\Leftrightarrow m_1 = m_2$.

$\Leftrightarrow$ means the statements imply each other.

○ Two lines $y = m_1x + c_1$ and $y = m_2x + c_2$ are **perpendicular** $\Leftrightarrow m_1 \times m_2 = -1$.

In the example, $2 \times -\frac{1}{2} = -1$

You can use these rules to decide whether a pair of lines is perpendicular, parallel or neither without drawing them.

EXAMPLE 1

Determine whether the lines $y - 3x + 3 = 0$ and $3y + x = 6$ are parallel, perpendicular or neither.

Rewrite equations in the form $y = mx + c$:

$$y - 3x + 3 = 0 \qquad\qquad 3y + x = 6$$
$$y = 3x - 3 \quad (1) \qquad\qquad y = -\frac{x}{3} + 2 \quad (2)$$

Equation(1) has gradient 3.   Equation(2) has gradient $-\frac{1}{3}$.

Find product of gradients: $3 \times \left(-\frac{1}{3}\right) = -1$

Hence the lines are perpendicular.

If you know the equation of one line, you can use the fact that two lines are perpendicular or parallel to find the equation of the other line.

EXAMPLE 2

The line $ax + by + c = 0$ is parallel to the line $y - 2x + 1 = 0$
Show that $a = -2b$

Rearrange the equations in the form $y = mx + c$:

(1): $ax + by + c = 0$ (2): $y - 2x + 1 = 0$

$\qquad\qquad by = -ax - c \qquad\qquad\qquad\qquad y = 2x - 1$

$\qquad\qquad y = -\dfrac{ax}{b} - \dfrac{c}{b}$

It helps to label the equations (1) and (2).

Hence find the gradient of each line:

Equation (1) has gradient $-\dfrac{a}{b}$.

Equation (2) has gradient 2.

Since the lines are parallel they both have the same gradient.

Hence $\quad -\dfrac{a}{b} = 2$

Rearrange: $a = -2b$ as required.

EXAMPLE 3

The line, L, joining the points $A(4k, -3)$ and $B(1, -k)$ is perpendicular to the line $2y = x - 3$.
Find the coordinates of the points where the line L cuts the axes.

The line $2y = x - 3$ has gradient $\dfrac{1}{2}$

$\therefore$ the line L perpendicular to this has gradient -2.

Perpendicular lines
$m_1 \times m_2 = -1$

For L, use $\dfrac{y_2 - y_1}{x_2 - x_1} = m$: $\quad \dfrac{-3 + k}{4k - 1} = -2$

Simplify: $\qquad\qquad\qquad -3 + k = -8k + 2$

$\qquad\qquad\qquad\qquad\quad 9k = 5$

Hence $\qquad\qquad\qquad\quad k = \dfrac{5}{9}$

Substitute for k in the coordinates of A and B: A is $\left(\dfrac{20}{9}, -3\right)$, B is $\left(1, -\dfrac{5}{9}\right)$

so the equation of line L is $\dfrac{y + 3}{x - \dfrac{20}{9}} = -2$

Using $\dfrac{y - y_1}{x - x_1} = m$

Simplify: $\qquad\qquad\qquad\qquad y = -2x + \dfrac{13}{9}$

$\left(-2 \times -\dfrac{20}{9}\right) - 3 = \dfrac{13}{9}$

When $x = 0$, $y = \dfrac{13}{9}$ and when $y = 0$, $x = \dfrac{13}{18}$

$\therefore L$ cuts the axes at $\left(0, \dfrac{13}{9}\right)$ and $\left(\dfrac{13}{18}, 0\right)$.

C1

Exercise 2.3

1 Rearrange the straight line equations in the form $y = mx + c$ and determine whether each pair of lines is parallel, perpendicular or neither.

   a $y = 2x + 1, y - 2x = 3$ **b** $2y + 4 = 3x, 4y + 8 = 3x$

   c $x + y + 1 = 0, y - x + 1 = 0$ **d** $y = 2x - 3, 2y = x - 3$

   e $2y + x + 3 = 0, 4y - 8x + 1 = 0$ **f** $1 + y = 4(x + 2), x + 2 = 4(1 + y)$

   g $x - 1 = y, y - 2 = x$ **h** $y = -x + 5, x = -y + 5$

2 **a** The line L is parallel to the line $2y = 3x + 4$ and passes through the point $(-1, 3)$.
   Find the equation of the line L.

   b The line L is perpendicular to the line $y + 2x = 4$ and passes through the point $(-2, 1)$.
   Find the equation of line L.

   c A line L is parallel to the line K whose equation is $4x + 3y + 2 = 0$
   Line L also passes through the point $(0, 4)$.
   Find the equation of line L.

   d Find the equation of the line joining the points $(1, -1)$ and $(-2, 3)$ and state whether this line is parallel, perpendicular or neither to the line with equation $4y - 3x + 4 = 0$

   e The line joining the point $P(x, y)$ to the point $Q(3, -2)$ is parallel to the line $2x - y + 4 = 0$
   Find the equation of the line PQ.

   f Line L is perpendicular to the line $2y - x + 3 = 0$
   at the point $\left(4, \frac{1}{2}\right)$.
   Determine the equation of the line L.

   g The line L is parallel to the line $3x + 6y - 2 = 0$ and goes through the point $(5, 0)$.
   What is the equation of the line?

   h Determine the equation of the line passing through the point $(1, -1)$ which is perpendicular to the line with equation $3 - 2y - 4x = 0$

3   **a**   The line $y = mx + 1$ is perpendicular to the line $y = \frac{1}{2}x - 3$
Find the value of m.

b   The line $2y = 3x + 2$ is parallel to the line $y = ax - 4$
Find the value of a.

c   A straight line with equation $y = mx + c$ passes through
the point $P(1, 3)$ and is parallel to the line $y + 2x = 0$
Find the value of m and c.
Hence write down the equation of the line.

d   The equation of a line is given by $x + 2y - 5 = 0$
Write this equation in form $y = mx + c$.
State the gradient of a line perpendicular to this line.

e   Write in the form $ax + by + c = 0$ the equation of the line
which is perpendicular to the line $y - x + 4 = 0$ and passes
through the point $(0, -2)$.

f   Find the equation of the line which is perpendicular to the
line $y = 3x - 1$ and passes through the point $(3, 2)$.
Give the equation in the form $y = mx + c$

g   The line $y = mx + c$ passes through the point $(4, 3)$ and is
parallel to the line $x + 2y = 4$
Determine the values of m and c and write down the
equation of the first line.

h   The line joining $A(3, a)$ and $B(2a, -1)$ is perpendicular
to the line $2y + x + 1 = 0$
Find the value of a.

INVESTIGATION

4   The two boxes below contain equations of straight lines.
Each line in Box A is perpendicular to a line in Box B.
Which line in Box B does not have a pair?

Box A	Box B
$y = \frac{1}{3}x + 1$	$y + 3x = 5$
$5y = -2x + 4$	$3y = -x - 1$
$y = 3x + 2$	$2y - 5x - 2 = 0$
	$x - 3y - 2 = 0$

◯ See Chapter 0 for revision on midpoints and lengths of lines and simultaneous equations.

1 Rewrite each equation in the form $y = mx + c$

   a $3 - x - y = 0$

   b $2x + 3y = 6$

   c $1 = 4y + 8x$

2 Rewrite each equation in the form $ax + by + c = 0$
where a, b and c are integers.

   a $3y - 2x = 5$

   b $y = \frac{1}{2}x - 1$

   c $\frac{3}{4}y = 2 - \frac{1}{2}x$

3 **a**   The line, $ax + y + c = 0$, passes through the point $(1, 2)$
      and has gradient 4. What are the values of a and c?

   b   Line L passes through the point $(-2, 3)$ and has equation
      $y = \frac{1}{2}x + c$
      Work out the value of c.

   c   Make y the subject of the straight line equation $4x - 2y + 5 = 0$
      Hence determine the gradient and y-intercept.

   d   A line has gradient b and y-intercept $(0, 2b)$.
      Show that the line has equation $y = b(x + 2)$
      Find the value of b if this line passes through the point $(-1, -2)$.

4 **a**   Are the lines $3 - y = x$ and $2 + y = x$ perpendicular?
      Show how you reach this conclusion.

   b   Find the equation of the line which is parallel to
      $4y + 8x - 7 = 0$ and goes through the point $(0, -3)$.

   c   The line L cuts the x- and y-axes at P and Q respectively.
      If the gradient of L is $-\frac{1}{2}$ and the y-intercept is 3 find the
      coordinates of P and Q.
      A second line K is perpendicular to L and passes through
      the point Q. What is the equation of line K?

   d   The line $y = ax + b$ is perpendicular to the line $x + 3y - 2 = 0$
      and goes through the point $(4, -2)$. Find the values of a and b.

5 For the line ABC, A is the point $(1, 4)$ and C is the point $(5, 8)$. The midpoint of the line is at $B(x, y)$. A line L is drawn through B and is perpendicular to ABC. Find the coordinates of B and the equation of line L.

6 A straight line, PQR, joins the points $P(-1, -1)$, $Q(3, 7)$ and $R(x, y)$, where Q is the midpoint of line PR. Another line, L, is drawn at point R and passes through the point $S(1, -4)$. Find the equation of line L.

7 The line L_1 passes through the point $(3, -9)$ and has gradient 2.

   a Find the equation of L_1 in the form $ax + by + c = 0$ where a, b and c are integers.

The line L_2 passes through the origin and has gradient $-\frac{1}{2}$. The lines L_1 and L_2 intersect at the point P.

   b Calculate the coordinates of P.

Given that L_1 crosses the y-axis at the point C

   c calculate the exact area of $\triangle OCP$.

8 The points, $A(1, 7)$, $B(20, 7)$ and $C(p, q)$ form the vertices of a triangle ABC, as shown in the diagram. The point $D(8, 2)$ is the midpoint of AC.

   a Find the value of p and the value of q.

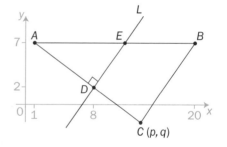

The line L, which passes through D and is perpendicular to AC, intersects AB at E.

   b Find an equation for L, in the form $ax + by + c = 0$ where a, b and c are integers.

   c Find the exact x-coordinate of E.

[(c) Edexcel Limited 2005]

9 The line L_1, $y = \frac{1}{2}x + 3$, is perpendicular to the line L_2, $y = -2x + 9$

   a Find the point of intersection, P, of these two lines.

Line L_1 cuts the y-axis at A.

   b Find the coordinates of A.

By considering the right-angled triangle, APB, as shown in the diagram, or otherwise

   c find the length AP.

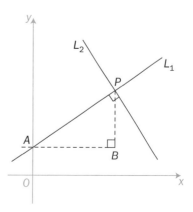

2

Exit ⟹

Summary   Refer to

- You can find the equation of a straight line if you know
  one point on the line and the gradient using $y - y_1 = m(x - x_1)$ 2.1

- You can find the gradient of a line if you know two points on the
  line using $m = \dfrac{y_2 - y_1}{x_2 - x_1}$ 2.1

- The equation of a straight line is generally written in the form
  $ax + by + c = 0$ or $y = mx + c$ 2.2

- Two straight lines are
  - parallel if their gradients are equal
  - perpendicular if the product of their gradients is –1.   2.3

C1

Links

Straight-line graphs are used in the real world to illustrate direct
proportion between two variables.

e.g. Conversion rates between different units of currency or between metric and
imperial measures.

They are also used commonly in physics where it is thought
that the relationship between two quantities is roughly linear.

e.g. Voltage and current ($V = IR$).

Straight-line graphs are an example of coordinate geometry,
which is an important branch of mathematics.

Coordinates are used to describe precisely the position of
a point in two dimensions or in three dimensional space.

3

Quadratic functions

This chapter will show you how to
- sketch quadratic graphs
- use different methods to solve quadratic equations
- understand and interpret the discriminant.

Before you start

You should know how to:

1 Simplify surd forms.

e.g. Simplify $\sqrt{75}$

Use the rule $\sqrt{ab} = \sqrt{a}\sqrt{b}$:

$$\sqrt{75} = \sqrt{25 \times 3}$$
$$= \sqrt{25}\sqrt{3}$$
$$= 5\sqrt{3}$$

2 Substitute values into an equation.

e.g. If $y = x^2 - 3x + 2$

find the value of y when

i $x = 3$ ii $x = -2$

i $y = (3)^2 - 3(3) + 2$
     $= 9 - 9 + 2$
     $= 2$

ii $y = (-2)^2 - 3(-2) + 2$
     $= 4 + 6 + 2$
     $= 12$

3 Expand double brackets.

e.g. Expand $(x - 3)(2x + 5)$

$(x - 3)(2x + 5) = 2x^2 + 5x - 6x - 15$

Simplify by collecting like terms:

$(x - 3)(2x + 5) = 2x^2 - x - 15$

Check in:

1 Simplify

  a $\sqrt{90}$

  b $\sqrt{60}$

  c $\sqrt{150}$

  d $\sqrt{8}$

  e $\sqrt{54}$

2 Find y when

  i $x = 2$ and   **ii** $x = -3$

  a $y = x^2 + 2x - 3$

  b $y = 2x^2 - 3x$

  c $y = 2 - x - x^2$

  d $y = 3(2x - 3)^2$

  e $y = (5 - x)(2 - x)$

  f $y = (x + 3)^2 - (x - 3)^2$

3 Expand

  a $(x + 2)(x + 5)$

  b $(2x - 1)(2x - 3)$

  c $(1 - x)(1 - 3x)$

  d $(2x + 1)(1 - 2x)$

  e $(5 - 2x)(2x - 5)$

The general form of a **quadratic function** is
$$f(x) = ax^2 + bx + c$$
where a, b and c are constant values and $a \neq 0$.

$f(x) = 2x^2 - 3x + 7$ is a quadratic function.

The simplest form of a quadratic function occurs when $a = 1$, $b = 0$ and $c = 0$ giving $f(x) = x^2$

When $a > 0$ the graph of $f(x)$ looks like

When $a < 0$ the graph of $f(x)$ looks like

The lowest point on the curve is called the minimum point (plural minima).

The highest point on the curve is called the maximum point (plural maxima).

The general form of a **quadratic equation** is
$$ax^2 + bx + c = 0$$

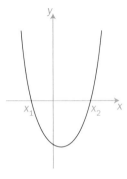

Many quadratic equations can be solved by factorising.

The solutions, x_1 and x_2, or **roots**, are the values of x at the x-intercepts.

EXAMPLE 1

Solve the equation $x^2 - 6x + 8 = 0$

Factorise: $(x - 4)(x - 2) = 0$

Either $x - 4 = 0$ or $x - 2 = 0$
             $x = 4$ $x = 2$

The quadratic equation has two solutions $x = 2$ or $x = 4$.

If two terms A and B multiply to give zero, then either $A = 0$ or $B = 0$ or $A = B = 0$

○ A quadratic equation usually has two solutions, but may have only one or none at all.

EXAMPLE 2

Find x when $(x + 4)(x - 1) = 0$

Either $x + 4 = 0$ or $x - 1 = 0$

giving $x = -4$ or $x = 1$

The solutions are $x = -4$ or $x = 1$.

You may find it useful to sketch the curve.

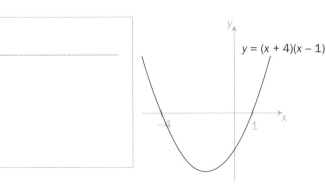

$y = (x + 4)(x - 1)$

C1

- A quadratic equation that can be written in the form $(x + p)(x + q) = 0$ has solutions $x = -p$ or $x = -q$.

This method only works if the quadratic expression equals zero. You may need to rearrange the equation before solving it.

EXAMPLE 3

Find the values of x that satisfy $x(2x + 1) = 4(2x + 1)$

If p is a solution, you can say that 'p **satisfies** the equation'.

$$x(2x + 1) = 4(2x + 1)$$

Rearrange: $\quad x(2x + 1) - 4(2x + 1) = 0$

Factorise: $\quad\quad\quad\quad (2x + 1)(x - 4) = 0$

Notice that $(2x + 1)$ is common to both terms.

Either $\quad 2x + 1 = 0 \quad$ or $\quad x - 4 = 0$

$\quad\quad\quad\quad 2x = -1 \quad\quad\quad\quad\quad x = 4$

$\quad\quad\quad\quad x = -\dfrac{1}{2}$

The solutions are $x = -\dfrac{1}{2}$ or $x = 4$.

Sometimes you will need to factorise the equation before you can solve it.

If you need to practise factorising quadratics, look at Chapter 0 on the CD-ROM.

EXAMPLE 4

Solve $\quad$ **a** $\; x^2 + 9x + 20 = 0 \quad\quad$ **b** $\; 2x^2 - x - 6 = 0$

a $\quad x^2 + 9x + 20 = 0$

$\quad (x + 4)(x + 5) = 0$

Either $\quad\quad x + 4 = 0 \quad\quad$ or $\quad\quad x + 5 = 0$

$\quad\quad\quad\quad\quad x = -4 \quad\quad\quad\quad\quad\quad x = -5$

The solutions are $x = -4$ and $x = -5$.

b $\quad\quad 2x^2 - x - 6 = 0$

$\quad (2x + 3)(x - 2) = 0$

Solve: Either $2x + 3 = 0 \quad\quad$ or $\quad\quad x - 2 = 0$

$\quad\quad\quad\quad\quad 2x = -3 \quad\quad\quad\quad\quad\quad x = 2$

$\quad\quad\quad\quad\quad x = -\dfrac{3}{2}$

The solutions are $x = -\dfrac{3}{2}$ or $x = 2$.

One factor will start with $2x$ and one with x.
One factor will have a $+$ and one a $-$. This is because the constant is negative.

It is often helpful to recognise an expression that is the **difference of two squares (DOTS)**.

See Chapter 0 on the CD-ROM.

$$X^2 - Y^2 = (X + Y)(X - Y)$$

EXAMPLE 5

a Factorise $4x^2 - 25$

b Hence solve $4x^2 - 25 = 0$

---

a Rewrite $4x^2 - 25$ in the form $X^2 - Y^2$:

$$4x^2 - 25 = (2x)^2 - (5)^2$$

Apply $X^2 - Y^2 = (X + Y)(X - Y)$:

$$4x^2 - 25 = (2x)^2 - (5)^2 = (2x + 5)(2x - 5)$$

b $4x^2 - 25 = 0$

so $(2x + 5)(2x - 5) = 0$

Either $\qquad$ $2x + 5 = 0$ $\qquad$ or $\qquad$ $2x - 5 = 0$

$\qquad\qquad\qquad 2x = -5 \qquad\qquad\qquad\qquad 2x = 5$

$\qquad\qquad\qquad x = -\dfrac{5}{2} \qquad\qquad\qquad\qquad x = \dfrac{5}{2}$

The solutions are $x = -\dfrac{5}{2}$ or $x = \dfrac{5}{2}$.

Exercise 3.1

1 Solve these equations.

a $(x - 2)(x - 3) = 0$ $\qquad$ **b** $x(x + 1) = 0$ $\qquad$ **c** $2x(x - 3) = 0$

d $3(x + 4)(x - 5) = 0$ $\qquad$ **e** $(x + 7)^2 = 0$ $\qquad$ **f** $5(2 - x)(3 - x) = 0$

g $-4(4 - x)^2 = 0$ $\qquad$ **h** $(x - 5)(2x + 1) = 0$ $\qquad$ **i** $x(2x - 3) = 0$

j $4x(1 - 3x) = 0$ $\qquad$ **k** $(2x - 5)(2x - 3) = 0$ $\qquad$ **l** $5(3x - 5)^2 = 0$

m $(4x + 2)(2 - 4x) = 0$ $\qquad$ **n** $3(2x + 5)(5x + 2) = 0$ $\qquad$ **o** $9(3 - 2x)^2 = 0$

2 Factorise these equations and hence find the values of x that satisfy each equation.

a $2(x - 1) + x(x - 1) = 0$ $\qquad$ **b** $3(4x + 1) + x(4x + 1) = 0$

c $7(3x - 1) = 2x(3x - 1)$ $\qquad$ **d** $x(4 - 3x) = \dfrac{1}{2}(4 - 3x)$

3 i Factorise these equations.

$\quad$ **ii** Hence find the values of x that satisfy each equation.

$\quad$ **iii** Sketch the graph of the associated quadratic function.
$\qquad$ In your sketch, mark the coordinates of the points where $\qquad$ *Let $y = 0$ and $x = 0$.*
$\qquad$ the curve crosses the x- and y-axes.

a $x^2 + 3x + 2 = 0$ $\qquad$ **b** $x^2 + x - 6 = 0$ $\qquad$ **c** $x^2 - 7x + 10 = 0$

d $x^2 - x = 30$ $\qquad$ **e** $x^2 = 11x - 28$ $\qquad$ **f** $x^2 = 24 - 2x$

g $x^2 = 5x + 36$ $\qquad$ **h** $x^2 = 13x - 30$ $\qquad$ **i** $24 + 25x + x^2 = 0$

4 Factorise these equations using the difference of two squares and solve them to find x.

a $x^2 - 9 = 0$

b $4x^2 - 1 = 0$

c $9x^2 - 16 = 0$

d $\dfrac{x^2}{4} - 1 = 0$

e $27x^2 - 12 = 0$

f $5 - 125x^2 = 0$

g $\dfrac{12x^2}{25} - 48 = 0$

h $2 - x^2 = 0$

i $3 - \dfrac{x^2}{4} = 0$

5 Factorise these equations and solve them to find x.

a $2x^2 - x - 1 = 0$

b $3x^2 - 7x + 2 = 0$

c $4x^2 + 4x + 1 = 0$

d $6x^2 + 5x + 1 = 0$

e $12x^2 + 13x + 3 = 0$

f $6 - 11x + 5x^2 = 0$

g $12x^2 = 25x - 12$

h $6x^2 = 25 - 5x$

i $12 + 7x = 10x^2$

6 Solve these equations to find the values of x.

a $4(x + 2)^2 = 0$

b $x(1 - 2x) = 0$

c $(3x + 2)(4x - 5) = 0$

d $5(x - 3) - x(x - 3) = 0$

e $x(2x - 1) = 2x - 1$

f $x^2 + 8x + 15 = 0$

g $25x^2 - 36 = 0$

h $3x^2 - 11x = 4$

i $30x^2 + 49x + 20 = 0$

j $21x^2 = 55x - 14$

7 Solve

a $-2x^2 - 3x - 1 = 0$

b $x^2 = -3x - 2$

c $-3x^2 + 7x = 2$

INVESTIGATIONS

8 Four equations and their solutions are given:

Equations:	Solutions:
1. $x^2 + 3x + 2 = 0$	$x = -1$ $x = 3$
2. $x^2 - 3x + 2 = 0$	$x = 1$ $x = -3$
3. $2x^2 - x - 3 = 0$	$x = -2$ $x = \dfrac{3}{2}$
4. $x^2 - 4x + 4 = 0$	$x = 2$ $x = -\dfrac{3}{2}$

Some solutions may be used more than once.

Match each equation with its solution(s).

9 The box contains some linear factors:

$(2x + 3)$ $(x - 2)$ $(2x + 1)$ $(3x + 1)$ $(x + 1)$ $(x + 4)$ $(x - 4)$ $(2x - 3)$ $(2x - 1)$

Use some of these factors to factorise the quadratics

a $2x^2 - 5x - 12 = 0$

b $2x^2 - 3x - 2 = 0$

c $4x^2 + 4x - 3 = 0$

Completing the square

Some quadratic expressions have two identical factors.
Such expressions are known as perfect squares.

Solve the equation $x^2 + 10x + 25 = 9$

$$x^2 + 10x + 25 = 9$$
$$(x + 5)^2 = 9$$

Take square roots of each side:

$$x + 5 = \pm 3$$

Rearrange: $x = -5 \pm 3$

Either $x = -5 + 3$ or $x = -5 - 3$

Hence $x = -2$ or $x = -8$

$x^2 + 10x + 25$ is a perfect square since it factorises into $(x + 5)^2$.

Remember to include both solutions of $x^2 = 9$.
$3^2 = 9$ and $(-3)^2 = 9$

○ You can rewrite any quadratic expression in factorised form like this:

$$ax^2 + bx + c \equiv a(x + p)^2 + q$$

Factorising an equation into this form is called completing the square.

$\equiv$ means 'is identical to'.

Complete the square for the expression $x^2 + 8x$

Try $(x + 4)^2$:

$$(x + 4)^2 = x^2 + 8x + 16$$

This is close, however you want $x^2 + 8x$

Subtract 16: $x^2 + 8x = (x + 4)^2 - 16$

4 is chosen because $4x + 4x = 8x$

If the coefficient of x^2 is not equal to 1, you can still complete the square.

Complete the square for the expression $2x^2 - 4x$

First take out the coefficient of x^2:

$$2x^2 - 4x = 2(x^2 - 2x)$$

Now complete the square inside the bracket:

$$= 2(x^2 - 2x + 1 - 1)$$
$$= 2[(x - 1)^2 - 1] = 2(x - 1)^2 - 2$$

$(x - 1)^2 = x^2 - 2x + 1$
so you must subtract 1.

You can use the method of completing the square to solve quadratic equations.

EXAMPLE 4

Use the method of completing the square to solve

a $x^2 + 10x + 7 = 0$ **b** $2x^2 + 5x - 4 = 0$

---

a
$$x^2 + 10x + 7 = 0$$

Rewrite:
$$x^2 + 10x = -7$$

The coefficient of x is 10.

$\frac{1}{2} \times 10 = 5$ so try $(x + 5)^2$: $(x + 5)^2 = x^2 + 10x + 25$

Subtract 25:
$$(x + 5)^2 - 25 = x^2 + 10x = -7$$

Hence
$$(x + 5)^2 - 25 = -7$$

Rearrange:
$$(x + 5)^2 = -7 + 25$$
$$(x + 5)^2 = 18$$

Take square roots:
$$x + 5 = \pm\sqrt{18}$$

Simplify:
$$x + 5 = \pm 3\sqrt{2}$$

Rearrange:
$$x = -5 \pm 3\sqrt{2}$$

Either $x = -5 + 3\sqrt{2}$ or $x = -5 - 3\sqrt{2}$

There is a simple rule that can help you in completing the square:

o If you rewrite $ax^2 + bx + c$
  as $a(x + p)^2 + q$

  then $p = \dfrac{b}{2a}$

Remember to include both solutions of $\sqrt{18}$.

$\sqrt{18} = \sqrt{(9 \times 2)}$

$\phantom{\sqrt{18}} = \sqrt{(3^2 \times 2)} = 3\sqrt{2}$

b
$$2x^2 + 5x - 4 = 0$$

Rewrite:
$$2\left(x^2 + \frac{5}{2}x - 2\right) = 0$$

Since $2 \neq 0$, the expression in the bracket must be equal to 0.

Hence
$$x^2 + \frac{5}{2}x - 2 = 0$$

Rearrange:
$$x^2 + \frac{5}{2}x = 2$$

The coefficient of x is $\frac{5}{2}$.

$\frac{1}{2} \times \frac{5}{2} = \frac{5}{4}$ so try $\left(x + \frac{5}{4}\right)^2$: $\left(x + \frac{5}{4}\right)^2 = x^2 + \frac{5}{2}x + \frac{25}{16}$

Subtract $\frac{25}{16}$: $\left(x + \frac{5}{4}\right)^2 - \frac{25}{16} = x^2 + \frac{5}{2}x = 2$

Hence $\left(x + \frac{5}{4}\right)^2 - \frac{25}{16} = 2$

Rearrange: $\left(x + \frac{5}{4}\right)^2 = 2 + \frac{25}{16}$

Simplify and take square roots: $x + \frac{5}{4} = \pm\sqrt{\frac{57}{16}}$

Rearrange: $x = -\frac{5}{4} \pm \frac{\sqrt{57}}{4}$

Hence $x = \dfrac{-5 + \sqrt{57}}{4}$ or $x = \dfrac{-5 - \sqrt{57}}{4}$

$\sqrt{\left(2 + \dfrac{25}{16}\right)} = \sqrt{\left(\dfrac{32}{16} + \dfrac{25}{16}\right)}$

$\phantom{\sqrt{\left(2 + \dfrac{25}{16}\right)}} = \sqrt{\dfrac{57}{16}}$

Leave your answer in surd form.

C1

Exercise 3.2

1 Take square roots to find the value of x.

   a $(x-3)^2 = 25$ **b** $(x+2)^2 = 25$

   c $(2x+1)^2 = 1$ **d** $(2x-3)^2 = 16$

   e $(5+2x)^2 = 1$ **f** $(3-4x)^2 = 36$

   g $(5x-7)^2 = 49$ **h** $\left(\dfrac{x}{2}+2\right)^2 = 25$

   i $(x+4)^2 = 3$ **j** $(2x-1)^2 = 5$

2 Complete the square for each expression, writing your final answer in the form $k(x+a)^2 + b$.

   a $x^2 + 4x$ **b** $x^2 - 4x$

   c $x^2 + 5x$ **d** $x^2 - 3x$

   e $x^2 - 2x$ **f** $2x^2 + 4x$

   g $3x^2 - 6x$ **h** $5x^2 - 3x$

   i $\dfrac{x^2}{2} + 4x$ **j** $\dfrac{3}{4}x^2 - 2x$

3 Use the method of completing the square to solve these equations, leaving your answers in surd form.

   a $x^2 + 4x + 1 = 0$

   b $x^2 - 4x - 2 = 0$

   c $2x^2 + 8x + 3 = 0$

   d $2x^2 - 4x + 1 = 0$

   e $2x^2 - 5 = 6x$

   f $5 + 4x - 2x^2 = 0$

INVESTIGATIONS

4   Completing the square has a useful purpose when
    sketching quadratics.
    Consider the equation $y = x^2 + 6x + 5$

    a Express y in the form $y = (x + a)^2 + b$

    b Find the value of x that gives the *minimum* value for y.

    c What is the minimum value of y? What is the
         y-coordinate of the minimum point?

    d Hence sketch the curve, showing the intersection
         with the axes and the minimum point.

5   Match the following equations with their minimum
    points:

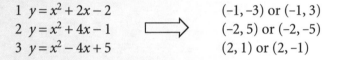

    1 $y = x^2 + 2x - 2$ (-1, -3) or (-1, 3)
    2 $y = x^2 + 4x - 1$ (-2, 5) or (-2, -5)
    3 $y = x^2 - 4x + 5$ (2, 1) or (2, -1)

6   Two graphs are shown:

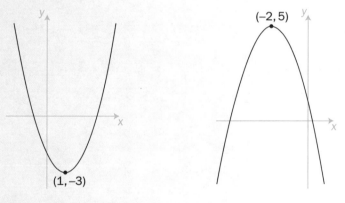

Fig. 1   Fig. 2

Find the equation of each graph giving your answer in
the form $y = ax^2 + bx + c$.

For Fig. 2, what would the equation be if the point (-2, 5)
was a minimum instead of a maximum?

The quadratic formula

You can apply the method of completing the square to the general quadratic equation $ax^2 + bx + c = 0$

$$ax^2 + bx + c = 0 \qquad a \neq 0$$

Rewrite as:
$$a\left(x^2 + \frac{b}{a}x + \frac{c}{a}\right) = 0$$

Hence
$$\left(x^2 + \frac{b}{a}x + \frac{c}{a}\right) = 0 \qquad \text{Dividing both sides by } a.$$

Rearrange:
$$x^2 + \frac{b}{a}x = -\frac{c}{a}$$

Complete the square:
$$x^2 + \frac{b}{a}x + \frac{b^2}{4a^2} = \frac{b^2}{4a^2} - \frac{c}{a}$$

Factorise:
$$\left(x + \frac{b}{2a}\right)^2 = \frac{b^2 - 4ac}{4a^2}$$

Take square roots:
$$x + \frac{b}{2a} = \pm\sqrt{\frac{b^2 - 4ac}{4a^2}}$$

Make x the subject:
$$x = -\frac{b}{2a} \pm \frac{\sqrt{(b^2 - 4ac)}}{2a} = \frac{-b \pm \sqrt{(b^2 - 4ac)}}{2a}$$

○ You can solve quadratic equations of the form
$ax^2 + bx + c = 0$ using the quadratic formula:

$$x = \frac{-b \pm \sqrt{b^2 - 4ac}}{2a}$$

You need to learn this formula. You can quote it without giving the proof.

The quadratic formula is particularly useful when a quadratic equation doesn't factorise easily.

EXAMPLE 1

Use the formula to solve the equation $x^2 - 2x - 5 = 0$

Compare $x^2 - 2x - 5 = 0$ with $ax^2 + bx + c = 0$:
$a = 1, b = -2, c = -5$

You should first try to factorise as it is quicker.

Use the formula:
$$x = \frac{-b \pm \sqrt{(b^2 - 4ac)}}{2a}$$

Put in the values:
$$x = \frac{-(-2) \pm \sqrt{(-2)^2 - 4(1)(-5)}}{2(1)}$$

Take care with the signs.
If b is negative then $-b$ is positive.
b^2 is always positive.

$\sqrt{24} = \sqrt{4 \times 6} = \sqrt{4} \times \sqrt{6} = 2\sqrt{6}$

Simplify:
$$x = \frac{2 \pm \sqrt{24}}{2} = 1 \pm \sqrt{6}$$

Remember to divide the whole of the numerator by 2, not just the square root.

The solutions are $x = 1 + \sqrt{6}$ or $x = 1 - \sqrt{6}$

Leave your answer in surd form unless the question indicates otherwise.

You can often use quadratic equations to solve word problems.

Three times a number subtracted from the reciprocal of that number is equal to 4.
Find the possible numbers in surd form.

First express the word problem as an equation using algebra.

Let x be the number: $\dfrac{1}{x} - 3x = 4$

So $\qquad\qquad 3x^2 + 4x - 1 = 0$

Multiply each term by x and rearrange.

Compare with $ax^2 + bx + c = 0$: $\quad a = 3, \quad b = 4, \quad c = -1$

Use the formula: $\qquad x = \dfrac{-b \pm \sqrt{(b^2 - 4ac)}}{2a}$

Put in the values: $\qquad x = \dfrac{-(4) \pm \sqrt{(4)^2 - 4(3)(-1)}}{2(3)}$

Evaluate: $\qquad x = \dfrac{-4 \pm \sqrt{(16 + 12)}}{6}$

Simplify: $\qquad x = \dfrac{-4 \pm \sqrt{28}}{6}$

$\sqrt{28} = \sqrt{4 \times 7} = \sqrt{4} \times \sqrt{7} = 2\sqrt{7}$

$$x = \dfrac{-4 \pm 2\sqrt{7}}{6}$$

Cancel down: $\qquad x = \dfrac{-2 \pm \sqrt{7}}{3}$

The solutions are $\qquad x = \dfrac{-2 + \sqrt{7}}{3} \quad$ or $\quad x = \dfrac{-2 - \sqrt{7}}{3}$

The discriminant

- In the quadratic function $f(x) = ax^2 + bx + c$ the expression $(b^2 - 4ac)$ is known as the discriminant.

If the coefficient of x^2 is negative, then the parabola will be upside down.

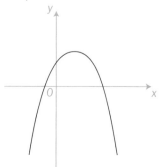

- You can use the discriminant to investigate the nature of the roots of a quadratic equation (two, one or no real roots).

There are three possible cases for the solution of a
quadratic equation.
The value of $(b^2 - 4ac)$ tells you what type of roots the equation has.

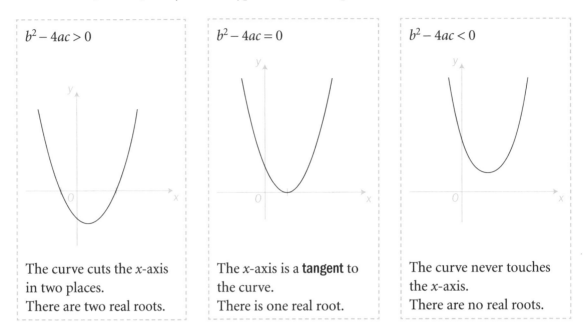

$b^2 - 4ac > 0$	$b^2 - 4ac = 0$	$b^2 - 4ac < 0$
The curve cuts the x-axis in two places. There are two real roots.	The x-axis is a **tangent** to the curve. There is one real root.	The curve never touches the x-axis. There are no real roots.

EXAMPLE 3

By finding the value of the discriminant, determine the
nature of the roots of these equations.

a $x^2 - 2x + 3 = 0$

b $x^2 - x - 2 = 0$

c $x^2 + 6x + 9 = 0$

Sketch a graph to illustrate each case.

a Write down the values of a, b and c:
  $a = 1, b = -2, c = 3$
  $b^2 - 4ac = 4 - 12$
  $\qquad = -8$
  $b^2 - 4ac < 0$
  so no real roots

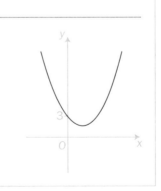

To sketch a graph, first find f(0) and another simple value e.g. f(1):
f(0) = 3, f(1) = 2

Example 3 continues on the next page.

EXAMPLE 3 (CONT.)

b Write down the values of a, b and c:

$a = 1, b = -1, c = -2$

$b^2 - 4ac = 1 - -8$

$\qquad = 9$

$b^2 - 4ac > 0$

so two real roots

$f(0) = -2, f(1) = -2$

c Write down the values of a, b and c:

$a = 1, b = 6, c = 9$

$b^2 - 4ac = 36 - 36$

$\qquad = 0$

$b^2 - 4ac = 0$

so one real root

$f(0) = 9, f(-1) = 4$

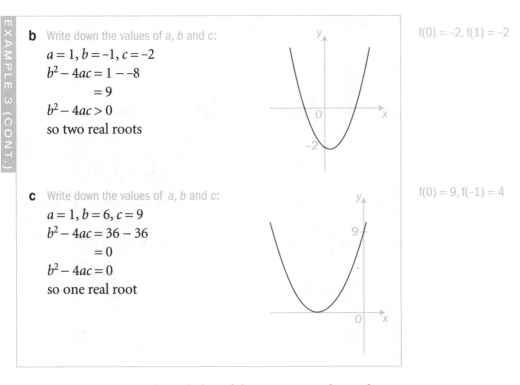

Sometimes you can use knowledge of the roots to work out the equation of a quadratic function.

EXAMPLE 4

a The equation $2x^2 + kx + 3k = 0$ has one (repeated) root. Find the value of k.

b The equation $x^2 + 5x + k = 0$ has two real and distinct roots. Find the range of possible values of k.

---

a For one (repeated) root $b^2 - 4ac = 0$

$$2x^2 + kx + 3k = 0$$
$$k^2 - 4 \times 2 \times 3k = 0$$

$a = 2, b = k, c = 3k$

Simplify: $\qquad k^2 - 24k = 0$

Factorise: $\qquad k(k - 24) = 0$

Solve: $\qquad k = 0 \quad \text{or} \quad k = 24$

b For two roots $b^2 - 4ac > 0$

$$x^2 + 5x + k = 0$$
$$5^2 - 4 \times 1 \times k > 0$$

$a = 1, b = 5, c = k$

Simplify: $\qquad 25 - 4k > 0$

$\qquad -4k > -25$

Divide both sides by -4: $\qquad k < \dfrac{25}{4}$

Remember to change the direction of the inequality sign when dividing by a negative number.

Exercise 3.3

1 Solve these equations by using the formula

$$x = \frac{-b \pm \sqrt{(b^2 - 4ac)}}{2a}$$

a $x^2 + 7x + 10 = 0$ b $x^2 + 2x - 3 = 0$ c $x^2 - 7x + 12 = 0$

d $x^2 - 2x - 8 = 0$ e $x^2 + 4x + 3 = 0$ f $2x^2 - 3x - 2 = 0$

g $2x^2 + x - 3 = 0$ h $6x^2 + 5x + 1 = 0$ i $8x^2 - 10x + 3 = 0$

2 Rearrange each equation, where necessary, into the form $ax^2 + bx + c = 0$ and use the quadratic formula to obtain solutions where possible. Give your solutions in simplified surd form.

> Look at the cases where a solution is not possible – try to think why.

a $x^2 + 3x + 1 = 0$ b $x^2 - 3x - 2 = 0$ c $x^2 - 5x + 3 = 0$

d $2x^2 + 6x + 1 = 0$ e $2x^2 + 3x - 4 = 0$ f $3x^2 - x + 1 = 0$

g $x^2 + 10x + 4 = 0$ h $2 - 4x - x^2 = 0$ i $(x + 1)^2 = x + 2$

3 Find the value of the discriminant, $(b^2 - 4ac)$, and decide whether each equation has one, two or no roots.

a $x^2 + 4x + 5 = 0$ b $x^2 - 3x - 10 = 0$

c $x^2 + 6x + 9 = 0$ d $x^2 - 2x - 1 = 0$

e $2x^2 + 3x - 5 = 0$ f $3x^2 - x - 1 = 0$

g $4x^2 - 5x + 2 = 0$ h $-2x^2 + 3x - 1 = 0$

4 Find the range of possible values of k if the following equations have

i no roots

ii one (repeated) root

iii two real and distinct roots   *distinct means not equal*

a $2x^2 - x + k = 0$

b $kx^2 - 4x - 1 = 0$

c $x^2 + k = 0$

5 The difference between two numbers a and b is 1, and the product of the two numbers is 9.
Show that there are two possible pairs of values which satisfy these conditions and evaluate the numbers.

6 The sum of a number and its reciprocal is 4.
What are the two possible numbers which satisfy this condition?

7   In a right-angled triangle the shorter sides are of lengths
    $(x + 3)$ and $(2x - 1)$ units and the length of the hypotenuse
    is $3x$ units.

    Find the lengths of the sides of the triangle.

8   The equation $ax^2 + bx + c = 0$ is such that $-b = p$, $2a = r$ and the
    discriminant is equal to q where p, q and r are constants.

    Show that $c = \dfrac{p^2 - q}{2r}$.

9   Given that the quadratic equation $ax^2 + bx + c = 0$
    has two solutions, show that the quadratic equation given by
    $a^2x^2 = b^2x - 2acx - c^2$, where a, b and c are constants and $b \neq 0$,
    also has two solutions.

INVESTIGATIONS

10 The golden ratio is a mathematically interesting number
    that supposedly represents divine proportion. The golden
    spiral, occurring in nature, is formed from the golden ratio.

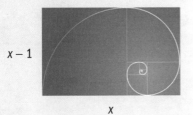

$x - 1$

x

The rectangle framing the golden spiral has sides in the
golden ratio if the area of the rectangle is equal to one.

a   Write an equation using this information.

b   Hence solve to find x, giving your answer in surd form.

11 Choose values of k to make each of these quadratic equations
    have just one real (repeated) root.

    a $x^2 + kx + 4 = 0$ b $x^2 + kx + 9 = 0$ c $x^2 + kx + 16 = 0$

    Can you generalise to a quadratic of the form
    $x^2 + kx + n^2 = 0$?

12 Which integer values for k result in the following equation having
    two real roots?

    $x^2 + kx + 5 = 0$

1 Solve these quadratic equations giving all values of x.

   a $(x-3)(x+7)=0$

   b $x(x+4)=0$

   c $5(x-3)^2=0$

   d $(3x-1)(2x-3)=0$

2 Factorise these equations and then solve to find the value(s) of x.

   a $x(2x-1)-3(2x-1)=0$

   b $4x^2-25=0$

   c $x^2+6x-7=0$

   d $2x^2+5x+3=0$

   e $\frac{4}{9}x^2-1=0$

   f $10x^2=12-7x$

   g $5x-4x^2=0$

   h $12x^2+12x-9=0$

3 Use the method of completing the square to solve these equations giving your answers in simplified surd form.

   a $x^2+4x+2=0$

   b $2x^2+6x-1=0$

   c $4-2x-x^2=0$

   d $(2x-3)^2=x+1$

4 Use the formula to solve these quadratic equations leaving your answers in simplified surd form where appropriate.

   a $x^2-3x-3=0$

   b $2x^2=4x+1$

   c $(x+2)^2-(2x+3)^2=0$

   d $\frac{3}{4}(x^2-2x+3)=x+1$

5 Factorise completely $x^3 - 7x^2 + 12x$

6 The equation $ax^2 + 8x + a = 0$, where a is a positive constant, has equal roots.
Find the value of a.

7 Given that $x^2 - 4x - 9 = (x + a)^2 + b$, where a and b are constants

  a   find the value of a and the value of b

  b   Show that the roots of $x^2 - 4x - 9 = 0$ can be written in the form
      $$p \pm q\sqrt{13}$$
      and hence determine the value of the integers p and q.

8 Given that $x^2 + 10x + 36 \equiv (x + a)^2 + b$, where a and b are constants:

  a   find the value of a and the value of b

  b   hence show that the equation $x^2 + 10x + 36$ has no real roots.

  The equation $x^2 + 10x + k = 0$ has equal roots.

  c   Find the value of k.

  d   For this value of k, sketch the graph of $y = x^2 + 10x + k$,
      showing the coordinates of any points at which the graph
      meets the coordinate axes.   [(c) Edexcel Limited 2003]

9 a   The equation $x^2 + ax + 12 = 0$ has equal roots.
      Find the values of a.

  b   The equation $kx^2 - 4x + k = 0$ has equal roots.
      Find the possible values of k.

  c   The equation $x^2 + 2kx + 2x + 7k - 3 = 0$ has repeated roots.
      Find the possible values of k.

10 a   Solve the equation $4x^2 + 12x = 0$

  $f(x) = 4x^2 + 12x + c$, where c is a constant.

  b   Given that $f(x) = 0$ has equal roots, find the value of c and
      hence solve $f(x) = 0$ [(c) Edexcel Limited 2003]

3

Exit

Summary

Refer to

- A quadratic function of the form $f(x) = ax^2 + bx + c$ has the shape

  when $a > 0$ when $a < 0$

  and

  minimum point   maximum point   3.1

- Quadratic equations of the form $ax^2 + bx + c = 0$ can be solved by
  - factorising   3.1
  - completing the square or   3.2
  - applying the formula   3.3

- The formula for solving the quadratic equation $ax^2 + bx + c = 0$

  is $x = \dfrac{-b \pm \sqrt{(b^2 - 4ac)}}{2a}$ 3.4

- The discriminant, $b^2 - 4ac$, may be used to determine how many roots a quadratic has.
  - $b^2 - 4ac > 0$ (two distinct real roots)
  - $b^2 - 4ac \geqslant 0$ (one or two real roots)
  - $b^2 - 4ac = 0$ (one real root)
  - $b^2 - 4ac < 0$ (no real roots)   3.4

C1

Links

Quadratic equations play a role in modelling the motion of objects ranging from the astronomical down to the subatomic scale.

Depending on how you slice a cone, you get four different **conic sections** – circle, ellipse, hyperbola and parabola. These are all described by equations of degree 2 and they all have practical applications. You will be most familiar with circles, but ellipses and hyperbolas describe the motion of planets around the sun, and parabolas are used in the design of radio telescopes and satellite dishes.

On a more down-to-earth level, each time you throw a stone or kick a ball the stone or ball traces a parabola (with its own quadratic equation) in the air.

4

Quadratic and linear relationships

This chapter will show you how to

○ solve simultaneous quadratic and linear equations

○ solve quadratic and linear inequalities.

Before you start

You should know how to:

1 Rearrange linear equations.

e.g. Make y the subject of the equation

$3x + 2y = 1$

Isolate the y-term: $2y = 1 - 3x$

Divide both sides by 2:

$y = \dfrac{1 - 3x}{2}$ or $y = \dfrac{1}{2} - \dfrac{3x}{2}$

2 Factorise a quadratic expression.

e.g. Factorise $x^2 - x - 6$

Factors of 6 are 2, 3 and 1, 6.

Difference is $-1x$.

Hence $x^2 - x - 6 = (x - 3)(x + 2)$

3 Solve linear equations.

e.g. Solve $3(x - 2) = 2$

Multiply out the brackets: $3x - 6 = 2$

Rearrange: $3x = 2 + 6$

Simplify: $3x = 8$

Divide by 3: $x = \dfrac{8}{3}$

4 Solve simultaneous linear equations.

e.g. Solve $7x + 2y = 17$ (1)

  $3x - y = 11$ (2)

Equation (1) + 2 × (2):

  $13x = 39$

  $x = 3$

Substitute $x = 3$ in (1):

  $21 + 2y = 17$

So $y = -2$

Check in:

1 Make y the subject of each equation.

 a $4x + 2y = 1$

 b $3(x + y) = 6$

 c $x - y - 3 = 0$

 d $5 - 2y = x$

 e $4(x - y) + 3(x + y) = 1$

2 Factorise

 a $x^2 + 2x - 8$

 b $x^2 - 5x - 6$

 c $x^2 - 6x + 9$

 d $x^2 + 7x - 18$

 e $2x^2 + 5x + 2$

3 Solve to find the unknown in each case.

 a $2(x - 1) = 3$

 b $4 - 3(t + 1) = 0$

 c $3 + y = 2 - y$

 d $5a = 4(2a - 1)$

 e $\dfrac{2}{1 + p} = 3$

4 Solve each pair of simultaneous equations.

 a $3x + y = 5$

  $2x + y = 4$

 b $2x + y = 4$

  $x - 2y = -13$

 c $2x + 3y = 8$

  $3x + 4y = 11$

C1

You know how to solve simultaneous linear equations.

See chapter 0 on the CD-ROM.

If the lines intersect there will be a single solution, which can be illustrated with a sketch graph.

A linear equation can also be solved simultaneously with a quadratic equation.

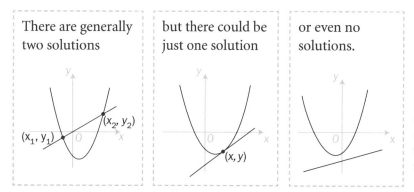

There are generally two solutions	but there could be just one solution	or even no solutions.

If one of the equations is of degree 1 (linear) and one is of degree 2 (e.g. quadratic) then there will be a maximum of two solutions.

You can use the substitution method to solve simultaneous equations when one is linear and one is quadratic.

EXAMPLE 1

Find the values of x and y which satisfy $x^2 + y = 0$ and $y = x - 6$

You can sketch a diagram to check that your solutions make sense.

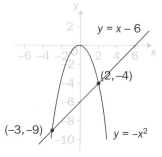

Label the equations:
$$x^2 + y = 0 \qquad (1)$$
$$y = x - 6 \qquad (2)$$

Substitute $y = x - 6$ into equation (1):
$$x^2 + (x - 6) = 0$$

Simplify:
$$x^2 + x - 6 = 0$$

Factorise:
$$(x + 3)(x - 2) = 0$$

Hence
$$x = -3 \text{ or } x = 2$$

Find y by substituting the x-values into equation (2):

$$y = x - 6$$

So when $x = -3,$ $y = -9$
and when $x = 2,$ $y = -4$

You could substitute into equation (1) and get the same y-values.

The solutions are $x = -3$ and $y = -9$
or $x = 2$ and $y = -4$

Make sure you write both pairs of solutions separately.

EXAMPLE 2

Solve the equations $y = x - 3$ and $x^2 - 3y^2 = 9$

$x^2 - 3y^2 = 9$ is the equation of a **hyperbola**.
Like a parabola, it is a conic section.

Label the equations:
$$y = x - 3 \quad (1)$$
$$x^2 - 3y^2 = 9 \quad (2)$$

Use equation (1) to find an expression for y^2:
$$y^2 = (x - 3)^2 = x^2 - 6x + 9$$

Substitute for y^2 in equation (2):
$$x^2 - 3(x^2 - 6x + 9) = 9$$

Expand the brackets:
$$x^2 - 3x^2 + 18x - 27 = 9$$

Simplify:
$$-2x^2 + 18x - 36 = 0$$

Take out the common factor -2:
$$-2(x^2 - 9x + 18) = 0$$

Divide both sides by -2:
$$x^2 - 9x + 18 = 0$$

Factorise:
$$(x - 3)(x - 6) = 0$$

Hence
$$x = 3 \quad \text{or} \quad x = 6$$

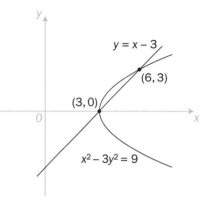

Find the y-values by substituting into equation (1):
$$y = x - 3$$

When $x = 3$ $\quad y = 3 - 3 = 0$
When $x = 6$ $\quad y = 6 - 3 = 3$

The solutions are $x = 3, y = 0$ or $x = 6, y = 3$

There are two x-values, so there should be two associated y-values.

Check your solutions. Make sure you have them in the correct pairs.

Exercise 4.1

1 Solve these pairs of simultaneous equations.

a $\quad y = x - 2$
$\quad x^2 + y = 0$

b $\quad y + 2x + 3 = 0$
$\quad x^2 + y = 0$

c $\quad y = 4(1 - x)$
$\quad x^2 + y = 0$

d $\quad y + 3x = 1$
$\quad 2x^2 + y = 0$

e $\quad y + 3x + 2 = 0$
$\quad 2x^2 + y = 0$

f $\quad y = 7x - 12$
$\quad x^2 - y = 0$

g $\quad y = 6x - 9$
$\quad x^2 - y = 0$

h $\quad y = 5x - 1$
$\quad 4x^2 - y = 0$

2   Solve for x and y.

a $y = 2x^2 + 3x - 2$
      $y = 2x - 1$

b $y = 3x^2 - 2x - 1$
      $y = 1 - x$

c $x = y^2 + 2y - 7$
      $y = x + 1$

d $4y = 2x^2 - 3x + 7$
      $y = 1 - 2x$

e $y = 5x^2 - 16$
      $y = 3x - 2$

f $x^2 = y + 5$
      $y = 3 - 2x$

g $3y^2 + 2x = 99$
      $y = 2x + 3$

h $\dfrac{y^2}{2} = \dfrac{x}{3} + \dfrac{5}{2}$
      $y = x - 3$

3   Find x and y.

a $x^2 + y^2 = 1$
      $y = x + 1$

b $x^2 - y^2 = 2$
      $y = x - 1$

c $x^2 + 2y^2 = 3$
      $y = 2x + 1$

d $2x^2 - y^2 = 1$
      $y = 2x - 1$

e $x^2 + y^2 = 1$
      $y = 1 - 2x$

f $x^2 - 2y^2 = 4$
      $x + y = 2$

g $2x^2 - 3y^2 = 20$
      $y + 2 = x$

h $3x^2 - 4y^2 - 8 = 0$
      $y = x - 1$

4   Solve for x and y.

a $y^2 - xy = 3$
      $y = x + 1$

b $x^2 + xy - y^2 = 1$
      $y = x + 1$

c $2x^2 - xy + y^2 = 2$
      $y = x - 1$

d $x^2 - xy + y^2 = 2 - x$
      $y = 2x - 1$

INVESTIGATIONS

5   Some circles have equations of the form

$x^2 + y^2 = r^2$

For the circle $x^2 + y^2 = 9$

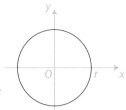

a   find the values of x and y on the coordinate axes and hence sketch the circle.

b   If the line $y = x + 3$ is drawn on the graph, how many times and where would it intersect the circle? Sketch your solution.

c   Investigate the number of solutions using the line $y = x + a$ for

   i $a = 0$ **ii** $a = 4$

C1

6 An ellipse is essentially a stretched circle.
Some ellipses have equations of the form

$$\frac{x^2}{a^2} + \frac{y^2}{b^2} = 1$$

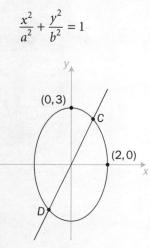

a How would you use the graph to find the values of
a and *b*?

b Use these values of *a* and *b* to express the ellipse in
a different form, without fractions.

c The line $y = 2x$ intersects the ellipse. Find the
coordinates of the points of intersection, *C* and *D*.

7 Use your knowledge of the discriminant to prove that
the line, $y = x$, is a tangent to the circle

$$(x - 2)^2 + y^2 = 2.$$

5

When you solve an equation, you find particular value(s) that satisfy the equation.
When you solve an inequality, you find a set of values that satisfies the inequality.

You can show an inequality on a number line:

$$-3 \quad -2 \quad -1 \quad 0 \quad 1 \quad 2$$

$$x \leqslant -\frac{1}{2}$$

Remember the general rule for multiplying an inequality by a negative number:

○ **When you multiply (or divide) an inequality by a negative number you must reverse the inequality sign.**

See Chapter 0 on CD-ROM for revision on linear inequalities.

This rule applies to the four inequality signs $<$, $>$, $\leqslant$ and $\geqslant$.

You may need to simplify an inequality before you can solve it.

EXAMPLE 1

Find the range of values of t which satisfies $2t - 3(2t + 4) < 0$

Simplifying an inequality is very similar to simplifying an equation.

$$2t - 3(2t + 4) < 0$$

Expand the brackets: $\quad 2t - 6t - 12 < 0$

Simplify: $\quad -4t - 12 < 0$

Rearrange: $\quad -4t < 12$

Divide by -4 and adjust sign: $\quad t > -3$

The solution is $\quad t > -3$

Remember to reverse the inequality sign when you divide by a negative number.

To solve a quadratic inequality rearrange it in a form where you can solve the associated quadratic equation $ax^2 + bx + c = 0$.

EXAMPLE 2

Find the ranges of values of x which satisfy $x^2 - 2x > 3$

$$x^2 - 2x > 3$$

Rearrange: $\quad x^2 - 2x - 3 > 0$

Factorise: $\quad (x + 1)(x - 3) > 0$

Consider the equation $\quad (x + 1)(x - 3) = 0$

This has solutions $\quad x = -1$ and $x = 3$

Sketch the graph of $y = x^2 - 2x - 3$:

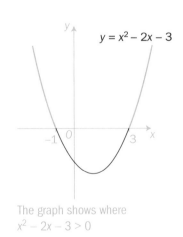

$$y = x^2 - 2x - 3$$

The required region is where the graph is above the x-axis.

There are two ranges which satisfy the inequality.
They are $\quad x < -1 \quad$ and $\quad x > 3$

The graph shows where $x^2 - 2x - 3 > 0$

You can solve a pair of inequalities simultaneously.

C1

EXAMPLE 3

Find the range of values of x which satisfies both the inequalities

$$x^2 - 2x - 3 > 0 \qquad (1)$$
and $$2x + 3 \leqslant 5 \qquad (2)$$

From Example 1 you know that $\qquad x^2 - 2x - 3 > 0$
is true when $\qquad x < -1 \quad$ and $\quad x > 3$

Consider equation (2): $\qquad 2x + 3 \leqslant 5$
This inequality has solutions in the range $\qquad x \leqslant 1$

Draw a number line to show this information:

$$-3 \quad -2 \quad -1 \quad 0 \quad 1 \quad 2 \quad 3 \quad 4 \quad 5 \quad 6$$

Inequality (1) ←———○   ○———————→
Inequality (2) ←————————●

○ indicates $<$ or $>$.
● indicates $\leqslant$ or $\geqslant$.
See Chapter 0 on CD-ROM. ○

The range which satisfies both inequalities is $x < -1$.

Exercise 4.2

1 Find the set of values of x which satisfy each inequality.

   a $4 + x > 1$
   b $2x - 3 \leqslant 0$
   c $5x + 3 \leqslant x$
   d $2x - 1 > 3x$

   e $x - 3 \geqslant 2x - 4$
   f $\frac{4}{3}x > x - 2$
   g $\frac{x}{2} - 1 > \frac{x}{3} + 1$
   h $4 - \frac{2x}{3} \leqslant 3 - \frac{x}{4}$

2 Find the range of values of the unknown which satisfy each inequality.

   a $3(t + 1) > 4(t + 2)$
   b $3y < 2(y - 1)$
   c $2y + 2(3 - 3y) \leqslant 0$

   d $7 - 3(a - 2) < 4$
   e $3 - 4(p + 2) \geqslant 0$
   f $2(4x - 3) - 4(3x - 1) > 0$

3 Find the set of values of x which satisfy each inequality.

   a $(x + 3)(x - 2) > 0$
   b $(x - 1)(x - 4) < 0$
   c $(x + 1)(x + 5) > 0$
   d $(2x - 1)(x + 2) < 0$

4 Factorise and solve these quadratic inequalities.

   a $x^2 + x - 2 > 0$
   b $t^2 + 7t + 12 > 0$

   c $p^2 < 3p + 4$
   d $q(q + 3) > 10$

5 Find the set of values which satisfy each inequality.

   a $2x^2 < 9x + 5$
   b $3t^2 < 2(t + 4)$
   c $p^2 > 9$
   d $4x^2 - 25 > 0$

6 Find the set of values of x which satisfy both inequalities.

   a $x^2 - 5x + 4 < 0 \qquad x < 3$ A number line may help.

   b $x^2 - x - 6 < 0 \qquad 2(x + 1) > 4$

   c $2x^2 - 9x + 9 > 0 \qquad 2x + 3 \leqslant x + 1$

57

Review 4

1 Use the substitution method to solve each pair of simultaneous equations.

   a $y = x - 3$ **b** $y = 2x - 1$
            $x^2 + 2y = 9$ $x^2 - 3y = 10$

   c $y = 2x^2 - 4x - 5$ **d** $y - 5 = x^2$
            $y = x + 7$ $y - 7 = x$

2 **a**   Find x and y when $x^2 + y^2 = 13$ and $y = 2x - 1$

   b   Solve the simultaneous equations $y^2 + xy = 0$ and $y = 2x + 1$

3 The diagram shows the curve with equation $y = x^2 - 2x$ and the
   line $y = x - 2$

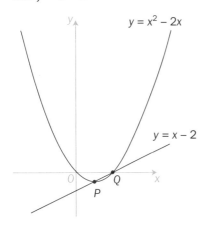

   Find, using algebra, the coordinates of P and Q.

4 The diagram shows the curve with equation $y = 2x^2 - 3$
   and the line $y = 7x + 1$

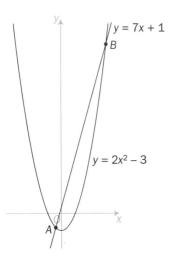

   Find the coordinates of the points A and B.

C1

5 Find the set of values of the variable which satisfies each inequality.

   a $4x + 7 > 1$ b $5(y - 1) < 2$ c $3(2t + 1) - 4(t - 2) \geqslant 0$

6 a Find the equations of the three lines
     on the graph.

  b Hence describe the shaded region
     using inequalities.

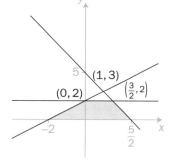

7 Solve the simultaneous equations
$$x - 2y = 1$$
$$x^2 + y^2 + 2y = 33$$

8 Find the set of values of x for which

   a $2(3x - 1) < 2 + 5x$ b $x^2 - 4x - 5 < 0$

   c both $2(3x - 1) < 2 + 5x$ and $x^2 - 4x - 5 < 0$

9 Solve the simultaneous equations
$$y^2 - x = 1$$
$$x = 2y + 2$$

10 a Solve the simultaneous equations
$$y + 2x = 5$$
$$2x^2 + 9x - y = 16$$

   b Hence, or otherwise, find the set of values of x for which
      $2x^2 + 9x - 16 > 5 - 2x$

11 The width of a rectangular sports pitch is x metres, $x > 0$.
   The length of the pitch is 20 m more than its width.
   Given that the perimeter of the pitch must be less than 300 m,

   a form a linear inequality in x.

   Given that the area of the pitch must be greater than 4800 m^2

   b form a quadratic inequality in x.

   c By solving your inequalities, find the set of possible values of x.   [(c) Edexcel Limited 2004]

4 Exit

Summary

Refer to

- You can solve quadratic and linear equations simultaneously by applying the substitution method.

  4.1

- Solving an inequality produces a solution set of values.

  4.2

- When multiplying or dividing both sides of an inequality by a negative number the inequality sign must be reversed.

  4.2

- To solve inequalities involving quadratic expressions you
  - solve the corresponding quadratic equation
  - use checking procedures and graph sketches to find the solution set.

  4.2

Links

The topics in this chapter are closely linked to the branch of mathematics known as linear programming – this is covered in detail in the Decision Mathematics modules.

Simultaneous equations and inequalities are commonly used in industrial processes, where procedures are determined by limiting restrictions and the aim is to maximise profits.

e.g In the research and development of commercial recipes, there may be governmental health limits on the proportions of a particular ingredient, and these may need to be balanced against making the product taste nice in order to optimise sales or against reducing production costs in order to maximise profits.

1 a Evaluate $25^{-\frac{1}{2}}$

   b Write $\sqrt{45}$ in the form $a\sqrt{b}$ where a and b are integers.

2 a Simplify $(a^2b\sqrt{c})^2$

   b Write $(3+\sqrt{2})(4-\sqrt{2})$ in the form $a+b\sqrt{c}$, where a, b and c are integers.

3 a For the expression x^2+3x+k find the value of the constant k which makes the expression a perfect square.

   b If $x^2+3x+l=(x+a)^2+b$ find the values of a and b in terms of l.

   c If $x^2+3x+m=1$ find the values of x in surd form.

4 a Plot the graphs of $y=x^2-1$ and the line $y=x+5$ on the same axes taking values of x in the range -3 to 4.

   b Use the graphs to estimate the solutions to the equation $x^2-x-6=0$

5 a Solve the simultaneous equations
      $$x^2+2y+4=0, \; x-y=6$$

   b Draw a number line to show the inequality $-1<x\leqslant 5$
      If the value of x also satisfies the inequality $x>2$ write down the integer values satisfying both inequalities.

6 a Find the gradient of the line joining the points $A(3,2)$ and $B(-1,5)$.

   b Hence find the equation of the line in part **a**.

   c The line AB crosses the x-axis at point P and the y-axis at point Q. Determine the coordinates of P and Q.

   d Deduce the area of the triangle POQ where O is the origin, $(0,0)$.

7 a Line L has equation $y-2x+3=0$
      Another line K is drawn which is perpendicular to line L at the point $A(-2,-7)$. What is the equation of line K?

   b The lines L and K cross the y-axis at points P and Q respectively. Find the distance PQ.

   c Write down the coordinates of the midpoint of line PQ and hence find the equation of the straight line joining $A(-2,-7)$ to this midpoint.

C1

8 **a** The roots of the equation $kx^2 + 3x + k = 0$ are equal.
Find the possible values of k.

b Using the values of k show that the value of x is +1 or –1.

c Another equation, $mx^2 + 3x + n = 0$, also has equal roots and
the sum of the two constants m and n is given by $m + n = \dfrac{15}{4}$
Determine the values of m and n.

9 **a** For the equation $x^2 + 4x - 2 \equiv (x + a)^2 + b$
find the values of a and b.

b Sketch the graph of $y = x^2 + 4x - 2$, indicating clearly the
coordinates of any intersections with the coordinate axes.

c Find the value of the discriminant of $x^2 + 4x - 2$
Explain how the sign of the discriminant relates to your
sketch in part **b**.

d The equation $x^2 + 4x + k = 0$, where k is a constant,
has no real roots. Find the set of possible values of k.

10 Given that $f(x) = x^2 - 6x + 18$, $x \geqslant 0$

a Express $f(x)$ in the form $(x - a)^2 + b$, where a and b are
constants.

The curve C with equation $y = f(x)$, $x \geqslant 0$, meets the y-axis
at P and has a minimum point at Q.

b Sketch the graph of C, showing the coordinates of P and Q.

The line $y = 41$ meets C at the point R.

c Find the x-coordinate of R, giving your answer in the
form $p + q\sqrt{2}$, where p and q are integers.

[(c) Edexcel Limited 2005]

C1

Graphs of functions

This chapter will show you how to
- sketch the graphs of cubic and reciprocal functions
- identify important features from the graph
- perform transformations involving functions.

Before you start

You should know how to:

1 Factorise an equation.

e.g. Factorise $y = x^3 + 5x^2 - 6x$

Take out the common factor, x:

$y = x(x^2 + 5x - 6)$

Factorise the quadratic:

$y = x(x - 1)(x + 6)$

Check by multiplying out.

2 Sketch the graph of the quadratic equation.

e.g. Sketch the graph of $y = x^2 - 2x - 8$

Factorise: $y = (x + 2)(x - 4)$

The graph cuts the x-axis where $y = 0$ and

$x = -2$ or 4

When $x = 0$, $y = -8$

The coefficient of x^2 is positive

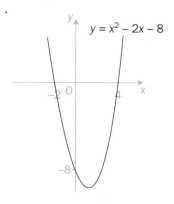

Check in:

1 Factorise each equation.

a $y = x^3 + 5x^2 + 6x$

b $y = 2x^3 - 2x$

c $y = x^3 - x^2 - 20x$

d $y = 3x^3 - 24x^2 + 36x$

e $y = 5x^3 - 80x$

f $y = 4x^3 - 5x^2$

2 Sketch the graph of each quadratic equation.

a $y = x^2 - x - 2$

b $y = x^2 + x - 12$

c $y = x^2 - 6x + 8$

d $y = x(x - 4)$

e $y = x^2 - 9$

f $y = 4x^2 - 100$

Remember to indicate the important features such as where the curve cuts the axes.

A general cubic equation has the form
$$y = ax^3 + bx^2 + cx + d$$
where a, b, c and d are constants.

e.g. $y = x^3$
$y = 2x^3 - 3x$
$y = x^3 + 3x^2 - 6x - 5$

Generally the graph of a cubic function has the shape

if $a > 0$ if $a < 0$

The points where the curve changes direction are called **turning points**. You will learn more about these in Chapter 7.

You can sketch a curve without plotting exact values.

EXAMPLE 1

Sketch the graph of $y = x(x + 1)(x - 2)$

Find the main features of the graph:

1 Consider the sign of the x^3-coefficient.
   Expand the brackets: $y = x^3 - x^2 - 2x$
   The coefficient of x^3 is positive.

This tells you the general shape of the curve:

2 Let $y = 0$: $x(x + 1)(x - 2) = 0$
   Solve for x: $x = 0, x = -1, x = 2$
   So the curve crosses the x-axis at $(0, 0)$, $(-1, 0)$ and $(2, 0)$.

The number of x-axis crossings is the same as the number of solutions of the equation $f(x) = 0$.

3 Substitute $x = 0$ into the equation: $y = 0$
   So the curve crosses the y-axis at $(0, 0)$.

Use these observations to sketch the curve:

The curve should be smooth. Draw it freehand – do not use a ruler.

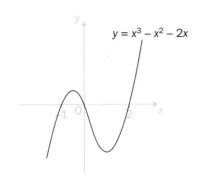

$y = x^3 - x^2 - 2x$

EXAMPLE 2

Sketch the graph of $y = (1-x)(3+x)(2+x)$

1 Expand the brackets: $y = -x^3 - 4x^2 - x + 6$
 The coefficient of x^3 is negative.

2 Let $y = 0$: $(1-x)(3+x)(x+2) = 0$
 Solve for x: $x = 1, x = -3, x = -2$
 The graph crosses the x-axis at $(1,0)$, $(-3,0)$ and $(-2,0)$.

3 Substitute $x = 0$ into the equation:
 $y = (1)(3)(2) = 6$
 The graph crosses the y-axis at the $(0,6)$.

Sketch the curve:

This tells you the general shape of the curve:

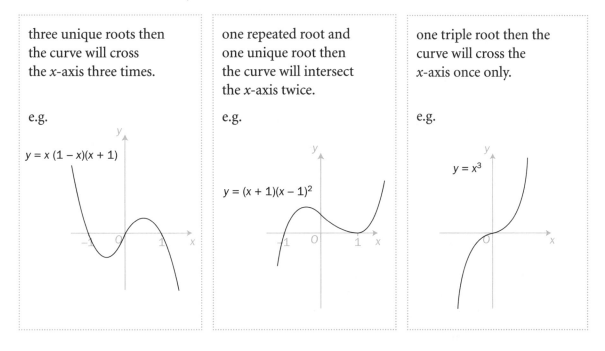

The number of roots of a cubic function determines how many times the curve crosses the x-axis. There are 3 cases: if the function has…

three unique roots then the curve will cross the x-axis three times.

e.g.

$y = x(1-x)(x+1)$

one repeated root and one unique root then the curve will intersect the x-axis twice.

e.g.

$y = (x+1)(x-1)^2$

one triple root then the curve will cross the x-axis once only.

e.g.

$y = x^3$

You can use alternative methods to find the number of solutions
of a cubic equation which is difficult to factorise.

EXAMPLE 3

By sketching suitable graphs estimate the number of solutions
there are to the equation $x^3 - x^2 + 2x + 3 = 0$

Rewrite:

$$x^3 = x^2 - 2x - 3$$

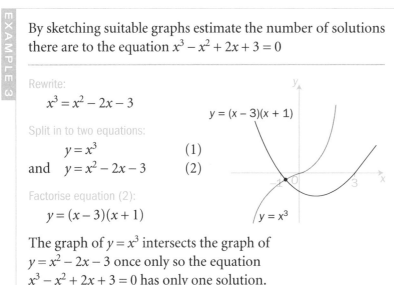

Split in to two equations:

$$y = x^3 \qquad (1)$$
$$\text{and} \quad y = x^2 - 2x - 3 \qquad (2)$$

Factorise equation (2):

$$y = (x - 3)(x + 1)$$

The graph of $y = x^3$ intersects the graph of
$y = x^2 - 2x - 3$ once only so the equation
$x^3 - x^2 + 2x + 3 = 0$ has only one solution.

This will make sketching the curve
easier.

The solution of the simultaneous
equations is the solution of the
original equation.

Exercise 5.1

1 State where each curve
   i   intersects or touches the x-axis
   ii   intersects the y-axis.

   a $y = x(x - 5)(x + 2)$ b $y = (x + 1)(x + 2)(x - 3)$

   c $y = (2x - 1)(x + 4)(1 - x)$ d $y = (x - 1)(x + 2)^2$

   e $y = x^2(2x + 5)$ f $y = -x(2x - 1)^2$

   g $y = x(x^2 - 4)$ h $y = (x - 2)^3$

   i $y = (2x + 3)^3$ j $y = x^3 - 3x^2 - 4x$

2 Sketch the curves given by each equation.
   Show the points of intersection with the x-axis.

   a $y = x(x - 2)(x + 3)$ b $y = x(x + 2)(x - 2)$

   c $y = x(x - 3)(x + 2)$ d $y = x^2(x - 3)$

3 Sketch each curve and mark the points of intersection with the axes.

   a $y = (x + 3)(x + 2)(x - 1)$ b $y = (1 - x)(x + 3)(x - 1)$

   c $y = (2x - 3)(x - 3)(x + 1)$ d $y = (2x + 5)(x - 2)(1 - x)$

4 Sketch the graph of each equation.

   a $y = (x + 2)^2(x - 1)$ b $y = (x + 1)(2x - 5)^2$

   c $y = (2x - 3)(x + 2)^2$ d $y = (1 - x)(2 + x)^2$

5 Sketch the curve given by each equation.

   a $y = x^3 + 2x^2 - 3x$ **b** $y = x^3 + 4x^2 + 4x$ Factorise the equation first.

   c $y = 6x - x^2 - x^3$ **d** $y = 2x^3 - 12x^2 + 16x$

6 Sketch the curve given by each equation.

   a $y = x^2(x + 2)$ **b** $y = (2x - 1)(2x + 3)(2 - x)$

   c $y = x(3 - 2x)^2$ **d** $y = 3x - 2x^2 - x^3$

7 Sketch the graphs of these pairs of equations on the same axes
   and state how many points of intersection there are.

   a $y = x + 4, y = x^3$ **b** $y = (x + 1)(x - 1), y = x + 1$

   c $y = x^2(x - 4), y = x + 1$ **d** $y = x(x - 2)(x + 4), y = x - 3$

8 By sketching suitable graphs estimate how many solutions there are
   to the equation
   $x^3 - x - 1 = 0$

INVESTIGATION

9 Find the equation of each curve using the information
   shown in the diagram.

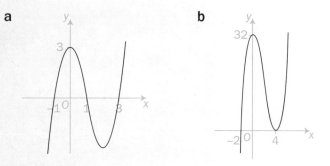

   a   **b**

10 A quadratic graph can intersect with the line $y = 0$ once
    or twice.

    How many intersections are possible between

    a a linear and a quadratic graph

    b a linear and a cubic graph?

    How could you prove your answers without drawing
    any graphs?

Sketching reciprocal graphs

A reciprocal curve has an equation of the form
$y = \dfrac{k}{x}$ where k is a constant.

For very small positive or negative values of x
$\quad y \to \infty \quad$ or $\quad y \to -\infty$
For very small positive or negative values of y
$\quad x \to \infty \quad$ or $\quad x \to -\infty$

The x- and y-axes are asymptotes of the curve $y = \dfrac{1}{x}$

The curve $y = \dfrac{k}{x}$ has asymptotes at $x = 0$ and $y = 0$.

A sketch of the graph looks like this:

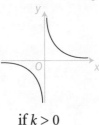

    if $k > 0$ if $k < 0$

e.g $y = \dfrac{1}{x} \qquad k = 1$

$\quad\quad y = -\dfrac{2}{x} \qquad k = -2$

Try some values of x and y for yourself.

An asymptote is a line which the curve approaches but never actually touches.

A reciprocal function can also be written in the form $yx = k$ its curve is called a **hyperbola**.

EXAMPLE 1

Plot the graph of $y = \dfrac{1}{x}$

The asymptotes are $x = 0$ and $y = 0$.

Make a table of values:

$x > 0$

x	$\frac{1}{4}$	$\frac{1}{2}$	$\frac{3}{4}$	1
y	4	2	$1\frac{1}{3}$	1

$x < 0$

x	$-\frac{1}{4}$	$-\frac{1}{2}$	$-\frac{3}{4}$	-1
y	-4	-2	$-1\frac{1}{3}$	-1

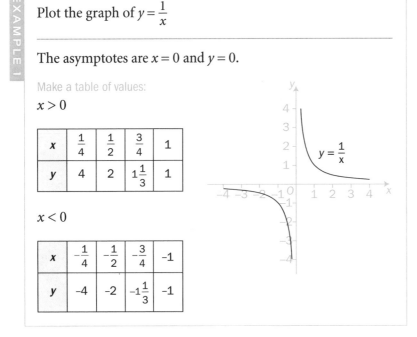

C1

EXAMPLE 2

Sketch the graph of $y = -\dfrac{4}{x}$ and $y = -\dfrac{1}{x}$ on the same diagram.

In both functions $k < 0$ so both curves will have the shape

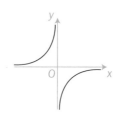

The asymptotes of each curve are $x = 0$ and $y = 0$.

Compare the functions:

When $x > 0$, $\quad -\dfrac{4}{x} < -\dfrac{1}{x}$

When $x < 0$, $\quad -\dfrac{4}{x} > -\dfrac{1}{x}$

Use this information to sketch the curves:

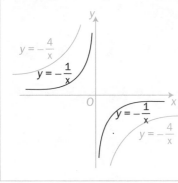

Exercise 5.2

1 Sketch each pair of curves on the same axes.

   a $y = \dfrac{1}{x}$ and $y = \dfrac{4}{x}$ **b** $y = -\dfrac{2}{x}$ and $y = -\dfrac{8}{x}$

   c $y = \dfrac{2}{x}$ and $y = \dfrac{1}{2x}$ **d** $y = -\dfrac{1}{x}$ and $y = -\dfrac{1}{4x}$

2 Sketch the curve of $y = \dfrac{1}{x}$ and use it to sketch the curve

   of $y = \dfrac{1}{x^2}$ on the same diagram. Label the graphs clearly.

3 Sketch the graphs of $y = \dfrac{2}{x}$ and $y = \dfrac{4}{x^2}$ on the same axes.

INVESTIGATION

4 Consider the curve $y = \dfrac{x}{x+1}$

   a Find the value of x that makes y impossible to calculate and hence state an asymptote of the curve.

   b Find the y-axis intercept.

   c If x took an infinitely large value, what would happen to y?

   d Use this information to sketch the curve.

5

Translating a graph

You can translate the graph of $y = f(x)$ parallel to the y-axis by adding a constant.

○ $f(x) \pm a$ represents **a** translation of $f(x)$ parallel to the y-axis by $\pm a$ units.

$+a$ moves the graph in the positive y-direction.
$-a$ moves the graph in the negative y-direction.

EXAMPLE 1

Sketch the graphs of $y = x^2 + 2$ and $y = x^2 - 3$ on the same diagram.

Sketch the graph of $f(x) = x^2$

The function $f(x) + 2$ represents a translation parallel to the y-axis by 2 units.

The function $f(x) - 3$ represents a translation parallel to the y-axis by -3 units.

Perform each translation to the graph of $f(x) = x^2$:

You know the graph of $y = x^2$

Using the rule for $f(x) + a$ with $a = 2$.

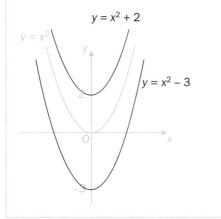

You can also translate the graph of $y = f(x)$ parallel to the x-axis.

○ $f(x \pm a)$ is a translation of $f(x)$ parallel to the x-axis by $\mp a$ units.

$+a$ moves the graph in the **negative** x-direction.
$-a$ moves the graph in the **positive** x-direction.

C5

EXAMPLE 2

Sketch the graphs of $y = (x+2)^2$ and $y = (x-3)^2$ on the same diagram.

Sketch the graph of $f(x) = x^2$

The function $f(x+2)$ represents a translation parallel to the x-axis by -2 units.

The function $f(x-3)$ represents a translation parallel to the x-axis by 3 units.

Perform each translation to the graph of $f(x) = x^2$:

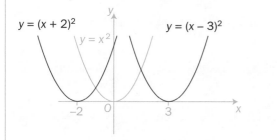

You can translate any known curve.

EXAMPLE 3

Sketch the graph of $y = \dfrac{1}{x-2}$.

First sketch the curve $y = \dfrac{1}{x}$

The function $f(x-2)$ represents a translation of 2 units parallel to the x-axis.

Perform the translation to sketch the curve of $y = \dfrac{1}{x-2}$:

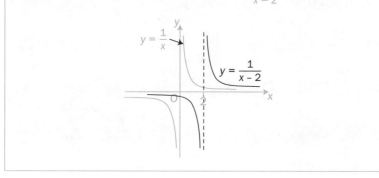

The graph of $y = \dfrac{1}{x}$ is familiar.

Replace the x in the original function with $x-2$ to give the new function.

Use the rule for $f(x+a)$ with $a = -2$.
Negative a moves the graph in the **positive** x-direction.

To make your two curves consistent you may find it helpful to draw the original asymptote and move this to draw the new curve.

You can combine translations in the x- and y-directions to give a translation in both directions.

EXAMPLE 4

If $f(x) = x^3$ sketch the graph of $f(x - 1) + 3$

First let $y = f(x)$
Sketch the curve of $y = x^3$

To create $f(x - 1) + 3$ you replace x with $x - 1$ and then add 3 to the whole function.

Apply the changes to the original function $f(x) = x^3$:

$$f(x - 1) + 3 = (x - 1)^3 + 3$$

This represents a translation of 1 unit parallel to the x-axis and a translation of 3 units parallel to the y-axis.

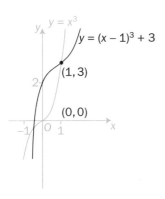

5

Exercise 5.3

1 Write the equation of $f(x) + a$ for $f(x)$ and a given in each case.

   a $f(x) = 2x$ and $a = 4$ **b** $f(x) = 3x - 1$ and $a = 3$

   c $f(x) = x^3$ and $a = -7$ **d** $f(x) = -x^2 + x + 1$ and $a = -4$

2 Write the equation of $f(x + a)$ for $f(x)$ and a given in each case.

   a $f(x) = 3x$ and $a = -1$ **b** $f(x) = 2x^2$ and $a = 1$

   c $f(x) = x^3$ and $a = -3$ **d** $f(x) = \dfrac{4}{x}$ and $a = 2$

   e $f(x) = x^2(x + 2)$ and $a = -2$ **f** $f(x) = x^2 + 3$ and $a = -3$

3 **a** Sketch the graphs of $f(x)$, $f(x) + 2$ and $f(x - 3)$ when
     i $f(x) = x(x - 2)$
     ii $f(x) = x^3$
     iii $f(x) = \dfrac{3}{x}$

   b Describe the transformations involved.

4 Sketch the graph of $f(x) = x(x - 2)(x + 2)$ and the graph of $y = f(x) + 4$ on the same diagram.
   Indicate clearly the points where the curves cross the x-axis.

5 Sketch the graph of $f(x) = x^3$
   On the same diagram sketch the graph of $y = f(x - 2)$
   Describe the transformation that has taken place.

6 Sketch the graph of $f(x) = x(x - 3)$ and the graph of $y = f(x + 3)$
   on the same diagram.
   Show clearly the points where the curves cross the x-axis.

7 On the same diagram sketch the graphs of $y = f(x)$ and
   $y = f(x - 1)$ for $f(x) = \dfrac{1}{x}$

8 On the same diagram sketch the graphs of $y = f(x)$ and $y = f(x + 2)$
   where $f(x) = x^2$. What transformation of $f(x) = x^2$ has taken place?

9 Sketch the graph of $f(x) = x(x + 2)^2$ and use this to sketch, on
   a separate graph, $y = f(x) + 2$ and $y = f(x + 2)$
   Describe the transformations.

10 Sketch the graph of $f(x) = \dfrac{1}{x}$ and use this to sketch, on
    a separate graph, $y = f(x - 2) + 3$

    Mark the new asymptotes on your diagram and write down
    their equations.

Ω

INVESTIGATION

11 The graph of $f(x) = x^2$ is shown:

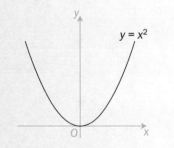

Find the equations of the following graphs:

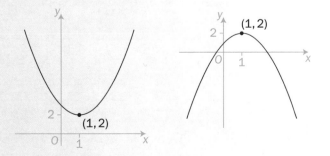

Reflecting in the x-axis

The graph of $y = -f(x)$ is a reflection in the x-axis of the graph of $y = f(x)$

EXAMPLE 1

Sketch the graph of $y = -x^2$

Sketch the graph of $f(x) = x^2$

The function $-f(x)$ represents a reflection in the x-axis.

You should know the shape of the graph of $y = x^2$

Perform the reflection to the graph of $f(x) = x^2$:

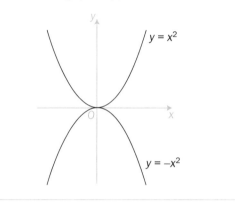

Reflecting in the y-axis

The graph of $y = f(-x)$ is a reflection in the y-axis of the graph of $y = f(x)$

C1

EXAMPLE 2

Write down the function $y = f(-x)$ and sketch the graph of $y = f(-x)$ where $f(x) = \frac{1}{x}$

$f(x) = \frac{1}{x}$

so $f(-x) = \frac{1}{-x} = \frac{-1}{x}$

Sketch the graph of $f(x) = \frac{1}{x}$

The function $f(-x)$ represents a reflection in the y-axis.

Perform the reflection to the graph of $f(x) = \frac{1}{x}$:

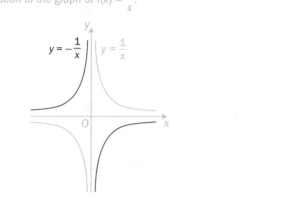

You should know the shape of the graph of $y = \frac{1}{x}$

See Section 5.2 for revision.

Stretching parallel to the x-axis

You can transform the graph of $y = f(x)$ by changing the function to $f(ax)$ where a is a constant.

- $f(ax)$ represents a stretch of $f(x)$ parallel to the x-axis by a scale factor of $\frac{1}{a}$.

If $a > 1$, $\frac{1}{a} < 1$ and the graph 'shrinks' parallel to the x-axis.
If $0 < a < 1$, $\frac{1}{a} > 1$ and the graph is stretched parallel to the x-axis.

EXAMPLE 3

If $f(x) = x^3$, sketch the graph of $y = f(2x)$ and write down the function it represents.

First sketch the curve of $f(x) = x^3$

Now let $y = f(2x)$.
This represents a stretch parallel to the x-axis with a scale factor of $\frac{1}{2}$.

$y = f(2x) = (2x)^3 = 8x^3$

Perform the stretch to the graph of $f(x) = x^3$:

You should know the shape of the graph of $f(x) = x^3$

Use the rule for $f(ax)$ with $a = 2$.

Remember to cube the 2 and the x.

Stretching parallel to the *y*-axis

You can also transform the graph of $y = f(x)$ by changing the function to $af(x)$ where a is a constant.

○ $af(x)$ represents a stretch of f(x) parallel to the *y*-axis by a scale factor of a.

If $a > 1$ the graph is *stretched* parallel to the *y*-axis.
If $0 < a < 1$ the graph 'shrinks' parallel to the *y*-axis.

EXAMPLE 4

If $f(x) = \dfrac{1}{x}$, sketch the graph of $y = 2f(x)$ and write down the function it represents.

First sketch the graph of $y = \dfrac{1}{x}$

Now let $y = 2f(x)$.
This represents a stretch along the *y*-axis with a scale factor of 2.

$$y = 2f(x) = \frac{2}{x}$$

Use the rule for $af(x)$ with $a = 2$.

Perform the stretch to the graph of $f(x) = \dfrac{1}{x}$:

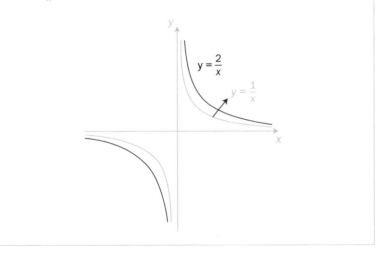

Sometimes you will be asked to stretch a curve in both directions.

On the same axes sketch the graphs of $y = f(2x)$ and $y = \frac{1}{2}f(x)$

where $f(x) = (x + 2)(x - 4)$

Write down the equations of $y = f(2x)$ and $y = \frac{1}{2}f(x)$

First consider $y = (x + 2)(x - 4)$

The curve cuts the y-axis at $x = -2$ and $x = 4$

These are solutions for $y = 0$.

The curve cuts the y-axis at $y = -8$

This is the value of y when $x = 0$.

Sketch the curve.

Now let $y = f(2x)$.

This represents a stretch parallel to the x-axis with a scale factor of $\frac{1}{2}$.

Using the rule for f(ax) with $a = 2$.

Replace x in the original equation with $2x$:

$y = (2x + 2)(2x - 4)$

Now let $y = \frac{1}{2}f(x)$.

This represents a stretch parallel to the y-axis with a scale factor of $\frac{1}{2}$.

Using the rule for af(x) with $a = \frac{1}{2}$.

Multiply f(x) by $\frac{1}{2}$:

$y = \frac{1}{2}(x + 2)(x - 4)$

Perform the stretches to the curve of f(x) = (x + 2)(x − 4):

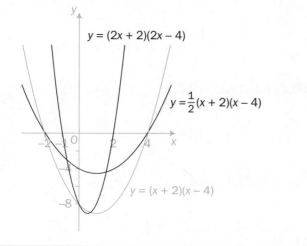

C

Exercise 5.4

1 Given $y = f(x)$ in each case, rewrite the equation for $y = f(ax)$ or $y = af(x)$ as indicated.

a $f(x) = x^2 + 1$, $y = f(2x)$

b $f(x) = x^2 + 1$, $y = 2f(x)$

c $f(x) = \dfrac{2}{x^2}$, $y = f(3x)$

d $f(x) = x(x - 2)$, $y = -f(x)$

e $f(x) = x(x - 2)$, $y = f(-x)$

f $f(x) = x^2$, $y = 2f(3x)$

g $f(x) = \dfrac{1}{1 - x}$, $y = -f(-x)$

h $f(x) = x^2(x + 1)$, $y = f(-2x)$

2 Sketch the graph of $f(x) = x^2 + 1$
   On the same diagram sketch the graph of $y = f(2x)$

3 Sketch the graph of $f(x) = \dfrac{1}{x}$
   On the same diagram sketch the graph of $y = 4f(x)$

4 On the same axes sketch the graphs of $y = f(x)$ and $y = f(-x)$ where $f(x) = x^3$

5 On the same axes sketch the graphs of $y = f(x)$ and $y = -f(x)$ where $f(x) = x(x - 4)$

6 Sketch the graph of $f(x) = (x - 3)(x + 5)$
   Sketch the curve $y = f(2x)$ on the same axes.
   From the graph estimate the values of x which satisfy the relationship $f(x) = f(2x)$

7 Sketch the graph of $f(x) = x(x^2 - 1)$
   Sketch the curve $y = 2f(x)$ on the same axes.
   Estimate the values of x which satisfy both equations.

8 On the same axes sketch the curves $y = f(x)$ and $y = f(-2x)$
for $f(x) = x^3 + 2$

Estimate the points of intersection of the two curves.

9 Sketch $y = f(x)$ and $y = 2f\left(\frac{1}{2}x\right)$ where $f(x) = x^2 - x$ on the
same axes.
From the graph estimate the values of x where the curves
intersect with the line $y = 0$

10 Sketch $y = f(x)$, $y = f(-x)$ and $y = -f(x)$ where $f(x) = (x-1)(x+2)$
on the same axes.

Estimate the coordinates of the turning points of each curve.

11 Sketch the curves $y = f(x)$ and $y = -f(-x)$ for $f(x) = x(x-2)$

Write down estimates of the coordinates of the minimum
and maximum turning points for each curve.

INVESTIGATIONS

12 Identify in which direction the following curves have been
stretched.

a $x^2 + 1$ ⟶ $9x^2$
b $x^2 + 1$ ⟶ $3x^2 + 3$
c x^3 ⟶ $8x^3$

13 Given $f(x) = x^2 + 4$, match each description with its
corresponding equation.

a Stretch in the x-direction, scale factor $= \frac{1}{2}$ i $2x^2 + 8$

b Stretch in the y-direction, scale factor $= 2$ ii $4x^2 + 4$

c Stretch in the x-direction, scale factor $= 2$ iii $\frac{1}{2}x^2 + 2$

d Stretch in the y-direction, scale factor $= \frac{1}{2}$ iv $\frac{1}{4}x^2 + 4$

Transforming graphs of functions

You can use the rules for transforming graphs to transform the graph of any function f(x).

To do this you first identify key features on the given sketch and then use these and the relevant rule to transform the graph.

Key features may include axis crossing points, or turning points of the curve.

You then mark the particular features on the new sketch.

EXAMPLE 1

The graph of $y = f(x)$ is shown in the diagram.
Use separate diagrams to show

a $y = f(x) + 2$ **b** $y = f(x + 2)$ **c** $y = f(2x)$

d $y = 2f(x)$ **e** $y = -f(x)$ **f** $y = f(-x)$

Identify the key features on the sketch of the graph of $y = f(x)$:
The curve cuts the x-axis at $x = -2$ and $x = 3$.
The curve cuts the y-axis at $y = 4$.
There is a maximum point between $x = 1$ and $x = 2$
with a y-value of about 6.
There is a minimum point at $x = -2$.

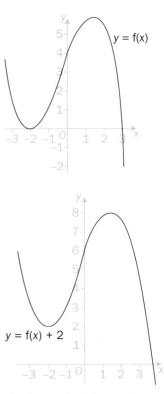

a $y = f(x) + 2$

This is a translation of $y = f(x)$ by 2 units parallel to the y-axis.
The curve cuts the y-axis at $y = 6$.
It has a minimum point at $x = -2$, $y = 2$.
The maximum point lies between $x = 1$ and $x = 2$.
Hence sketch the curve of $f(x) + 2$.

Use the rule for f(x) + a with $a = 2$.

b $y = f(x + 2)$

This is a translation of $y = f(x)$ by −2 units parallel to the x-axis.
The curve cuts the x-axis at $x = -4$ and $x = 1$.
It has a minimum point at $x = -4$, $y = 0$.
The maximum point lies between $x = -1$ and $x = 0$.
Hence sketch the curve of $f(x + 2)$.

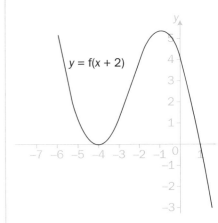

Use the rule for f($x + a$) with $a = 2$.

EXAMPLE 1 (CONT.)

c $y = f(2x)$

This is a stretch of $y = f(x)$ parallel to the x-axis by scale factor $\frac{1}{2}$.

The curve cuts the y-axis at $y = 4$.
The curve cuts the x-axis at the points $x = -1$ and $x = 1\frac{1}{2}$.
It has a minimum point at $x = -1, y = 0$.
The maximum point lies between $x = 0$ and $x = 1$.
Hence sketch the curve of $f(2x)$.

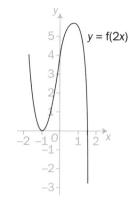

Use the rule for f(ax) with $a = 2$.

d $y = 2f(x)$

This is a stretch of $y = f(x)$ parallel to the y-axis by scale factor 2.
The curve cuts the y-axis at $y = 8$.
The curve cuts the x-axis at the points $x = -2$ and $x = 3$.
It has a minimum point at $x = -2, y = 0$.
The maximum point lies between $x = 1$ and $x = 2$
with a y-value of about 12.
Hence sketch the curve of $2f(x)$.

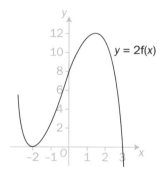

Use the rule for a f(x) with $a = 2$.

e $y = -f(x)$

This is a reflection of $y = f(x)$ in the x-axis.
The curve cuts the y-axis at $y = -4$.
The curve cuts the x-axis at the points $x = -2$ and $x = 3$.
There is a minimum point between $x = 1$ and $x = 2$ with a y-value of about -6.
There is a maximum point at $x = -2$.

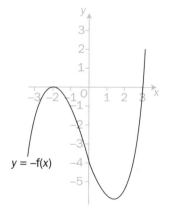

EXAMPLE 1 (CONT.)

f $y = f(-x)$

This is a reflection of $y = f(x)$ in the y-axis.
The curve cuts the y-axis at $y = 4$.
The curve cuts the x-axis at the points $x = -3$ and $x = 2$.
There is a maximum point between $x = -2$ and $x = -1$
with a y-value of about 6.
There is a minimum point at $x = 2$.

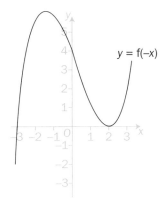

Exercise 5.5

1 The curve with equation $y = f(x)$ is shown in the diagram.
Sketch separate graphs to show the following transformations.
Identify the main features of each curve.

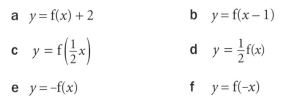

a $y = f(x) + 3$ **b** $y = f(x + 2)$

c $y = f(2x)$ **d** $y = 3f(x)$

e $y = -f(x)$ **f** $y = f(-x)$

2 The graph of $y = f(x)$ is shown in the diagram.
Sketch separate graphs to show the following transformations.
In each case state the equation of the asymptote.
Suggest a possible equation of the curve $y = f(x)$.

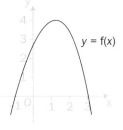

a $y = f(x) + 2$ **b** $y = f(x - 1)$

c $y = f\left(\frac{1}{2}x\right)$ **d** $y = \frac{1}{2}f(x)$

e $y = -f(x)$ **f** $y = f(-x)$

3 The diagram shows the sketch of the curve $y = f(x)$.
There is a local maximum point at $(0, 8)$ and a local
minimum point at $(2, 2)$.
Sketch separate graphs to show the following
transformations.
In each case state the coordinates of the maximum and
minimum points.

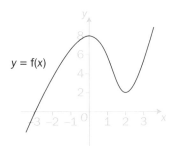

a $y = f(x) - 2$ **b** $y = f(x - 3)$

c $y = f(-x)$ **d** $y = -f(x)$

e $y = f(2x)$ **f** $y = \frac{1}{2}f(x)$

4 The graph of $y = f(x)$ is shown in the diagram.
The asymptotes have equations
$$x = 1 \quad \text{and} \quad y = 2.$$
Draw separate diagrams to show the following transformations.
In each case state the equations of the asymptotes.

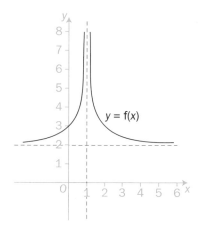

a $y = f(x) - 3$

b $y = f(x + 2)$

c $y = f(-2x)$

d $y = -2f(x)$

5 The graph of $y = 2f(x - 1)$ is drawn in the diagram.

The curve from which it is transformed has an equation
of the form $y = f(x)$.

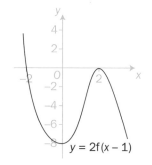

a Sketch the graph of the curve $y = f(x)$

b Identify the important features of this curve.

INVESTIGATION

6 Identify which of the following points

(1, 4)   (1, 5)   (2, 0)   (2, 2)

(1, 6)   (1, 3)   (0, 3)

would lie on the curve $f(x) = x^2 + 1$
after the following transformations.

a $f(x + 1)$

b $f(x) - 3$

c $3f(x)$

1 Sketch the graphs of these equations indicating where each curve intersects with the axes.

    a $y = (x - 1)(x + 5)$

    b $y = x^2(x - 2)$

    c $y = x(x - 2)(x + 2)$

    d $y = (x + 3)(x + 1)(x - 1)$

2 Sketch the graphs of these equations.

    a $y = (x - 3)(x^2 + 3x - 4)$

    b $y = (2x + 5)(x^2 - 4x)$

3 Sketch the graphs of these equations.

    a $y = \dfrac{8}{x}$

    b $y = 2 - \dfrac{4}{x}$

4 **a** Let $f(x) = 2x^2 + x - 15$
       Factorise the equation and solve for values of x when $f(x) = 0$.
       Sketch the graph of $y = f(x)$ and use it to sketch the graph
       of $y = f(x) + 5$ on the same diagram.

    b Sketch the graph of the function $f(x) = -\dfrac{4}{x - 2}$
       Show clearly the position of the asymptotes.
       On the same diagram, draw the line $y = x + 3$
       At how many points do the curve and the line intersect?

5 The graph of the function $y = f(x)$ is shown in the diagram.
It has a local maximum at $P\,(1, -2)$ and a local minimum
at $Q\,(-1, -4)$.
On separate diagrams sketch the graphs of the functions:

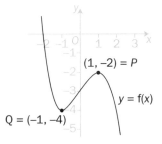

    a $y = f(x) + 3$

    b $y = f(x + 3)$

and state the new coordinates of points P and Q in
each case.

6 The diagram shows the sketch of a curve with equation $y = f(x)$.
The curve crosses the x-axis at points $(0, 0)$, $(-2, 0)$ and $(-4, 0)$.
The point P $(-3, 3)$ lies on the curve.
On separate diagrams sketch the curve with equations

  a $y = -f(x)$ **b** $y = 2f(x)$

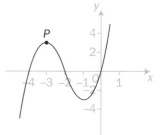

For each curve give the coordinates of the points where the
curve intersects the x-axis and show on each diagram the
new position of the point P under the given transformation.

7 The figure shows a sketch of the curve with equation $y = f(x)$.
The curve passes through the points $(0, 3)$ and $(3, 0)$ and
touches the x-axis at the point $(1, 0)$.
On separate diagrams sketch the curve with equation

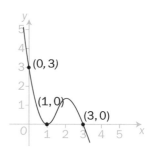

  a $y = f(x + 2)$ **b** $y = 2f(x)$

  c $y = f\left(\frac{1}{3}x\right)$ **d** $y = -f(x)$

On each diagram show clearly the coordinates of all the points
where the curve meets the axes.

8 The figure shows the sketch of the curve with equation $y = f(x)$.
The curve passes through the origin, O, and through the
point $(6, 0)$.
The maximum point on the curve is $(3, 4)$.
On separate diagrams, sketch the curve with equation

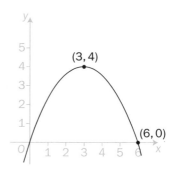

  a $y = 2f(x)$ **b** $y = f(x + 3)$

  c $y = -f(x)$ **d** $y = f(-x)$

On each diagram, show clearly the coordinates of the
maximum point and of each point at which the curve
crosses the x-axis.

9 The figure shows a sketch of the curve with equation $y = f(x)$.
The curve crosses the coordinate axes at the points $(0, 1)$ and
$(3, 0)$. The maximum point on the curve is $(1, 2)$.
On separate diagrams sketch the curve with equation

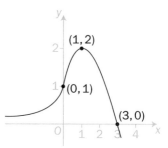

  a $y = f(x + 1)$ **b** $y = f(2x)$

  c $y = -f(x)$ **d** $y = f(-x)$

On each diagram, show clearly the coordinates of the
maximum point, and of each point at which the curve crosses
the coordinate axes.

[(c) Edexcel Limited 2003]

5 Exit

Summary

Refer to

○ The graph of a cubic equation, $y = ax^3 + bx^2 + cx + d$
   has this shape: and this shape:
   when $a > 0$ when $a < 0$

5.1

There are special cases such as $y = x^3$

○ The graph of a reciprocal curve, $y = \dfrac{k}{x}$
   has this shape: and this shape:
   when $k > 0$ when $k < 0$

5.2

○ You can sketch the graph of a function by considering
   its general shape
   the points where the graph crosses the x- and y-axes
   other key features.

○ The graph of $y = f(x)$ can be transformed.

$f(x) \pm a$	represents a translation of $f(x)$ parallel to the y-axis by $\pm a$ units	5.3
$f(x \pm a)$	is a translation of $f(x)$ parallel to the x-axis by $\mp a$ units	5.3
$-f(x)$	represents a reflection of $f(x)$ in the x-axis	5.4
$f(-x)$	represents a reflection of $f(x)$ in the y-axis	5.4
$f(ax)$	represents a stretch of $f(x)$ parallel to the x-axis by a scale factor of $\dfrac{1}{a}$	5.4
$af(x)$	represents a stretch of $f(x)$ parallel to the y-axis by a scale factor of a.	5.4

Links

Many situations in real life can be shown using
a reciprocal graph.

e.g In a chemical reaction, as time increases the
quantity of the reactant is likely to reduce.

Transformations of graphs can be used to show
a change in a situation.

e.g If the concentration in a chemical reaction
is increased then the quantity of the reactant
is likely to reduce more quickly.

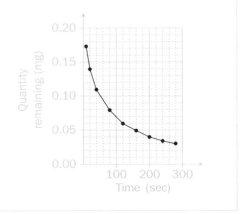

6

Sequences and series

This chapter will show you how to
- recognise, generate and analyse sequences
- formulate rules for obtaining a sequence
- work with an arithmetic series including the general term and its sum
- understand and use sigma notation, Σ, to describe a sum.

Before you start

You should know how to:

1 Solve simple equations of the type
$$ax + b = c$$
e.g. $4(x - 3) = 5$
Multiply out the bracket:
$$4x - 12 = 5$$
$$4x = 17$$
$$x = \frac{17}{4}$$

2 Factorise and solve quadratic equations of the type
$$ax^2 + bx + c = 0$$
e.g. $x^2 + 7x - 144 = 0$
Investigate factors of 144 which have a difference of 7:
$$(x - 9)(x + 16) = 0$$
Hence $x = 9$ or $x = -16$

3 Find the general term of a sequence of numbers.
e.g. $2, 7, 12, 17, \ldots$
Common difference is 5.
Use $5n$ where $n = 1, 2, 3, \ldots$
Adjust to obtain the sequence:
general term is $5n - 3$

Check in:

1 Solve
  a $3x + 9 = 15$
  b $2(x - 3) = 7$
  c $3x = 4(2x - 3)$
  d $2(3x - 1) = 3(x + 1)$
  e $\dfrac{3}{2x + 1} = \dfrac{4}{x - 2}$

2 Solve
  a $x^2 - 5x - 36 = 0$
  b $x^2 + 4x - 96 = 0$
  c $x^2 - x - 90 = 0$
  d $x^2 + 2x - 195 = 0$
  e $x^2 + 2x - 360 = 0$

3 Find the general term of each sequence of numbers.
  a $4, 5, 6, 7, \ldots$
  b $4, 6, 8, 10, \ldots$
  c $4, 7, 10, 13, \ldots$
  d $4, 2, 0, -2, \ldots$
  e $4, 0, -4, -8, \ldots$

6.1 General term of a sequence

- A sequence is a set of terms in which consecutive terms are related by a common rule.

Consider the sequence 1, 3, 5, 7, …

$$2 \times 1 - 1 \qquad 2 \times 2 - 1 \qquad 2 \times 3 - 1$$

The general term is $2n - 1$ where n is a positive integer.

- The general term of a sequence is usually denoted by u_n.

The common difference is 2. To find the general term use $2n$ where $n = 1, 2, 3, …$ and then adjust to obtain the sequence.

You may have come across the general term as a position-to-term rule at GCSE level.

EXAMPLE 1

The general term of a sequence is $u_n = 3 - 2n$
Find u_1, u_2, u_3 and u_4.

$u_n = 3 - 2n$

$u_1 = 3 - 2 \times 1 = 3 - 2 = 1$

$u_2 = 3 - 2 \times 2 = 3 - 4 = -1$

$u_3 = 3 - 2 \times 3 = 3 - 6 = -3$

$u_4 = 3 - 2 \times 4 = 3 - 8 = -5$

Hence the sequence begins $1, -1, -3, -5, …$

To find u_1, substitute $n = 1$ into the general term.

You can use the general term to find any term of a sequence.

EXAMPLE 2

Given $u_n = (n + 1)^2$ find u_2 and u_{19}.

$u_n = (n + 1)^2$

$u_2 = (2 + 1)^2 = 3^2 = 9$

$u_{19} = (19 + 1)^2 = 20^2 = 400$

Hence $u_2 = 9$ and $u_{19} = 400$

C1

EXAMPLE 3

The general term of a sequence is $u_n = (n + 1)(n + 4)$
Which term in the sequence is equal to 70?

Substitute $u_n = 70$: $(n + 1)(n + 4) = 70$

Expand the brackets: $n^2 + 5n + 4 = 70$

Rearrange: $n^2 + 5n - 66 = 0$

Factorise: $(n - 6)(n + 11) = 0$

Hence $n = 6$ or $n = -11$

$n = -11$ is not possible.

Hence $n = 6$ and $u_6 = 70$
so the sixth term is 70.

First rearrange so that one side of the quadratic equation = 0.

You can not have a –11th term.

Check your solution by substituting $n = 6$.into the general term.

EXAMPLE 4

Given $u_n = (-1)^n$ find u_5 and u_6.
What can you say about the behaviour of the terms in this sequence?

$u_n = (-1)^n$
$u_5 = (-1)^5 = -1$
$u_6 = (-1)^6 = 1$

The terms of the sequence will oscillate between –1 and 1.

Odd terms will have the value –1 and even terms will have the value 1.

Terms of a sequence may be algebraic rather than numerical.

EXAMPLE 5

If $u_n = n - n^2$ find u_{2k+1}

$$u_n = n - n^2$$

Substitute $2k + 1$ for n: $u_{2k+1} = (2k + 1) - (2k + 1)^2$

Expand: $u_{2k+1} = 2k + 1 - (4k^2 + 4k + 1)$

Simplify: $u_{2k+1} = 2k + 1 - 4k^2 - 4k - 1$

Hence $u_{2k+1} = -4k^2 - 2k$

Factorise: $u_{2k+1} = -2k(2k + 1)$

You can find the general term given information about specific terms of the sequence.

See Chapter 0 for revision on simultaneous equations. ⓞ

EXAMPLE 6

A sequence has general term $u_n = an + b$
Find a and b given that $u_2 = 0$ and $u_6 = -4$.

$u_n = an + b$

Use the information to form two simultaneous equations:

$u_2 = 0 \Rightarrow 2a + b = 0$ (1)

$u_6 = -4 \Rightarrow 6a + b = -4$ (2)

Subtract (1) from (2):

$$4a = -4$$
$$a = -1$$

Substitute $a = -1$ into (1):

$$-2 + b = 0$$
$$b = 2$$

Hence $u_n = -n + 2$

Check your solution by substituting $n = 2$ and $n = 6$ into the general term.

Exercise 6.1

1 Find the first four terms in each sequence given its general term.

a $u_n = 3n + 1$

b $u_n = (1 + n)^2$

c $u_n = 10 - 5n$

d $u_n = \dfrac{1}{n + 2}$

e $u_n = (2n - 3)^2$

f $u_n = (-1)^n$

g $u_n = (n + 1)(n - 1)$

h $u_n = (-2)^n n$

i $u_n = \dfrac{n + 1}{n + 2}$

j $u_n = (n + 1)^n$

2 Given the term u_n, find the value of k in each case.

In part a the general term is $4n - 2$. You are looking for the term in this sequence that is equal to 18. See Example 3 for help.

a $u_n = 4n - 2$, $u_k = 18$

b $u_n = 7 - 3n$, $u_k = -23$

c $u_n = 7 - 3n$, $u_k = -38$

d $u_n = \dfrac{1 - n}{1 + n}$, $u_k = -\dfrac{11}{13}$

e $u_n = 3 - \dfrac{2}{n}$, $u_k = 2.75$

f $u_n = (2n + 1)(2n - 1)$, $u_k = 195$

g $u_n = n^2 - 2$, $u_k = 398$

h $u_n = \dfrac{1 + 2n}{1 + 3n}$, $u_k = \dfrac{25}{37}$

i $u_n = (2n - 1)(3n + 1)$, $u_k = 286$

j $u_n = 4(-1)^n$, $u_k = -4$

3 A sequence has the general term $u_n = an + 3$.
Find a given that $u_{12} = 63$.

4 If $u_n = an + b$, $u_7 = 19$ and $u_{10} = 28$, find a and b.

5 Given $u_n = an^2 + bn$, $u_4 = 28$ and $u_8 = 120$, find the values
of a and b.

6 **a** The first two terms of a sequence are –1 and –4.
    If $u_n = a + bn$, find the values of a and b.

   b The first three terms of a sequence are 1, 3 and 7 where
    the general term is given by $u_n = an^2 + bn + c$.
    Find the values of the constants, a, b and c.

7 Show, by completing the square or otherwise, that all the
terms in the sequence given by $u_n = n^2 - 8n + 19$ are positive.

8 What is the smallest term in the sequence generated by
$u_n = n^2 - 6n + 13$?

9 **a** If $u_n = 2n - 3$ show that the terms of the sequence given
    by u_{2n+1} are odd numbers.

   b Given that $u_n = n^2 - 2n - 5$ show that u_{3n+1} generates a
    sequence in which all the terms are multiples of three.
    Hence write down the first three terms in the sequence.

INVESTIGATIONS

10 A sequence u_n takes three consecutive integers, $n - 1$,
n and $n + 1$, and multiplies them together.
Use logic to explain why the sequence gives terms which
are always multiples of 3.

11 Look at the following sequence:

$$\frac{2}{3}, \ \frac{3}{4}, \ \frac{4}{5}, \ \dots$$

   a Find u_n.

   b Now find u_n if the sequence has alternate positive
    and negative terms starting with $+\frac{2}{3}, \ -\frac{3}{4}, \ \frac{4}{5}, \ \dots$

Consider the sequence 2, 6, 10, 14, …
You add 4 to get the next term:

$u_1 = 2$ $u_2 = 6$ $u_3 = 10$ $u_4 = 14$

          +4   +4   +4

You can write $u_{n+1} = u_n + 4$
This is a recurrence formula for the sequence.

> - A recurrence formula is a relationship that links terms of a sequence.

You may have come across the recurrence formula as a term-to-term rule at GCSE level.

EXAMPLE 1

Use the recurrence formula $u_{n+1} = 2u_n - 1$ to find u_2, u_3 and u_4, given that $u_1 = 2$.

$u_{n+1} = 2u_n - 1$

Substitute $n = 1$ into the recurrence formula:

$u_2 = 2u_1 - 1$

Substitute $u_1 = 2$:

$u_2 = 2 \times 2 - 1$
$= 4 - 1$
$= 3$

Now use u_2 to find u_3

Substitute $n = 2$ into the recurrence formula:

$u_3 = 2u_2 - 1$
$= 2 \times 3 - 1$
$= 6 - 1$
$= 5$

and use u_3 to find u_4

$u_4 = 2u_3 - 1$
$= 2 \times 5 - 1$
$= 10 - 1$
$= 9$

Hence u_2, u_3 and u_4 are 3, 5 and 9 respectively.

A recurrence formula can also link three terms.
To evaluate one of the terms the two other terms must be known.

C1

EXAMPLE 2

A sequence is described by the recurrence formula
$$u_{n+2} = 3u_{n+1} - u_n$$
Find the next three terms in the sequence given that
$u_1 = 2$ and $u_2 = 3$.

$$u_{n+2} = 3u_{n+1} - u_n$$

Use $u_1 = 2$ and $u_2 = 3$ to find u_3:
$$u_3 = 3u_2 - u_1 = 3 \times 3 - 2 = 9 - 2 = 7$$

Use $u_2 = 3$ and $u_3 = 7$ to find u_4:
$$u_4 = 3u_3 - u_2 = 3 \times 7 - 3 = 21 - 3 = 18$$

Use $u_3 = 7$ and $u_4 = 18$ to find u_5:
$$u_5 = 3u_4 - u_3 = 3 \times 18 - 7 = 54 - 7 = 47$$

Hence the next three terms are 7, 18 and 47.

You can find a recurrence formula if you have information about
the sequence.

EXAMPLE 3

The sequence 2, –1, 5, –7, … is generated using the recurrence
formula $u_{n+1} = a + bu_n$
Find the values of a and b.

Substitute $n = 1$:
$$u_2 = a + bu_1$$
$$-1 = a + 2b$$

$u_1 = 2$ and $u_2 = -1$.

Substitute $n = 2$:
$$u_3 = a + bu_2$$
$$5 = a - b$$

$u_2 = -1$ and $u_3 = 5$.

Rewrite and label the equations:
$$a + 2b = -1 \quad (1)$$
$$a - b = 5 \quad (2)$$

These are **simultaneous equations**.

Subtract equation (2) from equation (1):
$$3b = -6$$
$$b = -2$$

| Take care when subtracting
| negative terms.

Substitute $b = -2$ into equation (2) to find a:
$$a + 2 = 5$$
$$a = 3$$

Hence $a = 3$ and $b = -2$

Check your values for a and b by
substituting them back into the
original equations.

and the recurrence formula is $u_{n+1} = 3 - 2u_n$

Check your final solution by
testing it with the given terms of
the sequence.

Sometimes you need to use trial-and-error to find a recurrence formula.

EXAMPLE 4

The sequence $1, 3, 5, 11, 21, \ldots$ can be obtained using the terms u_n, u_{n+1} and u_{n+2}

Using these terms, find the recurrence formula.

Look for a possible connection between the first three terms 1, 3 and 5.

Try to use the 1 and 3 to make 5:

$2 \times 3 - 1 = 5$ ✓ or

$3 + 2 \times 1 = 5$ ✓

Test for the next block of three terms 3, 5 and 11:

$2 \times 5 - 3 = 7$ ✗ or

$5 + 2 \times 3 = 11$ ✓

The first possibility doesn't work but the second one does.

Write the formula in terms of u_n, u_{n+1} and u_{n+2}:

$$u_{n+2} = u_{n+1} + 2u_n$$

Test your formula on the third batch of three terms 5, 11 and 21:

$11 + 2 \times 5 = 21$ ✓

The recurrence formula is $u_{n+2} = u_{n+1} + 2u_n$

Exercise 6.2

1 Write a recurrence formula in terms of u_n and u_{n+1} for each sequence.

a $4, 6, 8, 10, \ldots$

b $0, -1, -2, -3, \ldots$

c $1, 2, 4, 8, 16, \ldots$

d $2, 3, 5, 9, 17, \ldots$

e $1, 3, 1, 3, 1, 3, \ldots$

f $2, 2, 2, 2, \ldots$

g $-3, 3, -3, 3, -3, \ldots$

h $2, 4, 10, 28, 82, \ldots$

2 Find the terms u_2, u_3 and u_4 in each sequence.

a $u_{n+1} = u_n + 1; u_1 = 3$

b $u_{n+1} = 3u_n - 2; u_1 = 1$

c $u_{n+1} = 4 - u_n; u_1 = 4$

d $u_{n+1} = (u_n - 1)^2; u_1 = 2$

e $u_{n+1} = u_n^2; u_1 = 2$

f $u_{n+1} = u_n \div 2; u_1 = 2$

3 a If $u_{n+1} = ku_n + 1$ determine the value of k for the sequence $2, 7, 22, 67, \ldots$

b The recurrence formula $u_{n+1} = au_n + b$ produces the sequence $2, 5, 17, 65, \ldots$
Find the value of the constants a and b.

4 Find the next three terms in each sequence.

a $u_{n+2} = u_{n+1} + u_n; u_1 = 1, u_2 = 2$

b $u_{n+2} = 2u_{n+1} - u_n; u_1 = 1, u_2 = 2$

c $u_{n+2} = u_n(u_{n+1} - 1); u_1 = 1, u_2 = 3$

d $u_{n+2} = 3u_n - u_{n+1}; u_1 = 3, u_2 = 4$

e $u_{n+2} = 2(u_n + u_{n+1}); u_1 = 0, u_2 = 1$

f $u_{n+2} = 2 + u_n + u_{n+1}; u_1 = 1, u_2 = 3$

g $u_{n+2} = (-1)^n (u_{n+1} - u_n); u_1 = 1, u_2 = 4$

5 a The sequence 1, 1, 2, 3, 5, ... can be produced using a recurrence formula containing u_n, u_{n+1} and u_{n+2}
Find the formula.

b Determine the recurrence formula which will generate the sequence 1, 5, 9, 13, ... in terms of u_n, u_{n+1} and u_{n+2}

c Using the terms u_n, u_{n+1} and u_{n+2} find the recurrence formula for the sequence 1, 2, 2, 4, 8, 32, ...

d Determine the recurrence formula, using u_n, u_{n+1} and u_{n+2}, for the sequence 8, 5, 3, 2, 1, ...

6 The sequence $u_1, u_2, u_3, \ldots$, is defined by the recurrence relation
$u_{n+1} = (-1)^n u_n + d, \quad u_1 = 2, \quad$ where d is a constant.

a Show that $u_5 = 2$.

b Deduce an expression for u_{10}, in terms of d.

Given that $u_3 = 3u_2$

c find the value of d.

[(c) Edexcel Limited 2005]

C1

Arithmetic series

If you add together the terms of a sequence you get a series.

An arithmetic series is a series in which there is a common difference between consecutive terms.

Here are two arithmetic series:

$$+2 \quad +2 \quad +2 \quad +2$$
$$3 + 5 + 7 + 9 + \ldots \qquad \text{common difference is 2}$$

$$-4 \quad -4 \quad -4 \quad -4$$
$$5 + 1 + -3 + -7 + \ldots \qquad \text{common difference is } -4.$$

- An arithmetic series can be represented by the recurrence formula $u_{n+1} = u_n + k$ where k is a constant.

For the arithmetic series $3 + 5 + 7 + 9 + \ldots$
the recurrence formula is $u_{n+1} = u_n + 2$

If a is the first term and d is the common difference of an arithmetic series, then

$$u_1 = a$$
$$u_2 = a + d$$
$$u_3 = a + 2d$$
$$u_4 = a + 3d$$

For $3 + 5 + 7 + 9 + \ldots$
$u_1 = 3$
$u_2 = 3 + 2 = 5$
$u_3 = 3 + 2 \times 2 = 3 + 4 = 7$
$u_4 = 3 + 3 \times 2 = 3 + 6 = 9$

- The formula for the general term of an arithmetic series is
$$u_n = a + (n - 1)d$$
where a is the first term and d is the common difference.

u_n is the nth term.

A specific term, $u_r = a + (r - 1)d$

You can find the nth term of an arithmetic series if you know the first term, a, and the common difference, d.

EXAMPLE 1

Find the 10th and 15th terms of the arithmetic series which begins $\quad 3 + 5 + 7 + 9 + \ldots$

First term $a = 3$ and common difference $d = 2$.

Use the general formula $u_n = a + (n - 1)d$:

10th term
$$u_{10} = 3 + (10 - 1) \times 2 = 3 + 9 \times 2 = 21$$

15th term
$$u_{15} = 3 + (15 - 1) \times 2 = 3 + 14 \times 2 = 31$$

Make sure you use the correct order of operations; BIDMAS.

Hence the required terms are $u_{10} = 21$ and $u_{15} = 31$.

C1

You can calculate how many terms there are in a finite arithmetic series.

A finite series stops at a definite point. An infinite series carries on forever.

EXAMPLE 2

Determine how many terms there are in the arithmetic series
$$4 + 11 + 18 + 25 + \ldots + 144$$

First term $a = 4$
Common difference $d = 7$

Form an equation and solve it to find n:
Use the general formula $u_n = a + (n - 1)d$ where $u_n = 144$:

$$4 + (n - 1) \times 7 = 144$$
$$(n - 1) \times 7 = 140$$
$$n - 1 = 20$$
$$n = 21$$

Hence there are 21 terms in the series.

You can find the first term of an arithmetic series from given information.

EXAMPLE 3

The third term of an arithmetic series is 9 and the seventh term is 33.
Find the first and second terms.

Substitute $u_3 = 9$ into $u_n = a + (n - 1)d$:

$$a + (3 - 1)d = 9$$
$$a + 2d = 9 \quad (1)$$

Substitute $u_7 = 33$ into $u_n = a + (n - 1)d$:

$$a + (7 - 1)d = 33$$
$$a + 6d = 33 \quad (2)$$

Create a pair of simultaneous equations.

Subtract equation (1) from equation (2):

$$6d - 2d = 33 - 9$$
$$4d = 24$$
$$d = 6$$

Substitute $d = 6$ into equation (1) to find a:

$$a + 2 \times 6 = 9$$
$$a + 12 = 9$$
$$a = -3$$

You can check your solutions by substituting back into the original equations.

Hence the formula for the general term is
$$u_n = -3 + 6(n - 1)$$
$$u_1 = a \quad \text{so} \quad u_1 = -3$$
$$u_2 = a + 6 \times (2 - 1) = -3 + 6 \times 1 = 3$$

Hence the first and second terms are −3 and 3.

EXAMPLE 4

C1

Determine the first three terms in the arithmetic series
$$12 + 19 + 26 + 33 + \ldots$$
which are greater than 1000.

First term $a = 12$
Common difference $d = 7$
Let the number of terms be n.

Substitute the known values into $u_n = a + (n-1)d$:
$$u_n = 12 + (n-1) \times 7$$

Given $u_n > 1000$ set up an inequality:
$$12 + (n-1)7 > 1000$$

Solve for n:
$$12 + 7n - 7 > 1000$$
$$7n + 5 > 1000$$
$$7n > 1000 - 5$$
$$n > \frac{995}{7}$$
$$n > 142.14$$

Hence the 143rd term is the first one greater than 1000.

You need to **interpret** the decimal value. n is the first integer greater than 142.14 so it must be 143.

Use the general term $u_n = a + (n-1)d$:

143rd term is $\quad u_{143} = 12 + (143 - 1) \times 7$
$$= 12 + 142 \times 7 = 1006$$

and the next two terms are $u_{144} = 1006 + 7 = 1013$
$$u_{145} = 1013 + 7 = 1020$$

Hence the three required terms are 1006, 1013 and 1020.

Exercise 6.3

1 Which of the following are arithmetic series?

a $4 - 4 + 4 - 4 + \ldots$

b $-3 + 1 + 5 + 9 + \ldots$

c $\frac{1}{2} + 2\frac{1}{2} + 4\frac{1}{2} + 6\frac{1}{2} + \ldots$

d $0.1 + 0.01 + 0.001 + 0.0001 + \ldots$

e $-2 + 3 - 4 + 5 - 6 + \ldots$

f $10 + 5 + 2.5 + 1.25 + \ldots$

2 Use the recurrence formula to generate the next three terms in the arithmetic series whose first term is given.

a $u_{n+1} = u_n + 3; u_1 = 2$

b $u_{n+1} = u_n - 4; u_1 = 7$

c $u_{n+1} = u_n + \frac{1}{2}; u_1 = 1$

d $u_{n+1} = u_n - 10; u_1 = 4$

3 Determine the recurrence formula for these arithmetic series.

a $2 + 4 + 6 + 8 + \ldots$

b $12 + 15 + 18 + 21 + \ldots$

c $5 - 1 - 7 - 13 + \ldots$

d $1.5 + 0.8 + 0.1 - 0.6 + \ldots$

4 For each of these arithmetic series find the 10th, 20th and nth terms.

   a $2 + 5 + 8 + 11 + \ldots$

   b $\frac{1}{4} + 1 + 1\frac{3}{4} + 2\frac{1}{2} + \ldots$

   c $\frac{1}{5} + \frac{4}{5} + \frac{7}{5} + 2 + \ldots$

   d $-9 + -11 + -13 + -15 + \ldots$

   e $-0.5 + -0.9 + -1.3 + -1.7 + \ldots$

   f $3p + 9p + 15p + 21p + \ldots \ldots$

   g $\frac{1}{2}a + \frac{1}{4}a + 0 - \frac{1}{4}a - \frac{1}{2}a \ldots$

   h $x + (2x + 1) + (3x + 2) + (4x + 3) + \ldots$

5 How many terms are there in each of these finite arithmetic series?

   a $4 + 7 + 10 + 13 + \ldots + 34$

   b $17 + 15 + 13 + 11 + \ldots + -23$

   c $2 + 11 + 20 + 29 + \ldots + 272$

   d $-4 + -7 + -10 + -13 + \ldots + -49$

   e $0.7 + 0.3 + -0.1 + -0.5 + \ldots + -5.7$

   f $\frac{1}{2} + \frac{5}{8} + \frac{3}{4} + \frac{7}{8} + \ldots + 5$

   g $-1 + -\frac{1}{2} + 0 + \frac{1}{2} + \ldots + 30$

   h $\frac{2}{3} + \frac{5}{6} + 1 + \frac{7}{6} + \ldots + 14\frac{2}{3}$

6 Find the common difference in these arithmetic series.

   a First term 4, fourth term 19.

   b First term -3, seventh term 15.

   c Second term 5, fifth term -1.

7 **a** The seventh term in an arithmetic series is 15 and the eighth term is 20. Find the first term.

   b The fourth and sixth terms of an arithmetic series are $7\frac{1}{2}$ and $10\frac{1}{2}$ respectively. Work out the first and twelfth terms.

8 **a** For the arithmetic series $3 + 9 + 15 + 21 + \ldots$ which term in the series is the first one to be greater than 200?   *Set up an inequality equation.*

   b An arithmetic series consists of five terms; the second term is 7 and the last term is 22. Write out the full series.

   c The consecutive terms x, y and z form an arithmetic series. Show that y is the mean of the x and z values.

   d The first term of an arithmetic series is 5 and the common difference is -3. Find the first term in the series which is less than -100.

   e For the three consecutive terms, x^2, $5x$, and 9, find the two possible values of x which make these part of an arithmetic series.

INVESTIGATION

9   **a** Which three consecutive integers add to give 300?

    b Which four consecutive integers add to give 406?

6.4 Sum of an arithmetic series

Consider the challenge: *Add up the whole numbers from 1 to 1000.*
You can write this as the sum, S_{1000}, of the first 1000 natural numbers.

A natural number is a positive integer.

$$S_{1000} = 1 + 2 + 3 + \ldots + 998 + 999 + 1000$$

Reverse the order of the terms in this series:

$$S_{1000} = 1000 + 999 + 998 + \ldots + 3 + 2 + 1$$

Can you see why this is an arithmetic series?

Add the two series together term by term:

$$2S_{1000} = 1001 + 1001 + 1001 + \ldots + 1001 + 1001 + 1001$$

There are 1000 terms of value 1001

$$2S_{1000} = 1000 \times 1001$$

$$S_{1000} = \frac{1000 \times 1001}{2}$$

$$S_{1000} = 500\,500$$

The sum of the whole numbers from 1 to 1000 is 500 500.

In general, S_n denotes the sum of the first n natural numbers.

> You can apply this method to a general arithmetic series:
>
> $$S_n = a + [a + d] + [a + 2d] + [a + 3d] + \ldots + [a + (n - 2)d] + [a + (n - 1)d]$$
>
> Reverse the order of the terms:
>
> Add the two series together:
>
> Multiply the number of resulting terms by their value
>
> Arrive at the result:
>
> $$S_n = \frac{n}{2}[2a + (n - 1)d]$$

Work out this proof for yourself.

Learn this result and the proof. This is the sum of the first n natural numbers, S_n.

o **The sum to n terms of an arithmetic series is**

$$S_n = \frac{n}{2}[2a + (n - 1)d]$$

a is the first term and d is the common difference.

You can apply this result to any arithmetic series.

Sometimes arithmetic series are called **arithmetic progressions**.

C1

Find the sum of the series
$$4 + 9 + 14 + 19 + \dots \text{ to 20 terms}$$

First term $a = 4$
Common difference $d = 5$
Number of terms $n = 20$

Write down the facts you know.

Use the formula for the sum: $S_n = \frac{n}{2}[2a + (n-1)d]$

Substitute the values for a, d and n:

$$S_{20} = \frac{20}{2}[2 \times 4 + (20 - 1) \times 5]$$

$$S_{20} = 10[8 + 19 \times 5]$$

$$S_{20} = 1030$$

Hence the sum of the series to 20 terms is 1030.

The formula for S_n is sometimes written as
$$S_n = \frac{n}{2}[a + a + (n-1)d]$$
or $S_n = \frac{n}{2}[a + l]$ where l is the sum of the first and last terms.

Find the sum of the series
$$2 + 6 + 10 + 14 + \dots + 158$$

First you need to know how many terms there are in the series:

The nth term is $u_n = a + (n-1)d$
where $u_n = 158$, $a = 2$ and $d = 4$.

Substitute the values for u_n, a and d:
$$2 + (n-1) \times 4 = 158$$
$$4n - 4 = 156$$
$$4n = 160$$
$$n = 40$$

Use the formula to evaluate the sum to 40 terms:

$$S = \frac{n}{2}[2a + (n-1)d]$$

$$S = \frac{40}{2}[2 \times 2 + (40-1) \times 4]$$

$$S = 20 \times [4 + 39 \times 4]$$

$$S = 20 \times [4 + 156]$$

$$S = 3200$$

Hence the sum of the series is 3200.

You can use the sum of an arithmetic series to solve real-life problems.

EXAMPLE 3

Harry needs to save £1800 from his earnings to buy a car. In the first month he saves £50, the second month £60, and continues to add an extra £10 a month until it reaches the required sum.
How long will it take Harry to save this amount?

Write the information as a sum:

$$50 + 60 + 70 + \ldots = 1800$$

First term $a = 50$
Common difference $d = 10$
Let the number of terms be n.

Use the formula for the sum: $S = \dfrac{n}{2}[2a + (n-1)d]$

Substitute the values for a and d:

$$\frac{n}{2}[2 \times 50 + (n-1) \times 10] = 1800$$

$$\frac{n}{2}[100 + 10n - 10] = 1800$$

Simplify: $$n[90 + 10n] = 3600$$

Form a quadratic: $$10n^2 + 90n - 3600 = 0$$

Simplify: $$n^2 + 9n - 360 = 0$$

Factorise: $$(n - 15)(n + 24) = 0$$

Either $n = 15$ or $n = -24$.

n cannot be negative so $n = 15$.

It will take Harry 15 months to save up enough to buy the car.

C1

Exercise 6.4

1   Find the sum of each of these series.

    a $1 + 3 + 5 + 7 + \ldots$ (13 terms)

    b $4 + 8 + 12 + 16 + \ldots$ (11 terms)

    c $3 + 7 + 11 + 15 + \ldots$ (20 terms)

    d $-3 + -6 + -9 + -12 + \ldots$ (14 terms)

    e   What is the sum of the first 100 natural numbers?

2 **a** Determine how many terms there are in the series,
1 + 4 + 7 + 10 + ... + 37, and find the sum of the series.

  b Find how many terms there are in the series,
5 + 9 + 13 + 17 + ... + 81, and find its sum.

  c Find the sum of the series, 2 + 5 + 8 + 11 + ... + 62.

  d Find the sum of the series, 10 + 7 + 4 + 1 + ... + -26.

  e Find the sum of the first 50 odd numbers.

3 **a** The series, 2 + 5 + 8 + 11 + ... sums to 155.
How many terms are there in the series?

  b Find the number of terms needed in the series,
-20 + -18 + -16 + -14 + ..., to make the sum zero.

  c The series, 5 + 11 + 17 + 23 + ..., = 456.
How many terms are needed to arrive at this sum?

4 Ahmed plans to save £250 in the year 2001, £300 in
2002, £350 in 2003, and so on until the year 2020.

His planned savings form an arithmetic series with
common difference of £50.

  a Find the amount he plans to save in the year 2011.

  b Calculate his total planned savings over the 20-year period
from 2001 to 2020.

Ben also plans to save money over the same 20-year period.
He saves £A in the year 2001 and his planned yearly savings form
an arithmetic sequence with common difference of £60.

Given that Ben's total planned savings over the 20-year period
are equal to Ahmed's total planned savings over the same period,

  c calculate the value of A.

[(c) Edexcel Limited 2003]

INVESTIGATIONS

5 The sum of the first ten terms of an arithmetic series is 15.
The sum of the first sixteen terms is -24.

  a Write down 2 simultaneous equations to show this information.

  b Hence find a and d.

6 An alternative formula for the sum of the first n natural numbers is

$$S_n = \frac{n}{2}(a + l)$$

where a is the first term and l is the final term of the series.

Write a proof to show that this result is true.

Here is an arithmetic series with nine terms:

$$2 + 4 + 6 + 8 + \ldots + 18$$

You can express the sum of the series using the symbol Σ (sigma).

Σ is the Greek letter S. In mathematics it stands for 'sum'.

$$\sum_{r=1}^{r=9} 2r = 2 + 4 + 6 + 8 + \ldots + 18$$

Substituting the values $r = 1, 2, 3, \ldots, 9$ into the sum.

$\displaystyle\sum_{r=1}^{r=n}$ means the sum of the first n terms.

Sometimes this is written as $\displaystyle\sum_{1}^{n}$

You can evaluate a sum shown in sigma notation.

EXAMPLE 1

Evaluate $\displaystyle\sum_{r=1}^{r=4}(6r - 1)$

Substitute $r = 1, 2, 3, 4$ into $(6r - 1)$:

$$\sum_{r=1}^{r=4}(6r - 1) = 5 + 11 + 17 + 23 = 56$$

EXAMPLE 2

Evaluate $\displaystyle\sum_{1}^{10}(3r + 2)$

$\displaystyle\sum_{1}^{10}(3r + 2)$ is equivalent to

Substitute the values $r = 1, 2, 3, \ldots, 10$ to generate the sum:

$$5 + 8 + 11 + 14 + \ldots + 32$$

Hence $a = 5$, $d = 3$ and $n = 10$.

$\displaystyle\sum_{r=1}^{r=10}(3r + 2)$. You do not need to write '$r =$' in the sigma sign.

The sum is given by $S = \frac{n}{2}[2a + (n - 1)d]$

$$S = \frac{10}{2}[2 \times 5 + (10 - 1) \times 3]$$

$$S = 185$$

Hence the sum of the series is 185.

C1

The sum does not always start with the first term.

EXAMPLE 3

Write down the terms of the arithmetic series $\sum_{r=4}^{r=11}\left(7-\dfrac{r}{4}\right)$

Substitute the values 4, 5, 6, …, 11 for r:

$$\left(7-\dfrac{4}{4}\right)+\left(7-\dfrac{5}{4}\right)+\left(7-\dfrac{6}{4}\right)+\ldots+\left(7-\dfrac{11}{4}\right)$$

The series is

$$6+5\dfrac{3}{4}+5\dfrac{1}{2}+5\dfrac{1}{4}+5+4\dfrac{3}{4}+4\dfrac{1}{2}+4\dfrac{1}{4}$$

EXAMPLE 4

Use the sigma notation to denote the sum of the series
$$5+9+13+17+\ldots+37$$

First term $a=5$
Common difference $d=4$
Let $n=r$
The general term is given by $u_n=a+(n-1)d$

Substitute for a, d and n:

$$u_r=5+(r-1)\times 4=4r+1$$

Find the number of terms in the series:

Last term $\quad 37=a+(n-1)d$
$$\qquad\qquad =5+4(n-1)$$

Rearrange: $\quad 36=4n$
$$\qquad\qquad n=9$$

So there are nine terms in the series.

Hence the sum is shown by $\sum_{r=1}^{r=9}(4r+1)$

> Don't forget to swap the general n with the specific r.

Exercise 6.5

1 Write out the arithmetic series represented in each case.

a $\sum_{r=1}^{r=3}4r$

b $\sum_{r=1}^{r=5}(2r-1)$

c $\sum_{r=2}^{r=5}(5-2r)$

d $\sum_{r=10}^{r=15}(3r+2)$

e $\sum_{r=1}^{r=7}(-r)$

f $\sum_{r=4}^{r=6}\dfrac{r}{2}$

g $\sum_{1}^{6}\dfrac{(r+3)}{4}$

h $\sum_{12}^{15}\dfrac{r}{3}$

2 Find an expression for the general term and use sigma notation to *denote* the sum of each arithmetic series starting with $r = 1$.

You do not need to work out the sum.

   a $2 + 4 + 6 + 8 + \ldots + 14$

   b $1 + 3 + 5 + 7 + \ldots + 15$

   c $3 + 7 + 11 + 15 + \ldots + 39$

   d $-5 + -8 + -11 + -14 + \ldots + -35$

   e $2\frac{1}{2} + 4\frac{1}{2} + 6\frac{1}{2} + 8\frac{1}{2} + \ldots + 30\frac{1}{2}$

   f $15 + 20 + 25 + 30 + \ldots$ to 12 terms

   g $-3 + -9 + -15 + -21 + \ldots$ to 21 terms

   h $-\frac{1}{3} + -\frac{5}{3} + -3 + -\frac{13}{3} + \ldots$ to 10 terms

   i $3p + 8p + 13p + 18p + \ldots$ to q terms; p is a constant

   j $(a + 1) + (2a + 3) + (3a + 5) + (4a + 7) + \ldots$ to n terms; a is a constant

3 Work out the sum of each arithmetic series.

   a $\displaystyle\sum_{r=1}^{r=10} 5r$

   b $\displaystyle\sum_{r=1}^{r=10} (2r + 1)$

   c $\displaystyle\sum_{1}^{20} (3r - 1)$

   d $\displaystyle\sum_{1}^{20} (1 - 5r)$

   e $\displaystyle\sum_{1}^{40} (10 - r)$

   f $\displaystyle\sum_{1}^{40} \frac{(2r + 3)}{3}$

   g $\displaystyle\sum_{1}^{10} \frac{(2 - 3r)}{2}$

   h $\displaystyle\sum_{1}^{20} \frac{(3r + 5)}{2}$

   i $\displaystyle\sum_{3}^{20} (4r - 2)$

   j $\displaystyle\sum_{10}^{20} (r - 5)$

4 Show that $\displaystyle\sum_{r=1}^{n}(2r-5) = n(n-4)$

5 Express, in sigma notation, the arithmetic series
$14 + 8 + 2 - 4 \ldots$ to 12 terms.

6 Evaluate $\displaystyle\sum_{5}^{12}(4-3r)$

7 If $\displaystyle\sum_{1}^{n}(2r-1) = 900$, find n.

8 Show that $\displaystyle\sum_{r=1}^{r=n}(2r-1) = n^2$

9 Calculate $\displaystyle\sum_{r=1}^{20}(3r+1)$

INVESTIGATIONS

10 Gauss was a famous mathematician who examined the series

$$\sum_{k=1}^{n}k = 1+2+3+\ldots+n$$

a Use the formula for the sum of the first n numbers for an arithmetic progression to prove that

$$\sum_{k=1}^{n}k = \frac{n(n+1)}{2}$$

b Gauss used his formula to add up the numbers 1 to 100 very quickly. What is the answer?

11 Consider the arithmetic series

$11 + 9 + 7 + \ldots$

Investigate for which values of n the sum of the series is equal to the nth term itself by using the following steps:

a Prove that if $s_n = u_n$ then $n^2 - 14n + 13 = 0$

b Hence give the term numbers and their values which satisfy the sum being equal to the term itself.

Review 6

1 Find the first four terms in each sequence.

  a $u_n = (2n + 1)^2$　　　　　　　**b** $u_n = n^2 - 4$

  c $u_n = \dfrac{n + 1}{n}$　　　　　　　**d** $u_n = (2n + 1)(3n + 1)$

2 Find the value of k given the general term and the kth term in each sequence.

  a $u_n = 5 - 4n$, $u_k = -43$　　　　**b** $u_n = \dfrac{1 + 2n}{1 - 2n}$, $u_k = -\dfrac{31}{29}$

  c $u_n = n(3n - 1)$, $u_k = 234$　　　**d** $u_n = (2n - 1)(n + 1)$, $u_k = 135$

3 **a** The fourth and fifth terms of a sequence are 26 and 33. If $u_n = an + b$, find the values of the constants a and b.

  b If the eighth term of the sequence generated by $u_n = an^2 + 3$ is 131, find the value of a.

  c Given that $u_n = an^2 + bn + c$ and $u_3 = 6$, $u_7 = 38$ and $u_8 = 51$, find the values of the constants a, b and c.

4 **a** Write a recurrence formula in terms of u_n and u_{n+1} for the sequences

  i 4, 7, 10, 13, …　　　　　**ii** –1, 3, –5, 11, …

  b Find the terms u_2, u_3 and u_4 for the sequences

  i $u_{n+1} = u_n - 5$ and $u_1 = 4$
  ii $u_{n+1} = (u_n - 3)^2$ and $u_1 = 0$

5 The sequence of positive numbers $u_1, u_2, u_3, \ldots$ is given by $u_{n+1} = u_n(u_n + 1)$, $u_1 = 1$.
  i Find u_2, u_3 and u_4.
  ii Write down the value of u_5.

6 **a** Determine the 13th and 17th terms in the arithmetic series
  $-9 + -5 + -1 + 3 + \ldots$

  b How many terms are there in the series $11 + 5 - 1 - 7 + \ldots - 61$

  c The fifth term of an arithmetic series is $13\frac{1}{2}$ and the twelfth term is $34\frac{1}{2}$. Find the first term and the common difference.

7 **a** Find the sum to 20 terms of the series $-23 + -18 + -13 + -8 + \ldots$

  b The sum of the arithmetic series $4 + 13 + 22 + 31 + \ldots$ is to be greater than 1000. How many terms are needed to achieve this?

8 On Alice's 11th birthday she started to receive an annual allowance. The first annual allowance was £500 and on each following birthday the allowance was increased by £200.

  a Show that, immediately after her 12th birthday, the total of the allowances that Alice had received was £1200.

  b Find the amount of Alice's annual allowance on her 18th birthday.

  c Find the total of the allowances that Alice had received up to and including her 18th birthday.

When the total of the allowances that Alice had received reached £32 000 the allowance stopped.

  d Find how old Alice was when she received her last allowance.   [(c) Edexcel Limited 2006]

9 The rth term of an arithmetic series is $(3r - 2)$.

  a Write down the first three terms of this series.

  b State the value of the common difference.

  c Show that $\sum_{r=1}^{n}(3r - 2) = \frac{1}{2}n(3n - 1)$

10 An arithmetic series has first term a and common difference d.

  a Prove that the sum of the first n terms of the series is $\frac{1}{2}n[2a + (n - 1)d]$

Sean repays a loan over a period of n months. His monthly repayments form an arithmetic sequence.

He repays £149 in the first month, £147 in the second month, £145 in the third month, and so on. He makes his final repayment in the nth month, where $n > 21$.

  b Find the amount Sean repays in the 21st month.

Over the n months, he repays a total of £5000.

  c Form an equation in n, and show that your equation may be written as
    $n^2 - 150n + 5000 = 0$

  d Solve the equation in part **c**.

  e State, with a reason, which of the solutions to the equation in part **c** is not a sensible solution to the repayment problem.   [(c) Edexcel Limited 2005]

11 The sum of an arithmetic series is $\sum_{r=1}^{n}(80 - 3r)$

  a Write down the first two terms of the series.

  b Find the common difference of the series.

Given that $n = 50$,

  c find the sum of the series.   [(c) Edexcel Limited 2003]

6

Exit

Summary

Refer to

- A sequence is a set of terms which are generated by a common rule.   6.1
- The general term of a sequence can be denoted by u_n.   6.1
- A recurrence formula can be used to generate consecutive terms in a sequence.   6.2
- The recurrence formula for an arithmetic series is $u_{n+1} = u_n + k$, where k is a constant.   6.2
- A series is the sum of the terms of a sequence.   6.3
- An arithmetic series has a common difference between consecutive terms.   6.3
- The general term u_n of an arithmetic series is given by $u_n = a + (n-1)d$, where the first term is a, and common difference is d.   6.3
- The sum of an arithmetic series is given by $S = \frac{n}{2}[2a + (n-1)d]$ 6.4
- The sigma (Σ) notation is used to denote the sum of a series.   6.5

C1

Links

On a day-to-day level, series are used to calculate compound interest, and appreciation or depreciation of the value of goods.

Sequences have been used by code-builders and code-breakers; the Germans used the Enigma code during the second world war and British code-breakers deciphered it. Sequences are used commonly in banking, security and telecommunications, and the advances in computer technology over the past 20 years have seen a huge rise in sophistication in this field.

The Fibonacci sequence 1, 1, 2, 3, 5, 8, 13, 21, ... has recurrence relation $u_{n+2} = u_{n+1} + u_n$

If the numbers represent lengths, this sequence is found commonly in situations of natural growth, such as patterns in sunflowers, and also in art and architecture.

7

Differentiation

This chapter will show you how to
- find the gradient of a tangent to a curve
- find the derivative of a function from first principles
- differentiate expressions involving ax^n
- solve problems involving rates of change
- find second order derivatives
- find the equations of tangents and normals.

Before you start

You should know how to:

1 Perform calculations without using a calculator.

e.g. $(4.004001 - 4) \div 0.001$
$= 0.004\,001 \div 0.001$
$= 4.001$

2 Subtract algebraic expressions.

e.g. Subtract $2x - 3$ from $x^2 - 2x + 1$
$x^2 - 2x + 1 - (2x - 3)$
$= x^2 - 2x + 1 - 2x + 3$
$= x^2 - 4x + 4$

3 Manipulate powers and indices using the rules of indices.

e.g. Write $x^2\sqrt{x}$ in the form x^n

$x^2\sqrt{x}$

$= x^2 \times x^{\frac{1}{2}}$

$= x^{2 + \frac{1}{2}}$

$= x^{\frac{5}{2}}$

4 Express products and quotients as sums and differences.

e.g. Express $\dfrac{x^2 + 1}{\sqrt{x}}$ as a sum of two terms.

$\dfrac{x^2 + 1}{\sqrt{x}} = \dfrac{x^2}{\sqrt{x}} + \dfrac{1}{\sqrt{x}}$

$= x^{\frac{3}{2}} + x^{-\frac{1}{2}}$

Check in:

1 Perform these calculations.
  a $0.0303 \div 0.01$
  b $0.4141 \div 0.1$
  c $(2.0404 - 2) \div 0.001$
  d $(6.006\,006 - 6) \div 0.0001$

2 a Subtract $x^2 + 1$ from $2x^2 - 1$
  b Simplify $3x - 2 - (2x + 1)$
  c Subtract $(x + 1)^2$ from $(x + 2)^2$
  d Simplify $x^2 - 1 - (3x^2 - 2)$

3 Write each expression in the form x^n.
  a $x\sqrt{x}$

  b $\dfrac{x}{\sqrt{x}}$

  c $\dfrac{\sqrt{x}}{x^2}$

  d $\dfrac{1}{x^3}$

4 a Expand $(1 + 4x)(2 - 3x)$

  b Simplify $\dfrac{3x^3 - 2x}{x}$

  c Expand $x(4x - 3)(2 - 3x)$

  d Simplify $\dfrac{4x^3 - 5x^2}{\sqrt{x}}$

Consider the question:

How can you work out the exact value of the gradient at any point on a curve, without plotting the graph and making an estimate by drawing a tangent with a ruler?

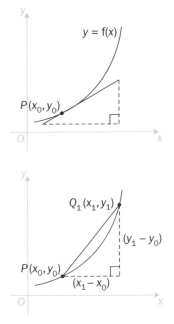

Consider the curve with equation $y = f(x)$ and a fixed point $P(x_0, y_0)$ which lies on the curve.

The diagram shows the tangent to the curve at P.

Imagine that Q is a neighbouring point that can move along the curve.

Initially Q has position $Q_1(x_1, y_1)$.

The gradient of the chord PQ_1 is given by $\dfrac{y_1 - y_0}{x_1 - x_0}$

Let Q move gradually closer towards the point P.

It first moves to $Q_2(x_2, y_2)$ then it moves to $Q_3(x_3, y_3)$ then it moves to $Q_4(x_4, y_4)$.

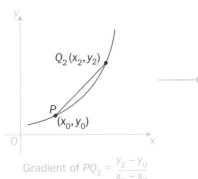

Gradient of $PQ_2 = \dfrac{y_2 - y_0}{x_2 - x_0}$ Gradient of $PQ_3 = \dfrac{y_3 - y_0}{x_3 - x_0}$ Gradient of $PQ_4 = \dfrac{y_4 - y_0}{x_4 - x_0}$

As Q moves towards P the gradient of the chord PQ gets closer to becoming the gradient of the tangent at P.

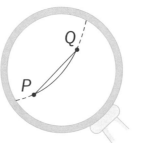

The graph is enlarged to show detail. In reality P and Q are very close together.

This leads to a general rule:

○ In the limit, as $Q \rightarrow P$,
   gradient of chord PQ = gradient of tangent at P.

You can use this result to deduce the gradient of the tangent at a point.

EXAMPLE 1

For the curve $y = x^2$ find the gradient of the chords PQ_1, PQ_2, PQ_3 and PQ_4 by joining the point $P = (1, 1)$ to the points

a $Q_1 = (1.1, 1.21)$ **b** $Q_2 = (1.01, 1.0201)$

c $Q_3 = (1.001, 1.002001)$ **d** $Q_4 = (1.0001, 1.0002)$

For Q_4, $y_4 = x_4^2$ and
$1.0001^2 = 1.00020001$
$= 1.0002$ to 5 s.f.

Hence deduce the gradient of the tangent at P.

Let P be $(x_0, y_0) = (1, 1)$ and let Q_n be (x_n, y_n).

Record the information in a table:

Chord PQ_n	x_n	y_n	$x_n - x_0$	$y_n - y_0$	Gradient of chord PQ_n $\dfrac{y_n - y_0}{x_n - x_0}$
PQ_1	1.1	1.21	0.1	0.21	2.1
PQ_2	1.01	1.0201	0.01	0.0201	2.01
PQ_3	1.001	1.002001	0.001	0.002001	2.001
PQ_4	1.0001	1.0002	0.0001	0.0002	2

The gradients are   **a**   2.1   **b**   2.01
                       c   2.001   **d**   2

Remember you cannot use a calculator in the C1 unit.

The gradient of the chord tends towards the value 2 as Q gets closer and closer to P. Hence you can deduce that the gradient of the tangent at P is 2.

This method is often referred to as the method of small increments. You can use it to deduce the gradient at a given point on any curve, without having to draw the curve.

Exercise 7.1

1   For the curve, $y = x^3$, determine the gradient of the chord AB joining A, $(1, 1)$, to B when B is at

    a $(1.1, 1.331)$ **b** $(1.01, 1.030301)$

    c $(1.001, 1.003003)$ **d** $(1.0001, 1.0003)$

    Hence deduce the gradient of the tangent at the point $A(1, 1)$.

2   The point P, $(2, 9)$, lies on the curve $y = x^2 + 2x + 1$ and a second point, Q, also lies on the curve. If the coordinates of Q are

    a $(2.1, 9.61)$ **b** $(2.01, 9.0601)$

    c $(2.001, 9.006001)$ **d** $(2.0001, 9.0006)$

    Find the gradient of the chord PQ and use the results to deduce the gradient of the tangent at P.

Differentiation from first principles

You can generalise the technique described in Section 7.1.

Consider the equation of the curve $y = x^2$

Let the point $P(x, y)$ lie on this curve and let Q be a neighbouring point, close to P.

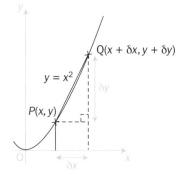

The coordinates of Q are
$(x + $ a small change in x, $y + $ a small change in $y)$
This is denoted by $Q(x + \delta x, y + \delta y)$

Looking at the diagram,

gradient of chord PQ is $\dfrac{\delta y}{\delta x}$

The aim is to find this ratio algebraically.

δ is the Greek letter delta.
δx means 'a small increase in the x-value'.

For point $P(x, y)$ $\qquad\qquad\qquad y = x^2 \qquad\qquad$ (1)

For point $Q(x + \delta x, y + \delta y)$ $\quad y + \delta y = (x + \delta x)^2 \quad$ (2)

Subtract (1) from (2): $\qquad\qquad \delta y = (x + \delta x)^2 - x^2$

$$\delta y = x^2 + 2x(\delta x) + (\delta x)^2 - x^2$$

Simplify: $\qquad\qquad\qquad\qquad \delta y = 2x(\delta x) + (\delta x)^2$

Divide by δx: $\qquad\qquad\qquad \dfrac{\delta y}{\delta x} = 2x + \delta x$

The term δx cannot be split up to give δ on its own.
So $(\delta x)^2 \neq \delta^2 x^2$

As $Q \to P$, $\delta x \to 0$ and $\dfrac{\delta y}{\delta x}$ gets closer and closer to becoming the gradient of the tangent to the curve at the point P.

δx and δy approach zero as Q gets closer to P and the chord becomes a tangent to the curve.

In the limit, as $\delta x \to 0$, $\quad \dfrac{\delta y}{\delta x}$ becomes $\dfrac{dy}{dx}$

so for the curve, $y = x^2 \quad \dfrac{dy}{dx} = 2x$

The δx term approaches zero, and is so small it can be ignored.

The expression $\dfrac{dy}{dx}$ can be used to find the gradient of the tangent to the curve $y = x^2$ for any value of x.

e.g. When $x = 3$

$$\dfrac{dy}{dx} = 2x = 2 \times 3 = 6$$

You can check by using the method of small increments.

So the gradient of the tangent to $y = x^2$ t the point where $x = 3$ is 6.

- $\dfrac{dy}{dx}$ is called the derivative of y with respect to x.

- $\dfrac{dy}{dx}$ is the value of $\dfrac{\delta y}{\delta x}$ in the limit as $\delta x \to 0$

- We say that you differentiate y to obtain $\dfrac{dy}{dx}$.

You can write:
$$\frac{dy}{dx} = \lim_{\delta x \to 0} \frac{\delta y}{\delta x}$$

You can use differentiation from first principles to find the gradient of the tangent at any point of any curve.

EXAMPLE 1

Find, from first principles, the gradient of the tangent to the curve with equation $y = x^2 + x + 3$ at the point $x = 2$.

Let point $P(x, y)$ and a neighbouring point $Q(x + \delta x, y + \delta y)$ lie on the curve.

For point P $\qquad y = x^2 + x + 3 \qquad\qquad$ (1)

For point Q $\qquad y + \delta y = (x + \delta x)^2 + (x + \delta x) + 3 \qquad$ (2)

Subtract (1) from (2): $\quad \delta y = (x + \delta x)^2 - x^2 + (x + \delta x) - x + 3 - 3$

$$\delta y = x^2 + 2x(\delta x) + (\delta x)^2 - x^2 + x + \delta x - x + 3 - 3$$

Simplify: $\qquad \delta y = 2x(\delta x) + (\delta x)^2 + \delta x$

Divide by δx: $\qquad \dfrac{\delta y}{\delta x} = 2x + \delta x + 1$

As $Q \to P, \delta x \to 0 \quad$ so $\displaystyle\lim_{\delta x \to 0} \frac{\delta y}{\delta x} \to 2x + 1$

Hence $\quad \dfrac{dy}{dx} = \displaystyle\lim_{\delta x \to 0} \frac{\delta y}{\delta x} = 2x + 1$

When $x = 2 \quad \dfrac{dy}{dx} = 2 \times x + 1 = 2 \times 2 + 1 = 5$

Hence the gradient of the tangent at the point $x = 2$ is 5.

EXAMPLE 2

Find, from first principles, an expression for $\dfrac{dy}{dx}$ when $y = x^3 - x$

Hence determine the gradient of the tangent to the curve at the point where $x = 0$.

Let point $P(x, y)$ and a neighbouring point $Q(x + \delta x, y + \delta y)$ lie on the curve.

For point P $\qquad y = x^3 - x$ $\qquad\qquad\qquad\qquad$ (1)

For point Q $\qquad y + \delta y = (x + \delta x)^3 - (x + \delta x)$ $\qquad$ (2)

Subtract (1) from (2): $\quad \delta y = (x + \delta x)^3 - x^3 - (x + \delta x) + x$

For this example it is useful to know that

$(x + a)^3 = x^3 + 3x^2 a + 3x a^2 + a^3$

Simplify: $\qquad\qquad\quad \delta y = 3x^2(\delta x) + 3x(\delta x)^2 + (\delta x)^3 - \delta x$

Divide by δx: $\qquad\qquad \dfrac{\delta y}{\delta x} = 3x^2 + 3x(\delta x) + (\delta x)^2 - 1$

As $Q \to P$, $\delta x \to 0$ and $\displaystyle\lim_{\delta x \to 0} \dfrac{\delta y}{\delta x} = 3x^2 - 1$

Hence $\quad \dfrac{dy}{dx} = 3x^2 - 1$

When $x = 0$ $\quad \dfrac{dy}{dx} = 3 \times (0)^2 - 1 = -1$

Hence the gradient of the tangent at the point where $x = 0$ is -1.

A sketch often helps to visualise the problem and to see whether your results are realistic.

$y = x^3 - x$ is a cubic equation with positive x^3 coefficient. You know the shape of this curve from Chapter 5.

Solve for x:

$y = x^3 - x$
$ = x(x^2 - 1)$

$x = 0, x = 1$ or $x = -1$
so the curve crosses the x-axis at $(0, 0)$, $(1, 0)$ and $(-1, 0)$.

You can see from the sketch that the function in Example 2 is decreasing at $x = 0$, so the gradient will be negative as expected.

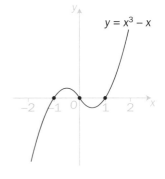

Exercise 7.2

1 In each of the following cases find expressions for

   i δy ii $\dfrac{\delta y}{\delta x}$ iii $\dfrac{dy}{dx}$

   a $y = 3x + 2$

   b $y = 1 - x^2$

   c $y = 2 - 3x$

   d $y = 2x^2$

   e $y = x(x + 1)$

   f $y = 2x(1 - x)$

2 Differentiate each equation from first principles.

   a $y = x^2 + 1$

   b $y = 4x$

   c $y = x^2 + 2x$

   d $y = 1 - x^2$

   e $y = x^3$

   f $y = x^4$

3 Find $\dfrac{dy}{dx}$ and hence find the gradient of the tangent
   at the given point.

   a $y = x^2 + 4$ at the point $(3, 13)$

   b $y = 3x^3$ at the point $(0, 0)$

   c $y = (x + 2)(x + 3)$ at the point $(1, 12)$

   d $y = x^3 + x$ at the point $(2, 6)$

Consider the results obtained when differentiating
the functions $y = x^2$, $y = x^3$ and $y = x^4$.

$$y = x^2 \quad \text{gives} \quad \frac{dy}{dx} = 2x$$

$$y = x^3 \quad \text{gives} \quad \frac{dy}{dx} = 3x^2$$

$$y = x^4 \quad \text{gives} \quad \frac{dy}{dx} = 4x^3$$

You can work out these derivatives
from first principles; look back at
the results from Section 7.2.

A pattern in these derivatives suggests a general result.

○ For any real value of n, if $y = x^n$ then $\dfrac{dy}{dx} = nx^{n-1}$

○ More generally, if $y = ax^n$ then $\dfrac{dy}{dx} = anx^{n-1}$

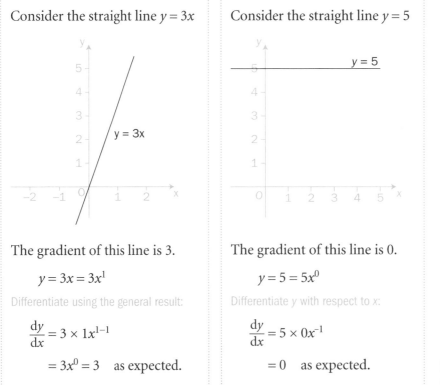

Consider the straight line $y = 3x$

$y = 3x$

The gradient of this line is 3.

$$y = 3x = 3x^1$$

Differentiate using the general result:

$$\frac{dy}{dx} = 3 \times 1x^{1-1}$$

$$= 3x^0 = 3 \quad \text{as expected.}$$

Consider the straight line $y = 5$

$y = 5$

The gradient of this line is 0.

$$y = 5 = 5x^0$$

Differentiate y with respect to x:

$$\frac{dy}{dx} = 5 \times 0x^{-1}$$

$$= 0 \quad \text{as expected.}$$

Remember $\frac{dy}{dx}$ gives you the
gradient.

You can use these rules to differentiate any power of x.

EXAMPLE 1

Find $\dfrac{dy}{dx}$ for the following functions.

a $y = 5x^2$ **b** $y = \sqrt{x}$

$\sqrt{x} = x^{\frac{1}{2}}$

a $y = 5x^2$

Differentiate y with respect to x:

$$\frac{dy}{dx} = 5 \times 2 \times x^{2-1}$$

$$\frac{dy}{dx} = 10x$$

b $y = \sqrt{x} = x^{\frac{1}{2}}$

Write roots in index form.

Differentiate y with respect to x:

$$\frac{dy}{dx} = \frac{1}{2} \times x^{\frac{1}{2}-1} = \frac{1}{2}x^{-\frac{1}{2}}$$

$$\frac{dy}{dx} = \frac{1}{2\sqrt{x}}$$

$x^{-\frac{1}{2}} = \dfrac{1}{x^{\frac{1}{2}}} = \dfrac{1}{\sqrt{x}}$

You can use the general result for differentiating to find the gradient at a particular point.

EXAMPLE 2

Find the gradient of the tangent to the curve,

$y = 2x^3$, at the point $A\left(\dfrac{1}{2}, \dfrac{1}{4}\right)$.

$$y = 2x^3$$

Differentiate y with respect to x: $\dfrac{dy}{dx} = 2 \times 3 \times x^{3-1}$

The gradient of the tangent is given by $\dfrac{dy}{dx}$.

Simplify: $\dfrac{dy}{dx} = 6x^2$

At the point A, $x = \dfrac{1}{2}$

Substitute $x = \dfrac{1}{2}$ into the expression for $\dfrac{dy}{dx}$:

$$\frac{dy}{dx} = 6 \times \left(\frac{1}{2}\right)^2$$

$$= \frac{6}{4} = \frac{3}{2}$$

Hence the gradient of the tangent at the point A is $\dfrac{3}{2}$.

Exercise 7.3

1 Use the general rule for differentiating x^n to differentiate these equations with respect to x.

a $y = 4x^2$

b $y = 7x$

c $y = -5$

d $y = 3x^3$

e $y = \frac{1}{4}x^4$

f $y = 6$

g $y = -2x$

h $y = \frac{2x}{3}$

2 Rewrite these equations using index notation and then differentiate y with respect to x.
Give your final answers in simplified form.

a $y = 2\sqrt{x}$

b $y = -3\sqrt{x}$

c $y = x\sqrt{x}$

d $y = -x^2\sqrt{x}$

e $y = \sqrt[3]{x}$

f $y = \frac{1}{x}$

g $y = -\frac{1}{x^2}$

h $y = \frac{1}{\sqrt{x}}$

i $y = \frac{2}{\sqrt{x}}$

j $y = \frac{4}{3x\sqrt{x}}$

k $y = -\frac{2}{\sqrt[3]{x}}$

l $y = \sqrt[3]{x^2}$

3 Find the gradient of each curve at the given point.

a $y = 5x^2$; $(1, 5)$

b $y = 7$; $(15, 7)$

c $y = \sqrt{x}$; $(4, 2)$

d $y = 6x$; $(-1, -6)$

e $y = 4x^3$; $\left(-\frac{1}{2}, -\frac{1}{2}\right)$

f $y = \frac{9}{x^2}$; $(3, 1)$

g $y = -\frac{4}{\sqrt{x}}$; $(4, -2)$

h $y = \frac{2}{x}$; $\left(\frac{1}{2}, 4\right)$

i $y = 2x\sqrt{x}$; $(9, 54)$

j $y = \frac{4x}{5}$; $(-5, -4)$

INVESTIGATIONS

4 Match each function with its derivative.

FUNCTION	DERIVATIVE
i $4\sqrt{x}$	a $12x^2$
ii $(x-3)(x+4)$	b $\dfrac{1}{4x^2}$
iii $\dfrac{x^2+9x}{x}$	c $6x^5$
iv $-\dfrac{1}{4x}$	d 1
v $4x^3$	e $\dfrac{2}{\sqrt{x}}$
vi	f $2x+1$

Function **vi** has been left for you to find.
Can you explain why this function is not unique?

5 **a** Sketch some quadratic and cubic curves.
   Investigate the behaviour of the gradient function as x
   approaches infinity

   i   when x is large and negative
   ii when x is large and positive.

   Are there any similarities in behaviour?

   b Use a graphics calculator or computer to investigate
   quartics (graphs of the form ax^4).

7.4 Differentiating polynomials

There is an alternative notation for differentiation.

When $y = f(x)$,　$\dfrac{dy}{dx} = f'(x)$

You can use the general result for $y = ax^n$ to differentiate expressions which have more than one term.

○ Generally if　$y = f(x) \pm g(x)$

then　　　　$\dfrac{dy}{dx} = f'(x) \pm g'(x)$

Differentiate each expression with respect to x.

a　$f(x) = 4x^2 + 3x$　　　　**b**　$y = 5 - x\sqrt{x}$

a　$f(x) = 4x^2 + 3x$

Differentiate f(x) with respect to x:

$$f'(x) = 4 \times 2 \times x^{2-1} + 3 \times 1 \times x^{1-1}$$

Differentiate each term with respect to x and then add the results together.

Simplify:　$f'(x) = 8x + 3$

$x^{1-1} = x^0 = 1$

b　$y = 5 - x\sqrt{x}$

Rewrite in index form:　　　　　$y = 5 - x^{\frac{3}{2}}$

$x \times \sqrt{x} = x \times x^{\frac{1}{2}} = x^{1+\frac{1}{2}} = x^{\frac{3}{2}}$

Differentiate y with respect to x:　$\dfrac{dy}{dx} = 0 - \dfrac{3}{2}x^{\frac{1}{2}}$

Differentiate each term with respect to x and then subtract the results.

Simplify:　　　　$\dfrac{dy}{dx} = -\dfrac{3}{2}x^{\frac{1}{2}}$

Hence　　　　$\dfrac{dy}{dx} = -\dfrac{3}{2}\sqrt{x}$

You can differentiate some products and quotients by splitting them into separate terms.

You will often be asked to differentiate expressions involving a variable other than x as in part **b** of Example 2.

EXAMPLE 2

Differentiate each expression with respect to the given variable.

a $y = (1 + x)(2 - x)$ **b** $f(t) = \dfrac{t^3 - t}{t^2}$

---

a
$$y = (1 + x)(2 - x)$$

Expand the brackets:
$$y = 2 + 2x - x - x^2$$
$$= 2 + x - x^2$$

Differentiate y with respect to x:
$$\frac{dy}{dx} = 1 - 2x$$

Differentiate each term separately – note that the 2 disappears when you differentiate.

b
$$f(t) = \frac{t^3 - t}{t^2}$$

Rewrite as the difference of two fractions:
$$f(t) = \frac{t^3}{t^2} - \frac{t}{t^2}$$

Cancel the fractions: $\quad f(t) = t - t^{-1}$

$\dfrac{t^3}{t^2} = t^{3-2} = t^1 = t$

$\dfrac{t}{t^2} = t^{1-2} = t^{-1}$

Differentiate $f(t)$ with respect to t:
$$f'(t) = 1 - (-1) \times t^{-1-1}$$

Simplify: $\quad f'(t) = 1 + t^{-2}$

■ Take care with negatives

Hence $\quad f'(t) = 1 + \dfrac{1}{t^2}$

$t^{-2} = \dfrac{1}{t^2}$

Exercise 7.4

1 Differentiate the following with respect to x.

  a $y = x^2 + 3$ **b** $y = 2x - 1$

  c $y = 3x^2 - x$ **d** $y = 3x + x^2$

  e $y = x^3 - 2x^2$ **f** $y = x^2 - x + 1$

2 Differentiate each expression with respect to x.

  a $(x - 1)(x + 2)$ **b** $x^2(1 - x)$

  c $(x^2 + 1)(x + 3)$ **d** $(x - 2)(x + 1)$

3 Differentiate the following with respect to x.

  a $y = 4 - \dfrac{1}{x}$ **b** $y = \dfrac{1}{x^2} + x$

  c $y = x - \sqrt{x}$ **d** $y = x\sqrt{x} - \dfrac{1}{\sqrt{x}}$

  e $\dfrac{x^2}{2} - x + \dfrac{1}{x}$ **f** $\sqrt{x}(x - 2)$

4 Differentiate each expression with respect to the given variable.

a $y = x(x+1)$

b $s = t^2(1-t)$

c $y = (r+1)(r-2)$

d $s = 4(2t-1)^2$

e $y = x(x-1)(x+1)$

f $V = 2r(r-4) + r(r+4)$

g $A = \sqrt{t}\,[t^2 + 1]$

h $y = \dfrac{1}{x}\left(\dfrac{1}{x} - x\right)$

i $s = (1-t)(1-2t)(1-3t)$

j $y = (x^3 - 1)(x-1)$

5 Given $y = f(x)$ find $f'(x)$ in each case.

a $f(x) = \dfrac{1+x}{x}$

b $f(x) = \dfrac{x^2 + x}{2x}$

c $f(x) = \dfrac{1 - \sqrt{x}}{x}$

d $f(x) = \dfrac{x^2 - 2x + 4}{x^2}$

e $f(x) = \dfrac{2 - x^2}{x^3}$

f $f(x) = \dfrac{2(x-1)}{\sqrt{x}}$

g $f(x) = \dfrac{(x+3)^2}{x}$

h $f(x) = (1-x)(2-x)$

i $f(x) = \dfrac{\sqrt{x} + x\sqrt{x}}{2}$

j $f(x) = \dfrac{ax + bx^3}{cx^2}$

a, b and *c* are constants
Treat them like numbers.

6 Differentiate the following with respect to the given variable.

a $s = t^2\sqrt{t} - \dfrac{1}{t}$

b $L = 2r(3r - r^2)$

c $r = \dfrac{5x - 4}{x^2}$

d $y = 7(t-1)(2t-3)$

e $A = (\sqrt{x} + 2)^2$

f $y = (r^3 - 1)(r^2 + 1)$

g $P = \sqrt{t}\,[t^2 - \sqrt{t} + 1]$

h $y = \dfrac{4a - bx}{3x^2}$

a and *b* are constants.

i $s = 2(t^2 - 1) - t^2(2 - t)$

j $V = \left(2 - \dfrac{1}{r}\right)^2$

INVESTIGATIONS

7 a Match each function with its derivative.

<table>
<tr><td>

function

$y = \dfrac{(2 + x)}{x}$

$y = \dfrac{(x + 1)}{x^{\frac{1}{2}}}$

$y = \dfrac{(x + 1)^2}{x}$

$y = \dfrac{2(x + 4)}{x^2}$

</td><td>

derivative

$\dfrac{dy}{dx} = 1 - \dfrac{1}{x^2}$

$\dfrac{dy}{dx} = -\dfrac{2}{x^2} - \dfrac{16}{x^3}$

$\dfrac{dy}{dx} = -\dfrac{2}{x^2}$

$\dfrac{dy}{dx} = \dfrac{1}{2}x^{-\frac{1}{2}} - \dfrac{1}{2}x^{-\frac{3}{2}}$

$\dfrac{dy}{dx} = 2 - \dfrac{3}{x^2}$

</td></tr>
</table>

b Identify the missing function.

8 Given two functions

$f(x) = (x + 3)$ and $g(x) = x^2$

a find $f'(x)$ and $g'(x)$.

b Let $h(x) = f(x)\,g(x)$
Find $h(x)$ and $h'(x)$.

c Is it true that $h'(x) = f'(x)\,g'(x)$?

d Let $p(x) = \dfrac{f(x)}{g(x)}$

   i Find $p(x)$ and $p'(x)$.

   ii Is it true that $p'(x) = \dfrac{f'(x)}{g'(x)}$?

Rates of change

When two or more variables are linked, you can study the relationship between them. They are called variables, since their value varies.

In this section you will look at what happens to linked variables when one changes.

If you change the radius, r cm, of a circle, you may like to know how the area, a cm^2, of the circle is changing in response.

when $r = 0$ cm $a = 0$ cm^2
when $r = 1$ cm $a = 3.14$ cm^2
when $r = 2$ cm $a = 12.56$ cm^2
when $r = 3$ cm $a = 28.27$ cm^2

As r changes from 0 cm to 1 cm the area increases by 3.14 cm^2.

As r changes from 2 cm to 3 cm the area increases by 15.71 cm^2.

It is clear from these results that the greater the radius, the greater the increase in the area as the radius increases by a constant amount.

You do not have to increase the amount by whole units. This is known as a continuous relationship.

So the rate of change of the area depends on the size of the radius.

The rate of change of the area as the radius changes is denoted $\dfrac{da}{dr}$. This is known as the rate of change of a with respect to r.

If you know an algebraic relationship between the variables a and r, then you can usually find $\dfrac{da}{dr}$.

$\dfrac{da}{dr}$ can be found by differentiating πr^2 with respect to r.

In this case you know that for a circle, $a = \pi r^2$

Differentiate with respect to r: $\dfrac{da}{dr} = 2\pi r$

π is a constant.

You can now use this to work out the rate of change of the area for any value of the radius.

e.g. When $r = 5$ cm, $\dfrac{da}{dr} = 2\pi \times 5 = 10\pi = 31.4$

When $r = 20$ cm, $\dfrac{da}{dr} = 2\pi \times 20 = 40\pi = 125.7$

This is the instantaneous rate when $r = 5$. When the radius is 5 cm, the rate of change of the area is 31.4 cm^2 per cm change in the radius.

In general, for two variables x and y, the rate of change of y with respect to x is given by $\dfrac{dy}{dx}$.

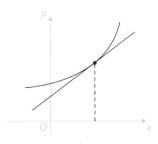

EXAMPLE 1

The volume, $V\,\text{cm}^3$, of a cube of side length x cm
is given by $V = x^3$
Find the rate of change of V with respect to x when

a $x = 10$ **b** $V = 64$.

$$V = x^3$$

Differentiate: $$\frac{\mathrm{d}V}{\mathrm{d}x} = 3x^2$$

So the rate of change of V with respect to x is $3x^2$.

a When $x = 10$, $\dfrac{\mathrm{d}V}{\mathrm{d}x} = 300$

So when the side length is $10\,\text{cm}$, the volume is increasing
at a rate of $300\,\text{cm}^3$ per cm increase in the side length.

b When $V = 64$, $x = \sqrt[3]{64} = 4$

So $\dfrac{\mathrm{d}V}{\mathrm{d}x} = 48$

So when the volume is $64\,\text{cm}^3$, the rate of increase of the
volume with respect to the side length is $48\,\text{cm}^3$ per cm
increase in the side length.

> Calculating the rate of change at a point is like calculating the gradient of the tangent at that point.

EXAMPLE 2

The rate of change of distance, s metres, with respect to time,
t seconds, is known as velocity, v metres per second (m/s).
Find the velocity when $t = 16$ if

a $s = 10$ **b** $s = 2t$ **c** $s = 6\sqrt{t}$.

a $$s = 10$$

Differentiate: $$\frac{\mathrm{d}s}{\mathrm{d}t} = 0$$

Therefore the velocity, $v = \dfrac{\mathrm{d}s}{\mathrm{d}t} = 0$ m/s

b $$s = 2t$$

Differentiate: $$\frac{\mathrm{d}s}{\mathrm{d}t} = 2$$

Therefore the velocity, $v = \dfrac{\mathrm{d}s}{\mathrm{d}t} = 2$ m/s

c $$s = 6\sqrt{t}$$

Differentiate: $$\frac{\mathrm{d}s}{\mathrm{d}t} = \frac{3}{\sqrt{t}}$$

Therefore the velocity, $v = \dfrac{\mathrm{d}s}{\mathrm{d}t} = \dfrac{3}{\sqrt{16}} = \dfrac{3}{4}$ m/s

> If the distance is constant at 10 m there must be zero velocity. The object is stationary.

> The velocity here is constant. The object is travelling at a steady speed of 2 m/s.

> The velocity is inversely proportional to the square root of the time, which means that velocity reduces as time increases.

EXAMPLE 3

The tension, T newtons (N), in a spring depends on how far the spring has been extended.
This distance is called the extension, x metres, of the spring.
The link between T and x is given as $T = 2x$.

Find   **a**   the tension in the spring

         b   the rate of change of the tension in the spring with respect to the extension

when $x = 1$ m.

---

a $T = 2x$, so when $x = 1$, $T = 2$.
This means that the tension is dependent on the extension of the spring.

b $T = 2x$

Differentiate T with respect to x: $\dfrac{dT}{dx} = 2$

This means that the rate of change of the tension with respect to the extension of the spring is constant at 2 newtons per cm and is independent of the extension.

Exercise 7.5

1   For each relationship, find the rate of change of y with respect to x and evaluate this when $x = 1$.

   a $y = 3x$ **b** $y = \dfrac{2}{x}$

   c $y = 2\sqrt{x}$ **d** $y = \dfrac{(x + 1)}{x^3}$

2   The relationship between p and q is given by $p = 2q^3 + q$
Find the rate of change of p with respect to q when $q = 4$.

3   The rate of change of y with respect to x on a graph is called the gradient. Find the gradient of each of these relationships at the point indicated.

   a $y = x$, $x = 10$

   b $y = x^2$, $x = 5$

   c $y = x^2 + 3x - 1$, $x = 0$

   d $y = x^2 + 4$, $y = 4$

4 The surface area of a sphere is given by $A = 4\pi r^2$, where r is the radius of the sphere.

Describe what happens to the surface area as the radius increases.

Find $\dfrac{dA}{dr}$, the rate of change of the surface area with respect to the radius and evaluate this when

a $r = 5$

b $A = 16\pi$

leaving your answers in terms of π where appropriate.

5 In a simplified mathematical model, the distance, x m, that a skydiver travels as he descends from an aeroplane is given by $x = 4t^2$ where t is the time in seconds that has elapsed after leaving the aeroplane.

Find the rate of change of the distance with respect to time (speed) when $t = 10$.

6 The variables x and y are linked by the equation $y = 2x^2 + x$
Find the value of x when the rate of change of y with respect to x is 9.

7 The variables a and b are linked by the equation $a = 2\sqrt[3]{b}$
Find the values of b when the rate of change of a with respect to b is $\dfrac{1}{6}$.

INVESTIGATION

8 The radius of a sphere increases at a constant rate of 1 cm/s.
Investigate what happens to the rate of increase of the volume of the sphere.

Use a spreadsheet or a graph plotter to calculate a table of values for the radius and the volume at increasing values of t and then plot them on a graph. You should then be able to find what the exact relationship is by looking at the shape of the graph.

7.6 Tangents and normals

For the equation, $y = f(x)$, the gradient of the tangent to its curve at any point is given by

$$\frac{dy}{dx} \quad \text{or} \quad f'(x).$$

You can find the equation of the tangent at any given point.

EXAMPLE 1

Find the equation of the tangent drawn to the curve
$y = 4x^2 + 12x$ at the point $(-2, -8)$.

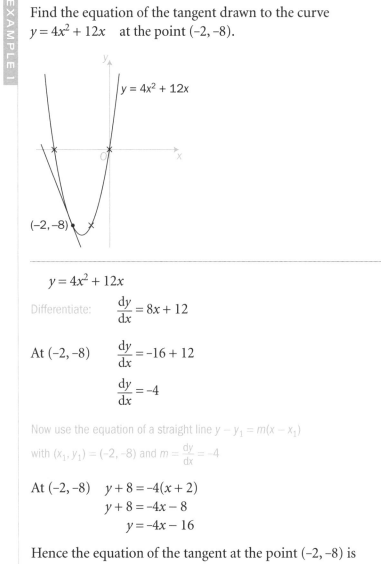

$$y = 4x^2 + 12x$$

Differentiate: $\quad \dfrac{dy}{dx} = 8x + 12$

At $(-2, -8)$ $\quad \dfrac{dy}{dx} = -16 + 12$

$$\frac{dy}{dx} = -4$$

Now use the equation of a straight line $y - y_1 = m(x - x_1)$

with $(x_1, y_1) = (-2, -8)$ and $m = \dfrac{dy}{dx} = -4$

At $(-2, -8)$ $\quad y + 8 = -4(x + 2)$
$$y + 8 = -4x - 8$$
$$y = -4x - 16$$

Hence the equation of the tangent at the point $(-2, -8)$ is
$y = -4x - 16$.

The normal to a curve at any point is the straight line which is perpendicular to the tangent at that point.

Perpendicular means the lines are at right-angles.

Let the gradient of the tangent at a point on a curve $y = f(x)$ be m_1 and the gradient of the normal at this point be m_2.

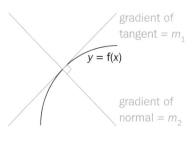

gradient of tangent = m_1

$y = f(x)$

gradient of normal = m_2

- Then $m_1 \times m_2 = -1$ as the gradient and the normal are perpendicular to each other.

e.g. When the gradient of the tangent is 2 the gradient of the normal will be $-\frac{1}{2}$.

You can use this result to find the equation of the normal at a given point on a curve.

EXAMPLE 2

For the curve with equation $y = 3x^2 - 8x$ find the equations of the tangent and normal at the point $(2, -4)$.

$$y = 3x^2 - 8x$$

Differentiate: $\dfrac{dy}{dx} = 6x - 8$

At $(2, -4)$: $\dfrac{dy}{dx} = 6 \times 2 - 8$

$\qquad\qquad = 4$

Hence the gradient of the tangent $= 4$

and the gradient of the normal $= -\dfrac{1}{m} = -\dfrac{1}{4}$

Draw a rough sketch to help:

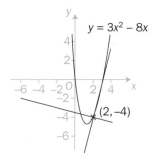

$y = 3x^2 - 8x$

$(2, -4)$

Now use the equation of a straight line $y - y_1 = m(x - x_1)$

Write down the equations of the tangent and normal at $(2, -4)$:

Tangent:	Normal:
$y + 4 = 4(x - 2)$	$y + 4 = -\frac{1}{4}(x - 2)$

Rearrange: $\quad y + 4 = 4x - 8 \qquad\qquad 4y + 16 = -x + 2$

$\qquad\qquad\quad y = 4x - 12 \qquad\qquad\quad 4y = -x - 14$

Hence the equation of the tangent is $y = 4x - 12$
and the equation of the normal is $4y = -x - 14$

You can find the coordinates of a point if you are given information about a curve at that point.

EXAMPLE 3

The tangent drawn to the curve $y = 5x^2 + 4x - 2$ at the point $P(x, y)$ is parallel to the x-axis. Determine the coordinates of P.

Sketch the graph to help you visualise the question.

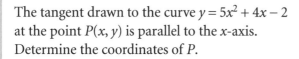

$$y = 5x^2 + 4x - 2$$

Differentiate: $\dfrac{dy}{dx} = 10x + 4$

The tangent is parallel to the x-axis, so $\dfrac{dy}{dx} = 0$

Solve $10x + 4 = 0$:

$$x = -\frac{4}{10} = -\frac{2}{5}$$

Substitute $x = -\dfrac{2}{5}$ into the equation of the curve to find y:

When $x = -\dfrac{2}{5}$, $y = 5\left(-\dfrac{2}{5}\right)^2 + 4\left(-\dfrac{2}{5}\right) - 2$

$$= \frac{20}{25} - \frac{8}{5} - 2 = -\frac{14}{5}$$

Hence P is the point $\left(-\dfrac{2}{5}, -\dfrac{14}{5}\right)$.

Exercise 7.6

1 **a** Find the gradient of the tangent to the curve $y = 5x^2$ at the point where $x = -2$.

b Determine the equation of the tangent at the point $P(1, -2)$ on the curve whose equation is $y = 1 - 3x^2$

c A tangent is drawn at the point $P(1, -1)$ on the curve
$$y = -\frac{1}{x^2}$$
What is the equation of this tangent?

d Find the gradient of the tangent to the curve $y = x^3 - 3x$ at the point where $x = 2$.

e Find the equation of the tangent to the curve
$y = x^2 - 3x - 4$
at the point $(2, -6)$.

2 a Find the gradient of the tangent and normal to the curve
       $y = 6x^2 - 5x + 1$ at the point where $x = 1$.

   b Find the equation of the normal to the curve $y = \dfrac{1}{x}$
       at the point where $x = 2$.

   c Determine the gradients of the tangent and normal at the
       point $P(1, 2)$ on the curve whose equation is $y = 3x^2 - 2x + 1$

   d Find the equations of the tangent and normal to the curve $y = \dfrac{2}{x^2}$
       at the point $\left(-2, \dfrac{1}{2}\right)$.

3 a The tangent drawn to the curve $y = 2x^2 + 3x$
       at the point $P(x, y)$ is parallel to the x-axis.
       Determine the coordinates of P.

   b The line $y = 2x - 4$ is a tangent to the curve $y = x^2 - 2x$
       at the point $P(x, y)$. What are the coordinates of P?

4 The tangent and normal to the curve $y = x^3 + 2x^2 - 4x + 5$
   are drawn at the point $(1, 4)$ as shown in the diagram.

   a Find the equations of the tangent and normal at this point.

   The tangent cuts the x-axis at A and the y-axis at B.

   b Find the coordinates of A and B.

   The normal cuts the x-axis at C and the y-axis at D.

   c Find the coordinates of C and D.

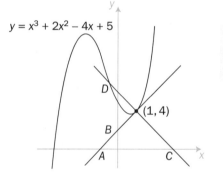

5 The tangent drawn to the curve with equation $y = \dfrac{3}{x}$
   at the point $\left(2, \dfrac{3}{2}\right)$ meets the x-axis at A and the y-axis at B.

   What is the area of the triangle AOB where O is the point $(0, 0)$?

   Sketch the graph to visualise the question.

INVESTIGATION

6 Sketch the graph of $y = x^2$

   a What happens to the values of the gradient of the tangents to
      the graph as x moves from negative to positive values?

   b What happens to the values of the gradient of the normals
      to the graph as x moves from negative to positive values?

   c Would this agree with $m_1 \times m_2 = -1$?

7.7 Second order derivatives

Let $y = f(x)$

The derivative of y with respect to x is $\dfrac{dy}{dx}$ or $f'(x)$.

$f'(x)$ is the first derivative of $f(x)$.

Differentiating again gives

$$\frac{d^2 y}{dx^2} \quad \text{or} \quad f''(x).$$

○ $\dfrac{d^2 y}{dx^2}$ is the second derivative of y with respect to

$\dfrac{d^2 y}{dx^2}$ is known as a 2nd order derivative. It measures the rate of change of the gradient.

EXAMPLE 1

Find $\dfrac{dy}{dx}$ and $\dfrac{d^2 y}{dx^2}$ when

a $y = 5x^3 + 3x^2 + 2$ **b** $y = x\sqrt{x}$

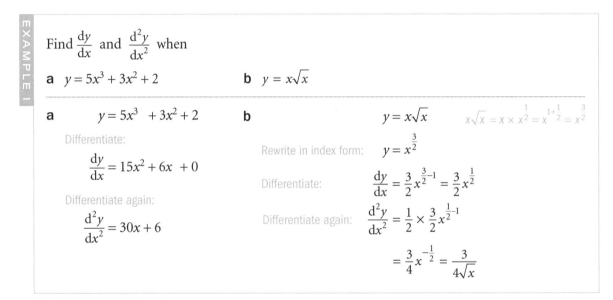

a $y = 5x^3 + 3x^2 + 2$

Differentiate:

$$\frac{dy}{dx} = 15x^2 + 6x + 0$$

Differentiate again:

$$\frac{d^2 y}{dx^2} = 30x + 6$$

b $y = x\sqrt{x}$ $x\sqrt{x} = x \times x^{\frac{1}{2}} = x^{1+\frac{1}{2}} = x^{\frac{3}{2}}$

Rewrite in index form: $\quad y = x^{\frac{3}{2}}$

Differentiate: $\quad \dfrac{dy}{dx} = \dfrac{3}{2}x^{\frac{3}{2}-1} = \dfrac{3}{2}x^{\frac{1}{2}}$

Differentiate again: $\quad \dfrac{d^2 y}{dx^2} = \dfrac{1}{2} \times \dfrac{3}{2}x^{\frac{1}{2}-1}$

$$= \frac{3}{4}x^{-\frac{1}{2}} = \frac{3}{4\sqrt{x}}$$

You can find the second derivative for a given value of x.

EXAMPLE 2

Find $f'(-2)$ and $f''(-2)$ for the function
$$f(x) = x(x+1)(2x-3)$$

Expand the brackets: $f(x) = 2x^3 - x^2 - 3x$

Differentiate: $\qquad f'(x) = 6x^2 - 2x - 3$

When $x = -2$ $f'(-2) = 6 \times (-2)^2 - 2 \times (-2) - 3$
$$= 25$$

This answer tells you that when $x = -2$ the rate of change of $f(x)$ with respect to x is 25.

Differentiate again: $f''(x) = 12x - 2$

When $x = -2$ $f''(-2) = 12 \times (-2) - 2$
$$= -26$$

This answer tells you that when $x = -2$ the rate of change of $f'(x)$ with respect to x is −26.

C1

Exercise 7.7

1 For each equation find

   i $\dfrac{dy}{dx}$ **ii** $\dfrac{d^2y}{dx^2}$.

   a $y = 3x^2 + 2x$ **b** $y = 5x^3$ **c** $y = 1 - \sqrt{x}$

   d $y = x - \dfrac{2}{x}$ **e** $y = (2x + 1)(3x + 1)$ **f** $y = x^2(x + 1)$

2 For each function find

   i $f'(3)$ **ii** $f''(3)$.

   a $f(t) = 3t^2 - 4$ **b** $f(t) = \dfrac{2}{t^2}$ **c** $f(t) = \dfrac{1+t}{t}$

   d $f(t) = 4\sqrt{t}$ **e** $f(t) = \dfrac{1}{2\sqrt{t}}$ **f** $f(t) = \dfrac{t^2 - 1}{t^3}$

3 **a** $A = \pi r^2$ is the formula for the area of a circle.

      Find $\dfrac{dA}{dr}$ and $\dfrac{d^2A}{dr^2}$.

      Hence evaluate $\dfrac{dA}{dr}$ and $\dfrac{d^2A}{dr^2}$ when $r = 4$.

      Leave your answers in terms of π.

   b $V = \dfrac{4}{3}\pi r^3$ is the formula for the volume of a sphere.

      Find $\dfrac{dV}{dr}$ and $\dfrac{d^2V}{dr^2}$.

      Hence evaluate $\dfrac{dV}{dr}$ and $\dfrac{d^2V}{dr^2}$ when $r = \dfrac{3}{4}$.

      Leave your answers in terms of π.

   c   What is the physical significance of your answers to **a** and **b**?   Look back at section 7.5 on rates of change.

INVESTIGATION

4 The following two boxes contain first and second derivatives.

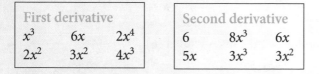

First derivative		
x^3	$6x$	$2x^4$
$2x^2$	$3x^2$	$4x^3$

Second derivative		
6	$8x^3$	$6x$
$5x$	$3x^3$	$3x^2$

   a   Put the derivatives in pairs.

   b   Which derivative (s) do not form a pair?

   c   Find the missing derivatives and put them in the correct pairs.

1 **a** Determine the gradient of the tangent and normal at the point $(1, 4)$ on the curve with equation $y = 3x^2 + 2x - 1$

  b The curve $y = \dfrac{1}{x}$ has a tangent whose gradient is –4 at two points on the curve. Find the coordinates of these points.

  c For the curve with equation $y = x^3 - 2x^2$ find the points where the tangents are parallel to the x-axis.

  d The tangent and normal to the curve $y = x^2 - 2x + 1$ at the point where $x = 2$ meet the x-axis at points A and B respectively. Find the length AB.

2 Find the equation of the normal to the curve $y = \dfrac{4}{x^2}$ at the point $(2, 1)$.
The normal cuts the x-axis at P and the y-axis at Q.
Determine the length PQ in surd form.

3 Given that $y = x^2 - \dfrac{6}{x^3}$, $x \neq 0$ find $\dfrac{dy}{dx}$.

4 The gradient of the curve C is given by $\dfrac{dy}{dx} = (x + 1)(x - 2)$.
The point $P(1, 2)$ lies on C.
Find the equation of the normal to C at P.

5 The figure shows part of the curve, C, with equation $y = (x - 1)(x^2 - 4)$
The curve cuts the x-axis at the points $P(1, 0)$ and Q, as shown in the diagram.

  a Write down the x-coordinates of P and Q.

  b Show that $\dfrac{dy}{dx} = 3x^2 - 2x - 4$

  c Show that $y = x + 7$ is the equation of the tangent to C at the point $(-1, 6)$.

The tangent to C at the point R is parallel to the tangent at $(-1, 6)$.

  d Find the exact coordinates of R.

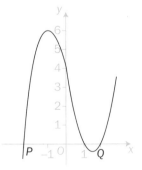

[(c) Edexcel Limited 2006]

6 The curve C has equation $y = \dfrac{2x^2 + x - 3}{x}$, $x \neq 0$.

The point P on C has x-coordinate 2.

a Find an expression for $\dfrac{dy}{dx}$.

b Find the value of $\dfrac{dy}{dx}$ at the point P.

c Find the equation of the tangent to C at P.

This tangent meets the x-axis at the point $(k, 0)$.

d Find the value of k.

7 The curve C has equation $y = \dfrac{2}{3}x^3 - x^2 + 4x - 3$.

The point P has coordinates $(3, 18)$.

a Show that P lies on C.

b Find the equation of the tangent to C at P, giving your answer in the form $y = mx + c$, where m and c are constants.

Another point Q also lies on C. The tangent to C at Q is parallel to the tangent to C at P.

c Find the coordinates of Q.

8 For the curve C with equation $y = f(x)$,

$$\dfrac{dy}{dx} = x^3 + 2x - 7.$$

a Find $\dfrac{d^2y}{dx^2}$.

b Show that $\dfrac{d^2y}{dx^2} \geq 2$ for all values of x.

Given that the point $P(2, 4)$ lies on C,

c find y in terms of x,

d find an equation for the normal to C at P in the form $ax + by + c = 0$, where a, b and c are integers.

[(c) Edexcel Limited 2002]

7

Exit

Summary   Refer to

- The method of small increments can be used to determine
  the gradient of the tangent to a curve at a particular point.   7.1
- The derivative of $y = f(x)$ is a function that gives the
  gradient at any point, and is denoted by $\dfrac{dy}{dx}$ or $f'(x)$.   7.2

- You can differentiate from first principles to find $\dfrac{dy}{dx}$.

  This involves using $\dfrac{dy}{dx} = \lim\limits_{\delta x \to 0} \dfrac{\delta y}{\delta x}$ 7.2

- If $y = ax^n$ then $\dfrac{dy}{dx} = anx^{n-1}$
  where y is differentiated with respect to x.   7.3

- Generally if $y = f(x) \pm g(x)$ then $\dfrac{dy}{dx} = f'(x) \pm g'(x)$ 7.4

- $\dfrac{dy}{dx}$ is the rate of change of y with respect to x.   7.5

- The gradient of the tangent, m_1, and the gradient of the
  normal, m_2, at a point are such that $m_1 \times m_2 = -1$ 7.6

- $\dfrac{d^2y}{dx^2}$ or $f''(x)$ is the second order derivative of
  y with respect to x.   7.7

Links

Differentiation is part of the branch of mathematics known as
calculus. Differentiation describes rates of change.

Astronomers use calculus to describe the motion of the planets,
mechanical and aeronautical engineers use it to describe the
movement of fluids among other things, and geographers
use it to describe population change.

On an everyday level, cars change speed when they accelerate or
decelerate, and differentiation allows you to work out the speed
and acceleration or deceleration at a particular time.

Calculations involving rates of change are used when designing
modern engines. If the acceleration of an aeroplane wasn't large
enough then it would never be able to take off.

8

Integration

This chapter will show you how to
- perform integration as the reverse process of differentiation
- integrate algebraic terms and functions
- find the equation of a curve from a gradient equation.

Before you start

You should know how to:

1 Perform calculations with fractions.

e.g. Evaluate $\dfrac{2}{3} - \dfrac{3}{8}$

Common denominator of 3 and 8 is 24.

$\dfrac{2}{3} - \dfrac{3}{8} = \dfrac{16-9}{24}$

$\qquad = \dfrac{7}{24}$

2 Multiply out brackets.

e.g. Find $(x + 3)(2x - 1)$

$(x + 3)(2x - 1)$

$= 2x^2 - x + 6x - 3$

Combine like terms:

$= 2x^2 + 5x - 3$

3 Apply the rules of indices.

e.g. Simplify $\left(\sqrt{x}\right)^3$

$\sqrt{x} = x^{\frac{1}{2}}$

Write in index form: $(\sqrt{x})^3 = \left(x^{\frac{1}{2}}\right)^3$

Apply $(x^m)^n = x^{m+n}$:

Hence $(\sqrt{x})^3 = x^{\frac{3}{2}}$

Check in:

1 Evaluate

a $\dfrac{3}{5} - \dfrac{4}{9}$

b $\dfrac{9}{4} + \dfrac{5}{3}$

c $1 - \dfrac{4}{7} + \dfrac{3}{5}$

d $-2 - \dfrac{2}{3} - \dfrac{3}{4}$

2 Multiply out
a $x(x^2 + 3x - 1)$
b $(x - 4)(2x + 3)$
c $(x^2 - 1)(x + 4)$
d $(x + 1)(x - 2)(x - 5)$
e $(x - 3)^3$

3 Write each term in index form.

a $\left(x^4\right)^{\frac{1}{2}}$

b $\dfrac{1}{2\sqrt{x}}$

c $\dfrac{1}{x\sqrt{x}}$

d $\sqrt{x^3}$

The integration process

Consider the equations $y = x^2$ and $y = x^2 + 3$

For $y = x^2$
and $y = x^2 + 3$ } differentiating gives $\dfrac{dy}{dx} = 2x$ for both equations.

Now try to reverse the process:

Reversing $\dfrac{dy}{dx} = 2x$ gives
$$\begin{cases} y = x^2 \\ y = x^2 + 1 \\ y = x^2 + 2 \\ \text{etc.} \end{cases}$$

Sketching the graphs of these functions might help you to see why this is true.

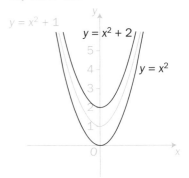

Starting with $\dfrac{dy}{dx} = 2x$ could give you an infinite number of possibilities, all of the form $y = x^2 + c$ where c is a constant.

Similarly, differentiating $y = x^3$ and $y = x^3 - 7$ both give the same result $\dfrac{dy}{dx} = 3x^2$

The derivative of a constant is 0.

○ The inverse of differentiation is called integration.

$$\begin{array}{c|c} y & \xrightarrow{\text{differentiate}} & \dfrac{dy}{dx} \\ & \xleftarrow{\text{integrate}} & \\ f(x) & & f'(x) \end{array}$$

Reversing the rule for differentiation produces a rule for integration.

Integrating $\dfrac{dy}{dx} = 3x^2$ gives $y = x^3 + c$, where c is a constant.

The constant c shows that there are an infinite number of solutions.

If you integrate $\dfrac{dy}{dx} = x^2$ you get $y = \dfrac{1}{3}x^3 + c$

INVESTIGATION

Here are some results you can verify for yourself.

Differentiate y to find $\dfrac{dy}{dx}$.

$\dfrac{dy}{dx}$	x	x^2	x^3	x^4
y	$\dfrac{1}{2}x^2 + c$	$\dfrac{1}{3}x^3 + c$	$\dfrac{1}{4}x^4 + c$	$\dfrac{1}{5}x^5 + c$

C1

○ If $\dfrac{dy}{dx} = x^n$ then $y = \dfrac{x^{n+1}}{n+1} + c$ (for any $n \neq -1$)

'Raise the power by 1 and divide by the new power'.

The general rule for integrating any expression ax^n is:

○ if $\dfrac{dy}{dx} = ax^n$

then integrating gives

$y = \dfrac{ax^{n+1}}{n+1} + c$ for any $n \neq -1$

If $n = -1$, then $n + 1 = 0$ and division by 0 is not defined.

○ The value c is called the constant of integration.

You can use this rule to find y, given $\dfrac{dy}{dx}$.

EXAMPLE 1

Find y when

a $\dfrac{dy}{dx} = 6x^2$ b $\dfrac{dy}{dx} = 5x$

---

a $\dfrac{dy}{dx} = 6x^2$ b $\dfrac{dy}{dx} = 5x$

$y = 6\dfrac{x^{2+1}}{(2+1)} + c$ $y = 5\dfrac{x^{1+1}}{(1+1)} + c$

$= \dfrac{6x^3}{3} + c$ $y = \dfrac{5}{2}x^2 + c$

so $y = 2x^3 + c$

$5x = 5x^1$

Remember to add the constant of integration, c.

Sometimes the index is negative.

EXAMPLE 2

Find y when

a $\dfrac{dy}{dx} = x^{-3}$ b $\dfrac{dy}{dx} = \dfrac{6}{x^2}$

---

a $\dfrac{dy}{dx} = x^{-3}$ b $\dfrac{dy}{dx} = \dfrac{6}{x^2}$

$y = \dfrac{x^{-2}}{-2} + c$ $y = 6 \times \dfrac{x^{-1}}{-1} + c$

$y = -\dfrac{1}{2x^2} + c$ $y = -\dfrac{6}{x} + c$

$\dfrac{1}{x^2} = x^{-2}$

The general rule for integration applies to fractional indices as well as integer powers.

See Chapter 1 for a reminder of the rules of indices.

You will often need to simplify an expression before integrating.

EXAMPLE 3

Find y if $\dfrac{dy}{dx} = \dfrac{1}{x\sqrt{x}}$

Rewrite: $\dfrac{dy}{dx} = \dfrac{1}{x^{\frac{3}{2}}} = x^{-\frac{3}{2}}$

$x\sqrt{x} = x^1 \times x^{\frac{1}{2}} = x^{\frac{3}{2}}$

Integrate: $y = \dfrac{x^{-\frac{3}{2}+1}}{\left(-\frac{3}{2}+1\right)}$

Simplify: $= \dfrac{x^{-\frac{1}{2}}}{-\frac{1}{2}} + c$

$= -2x^{-\frac{1}{2}} + c$

Hence $y = -\dfrac{2}{\sqrt{x}} + c$

Give your answer in the same form as the question.

C1

Exercise 8.1

1 These are all expressions for $\dfrac{dy}{dx}$.

Integrate to find an equation for y in each case.

a x^4 b x^7 c $3x^2$

d x^{10} e $5x^4$ f $\dfrac{1}{2}x^5$

g $-2x^5$ h $-\dfrac{1}{4}x^7$ i $4x$

2 These are all expressions for $\dfrac{dy}{dx}$.

Integrate to find an equation for y in each case.

a x^{-3} b $3x^{-4}$ c $\dfrac{1}{x^2}$

d $\dfrac{2}{x^3}$ e $-x^{-5}$ f $-\dfrac{5}{x^3}$

g $\dfrac{2}{3}x^{-3}$ h $-\dfrac{4}{5x^5}$ i 3

3 Simplify the right-hand side of each equation and then integrate to find an equation for y.

a $\dfrac{dy}{dx} = (x^2)^2$ b $\dfrac{dy}{dx} = (2x)^3$ c $\dfrac{dy}{dx} = (x^{-2})^3$ d $\dfrac{dy}{dx} = \left(\dfrac{3}{x}\right)^2$

e $\dfrac{dy}{dx} = \left(\dfrac{2}{x}\right)^3$ f $\dfrac{dy}{dx} = \left(\dfrac{2x}{3}\right)^3$ g $\dfrac{dy}{dx} = \left(-\dfrac{1}{x}\right)^4$ h $\dfrac{dy}{dx} = (3\sqrt{x})^4$

4 Integrate each expression with respect to x.

a $\sqrt{x}$ b $(\sqrt{x})^{\frac{1}{2}}$ c $\dfrac{1}{2\sqrt{x}}$

d $x\sqrt{x}$ e $-\dfrac{1}{x^2\sqrt{x}}$ f $\left(\dfrac{2}{\sqrt{x}}\right)^3$

INVESTIGATIONS

5 Consider the following graph of a quadratic function $f(x)$:

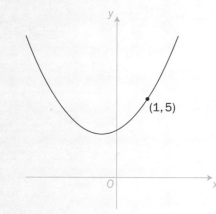

(1, 5)

The gradient function is of the form $f'(x) = ax + b$

a Given that when $x = 1$ the gradient is 3 and when $x = -1$ the gradient is -1, prove that $a = 2$ and find the value of b.

b Hence find the equation of $f(x)$ using the point shown on the graph.

6

$\dfrac{dy}{dx}$	$x^{\frac{1}{2}}$	$x^{-\frac{1}{2}}$	$x^{\frac{3}{2}}$	$x^{-\frac{3}{2}}$
y	$2x^{\frac{1}{2}} + c$		$-2x^{-\frac{1}{2}} + c$	$\dfrac{2}{5}x^{\frac{5}{2}} + c$

Match each expression for $\dfrac{dy}{dx}$ with one for y.

Identify the missing expression for y.

Using integral notation

If you know $\dfrac{dy}{dx}$, you can find an expression for y in terms of x by integrating. The standard notation for integration is the integral sign $\displaystyle\int$, together with something to say what variable you are integrating with respect to.

To integrate a function f(x) with respect to x,

you write $\qquad\qquad \displaystyle\int f(x)\, dx$

read this as the integral   of f(x)   with respect to x.

e.g. dx if you are integrating with respect to x, dt if you are integrating with respect to t etc.

f(x) is the function to be integrated, also known as the **integrand**.

The general rule for integrating any expression ax^n can now be written

$$\int ax^n\, dx = \frac{ax^{n+1}}{n+1} + c$$

EXAMPLE 1

Given that $\dfrac{dy}{dx} = 6x^2$, find an expression for y in terms of x.

$$\frac{dy}{dx} = 6x^2$$

Write as an integrand: $\qquad y = \displaystyle\int 6x^2\, dx$

Integrate: $\qquad y = 2x^3 + c$

Using the notation reduces the amount of writing you need to do and is clear and unambiguous.

EXAMPLE 2

Find $\qquad \displaystyle\int \frac{3t}{2}\, dt$

$$\int \frac{3t}{2}\, dt$$

Integrate: $\quad = \dfrac{3t^2}{4} + c$

The variable this time is t.

You can integrate expressions involving fractional indices.
Simplify the expression first.

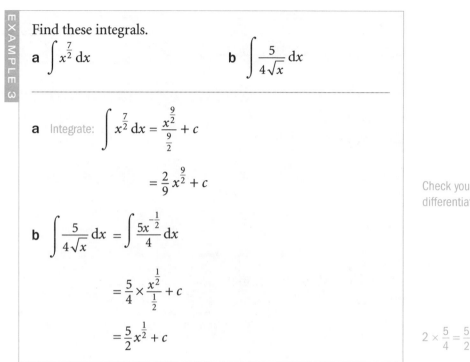

EXAMPLE 3

Find these integrals.

a $\displaystyle\int x^{\frac{7}{2}}\,dx$

b $\displaystyle\int \frac{5}{4\sqrt{x}}\,dx$

a Integrate: $\displaystyle\int x^{\frac{7}{2}}\,dx = \frac{x^{\frac{9}{2}}}{\frac{9}{2}} + c$

$$= \frac{2}{9}x^{\frac{9}{2}} + c$$

Check your answer by differentiating.

b $\displaystyle\int \frac{5}{4\sqrt{x}}\,dx = \int \frac{5x^{-\frac{1}{2}}}{4}\,dx$

$$= \frac{5}{4} \times \frac{x^{\frac{1}{2}}}{\frac{1}{2}} + c$$

$$= \frac{5}{2}x^{\frac{1}{2}} + c$$

$2 \times \dfrac{5}{4} = \dfrac{5}{2}$

When an expression is the sum or difference of more than one term, you can integrate each term separately.

Generally, if $f(x)$ and $g(x)$ are functions of x then
$$\int f(x) + g(x)\,dx = \int f(x)\,dx + \int g(x)\,dx$$

EXAMPLE 4

Find $\displaystyle\int (2x^3 - 3x^{-2})\,dx$

$$\int (2x^3 - 3x^{-2})\,dx = \int 2x^3\,dx - \int 3x^{-2}\,dx$$

The brackets emphasise that the whole expression $(2x^3 - 3x^{-2})$ is being integrated.

Simplify:
$$= 2\frac{x^4}{4} + c_1 - 3\frac{x^{-1}}{-1} + c_2$$

$$= \frac{x^4}{2} + \frac{3}{x} + c$$

Both terms have constants, c_1 and c_2. $c_1 + c_2$ is a constant so you write it as one constant, c.

C1

Remember to rewrite roots in index form before you integrate.

EXAMPLE 5

Find $\displaystyle\int \left(2\sqrt{t} - \frac{1}{\sqrt{t}} \right) dt$

$$\int \left(2\sqrt{t} - \frac{1}{\sqrt{t}} \right) dt = \int \left(2t^{\frac{1}{2}} - t^{-\frac{1}{2}} \right) dt$$

Integrate:

$$= 2\frac{t^{\frac{3}{2}}}{\frac{3}{2}} - \frac{t^{\frac{1}{2}}}{\frac{1}{2}} + c$$

$$= \frac{4}{3}t^{\frac{3}{2}} - 2t^{\frac{1}{2}} + c$$

$$= \frac{4}{3}t\sqrt{t} - 2\sqrt{t} + c$$

Give the answer in a similar form to the question.

You can integrate some products and quotients by expressing them in the form of a sum or difference.

EXAMPLE 6

Find $\displaystyle\int (x+2)(x-3)\, dx$

Expand the brackets:

$$\int (x+2)(x-3)\, dx = \int (x^2 - x - 6)\, dx$$

Integrate term by term:

$$= \frac{x^3}{3} - \frac{x^2}{2} - 6x + c$$

EXAMPLE 7

Find $\displaystyle\int \left(\frac{1+x^3}{x^2} \right) dx$

Rewrite as two fractions:

$$\int \left(\frac{1+x^3}{x^2} \right) dx = \int \left(\frac{1}{x^2} + \frac{x^3}{x^2} \right) dx$$

$$= \int (x^{-2} + x)\, dx$$

Integrate:

$$= \frac{x^{-2+1}}{(-2+1)} + \frac{x^2}{2} + c$$

Simplify:

$$= \frac{x^{-1}}{-1} + \frac{x^2}{2} + c$$

$$= -\frac{1}{x} + \frac{x^2}{2} + c$$

$\dfrac{x^3}{x^2} = x^{3-2} = x^1 = x$

Exercise 8.2

1 Evaluate the following integrals.

a $\displaystyle\int 4x \, dx$

b $\displaystyle\int p \, dp$

c $\displaystyle\int 3s^5 \, ds$

d $\displaystyle\int \frac{2}{w^2} \, dw$

e $\displaystyle\int \frac{3x}{4} \, dx$

f $\displaystyle\int -\frac{5}{2y^3} \, dy$

g $\displaystyle\int \frac{a}{5} \, da$

h $\displaystyle\int (4x)^2 \, dx$

i $\displaystyle\int 3z^{-4} \, dz$

2 The solution to a problem starts with $\dfrac{dx}{da} = \dfrac{2}{3a^2}$

The last line of the solution starts with $x =$

Write out the solution in full using the integral notation.

3 Evaluate these integrals.

a $\displaystyle\int x^{\frac{3}{2}} \, dx$

b $\displaystyle\int 3x^{\frac{1}{2}} \, dx$

c $\displaystyle\int 4x^{\frac{5}{2}} \, dx$

d $\displaystyle\int x^{\frac{2}{3}} \, dx$

e $\displaystyle\int x^{\frac{4}{3}} \, dx$

f $\displaystyle\int x^{\frac{1}{5}} \, dx$

4 Evaluate

a $\displaystyle\int x^{-\frac{1}{2}} \, dx$

b $\displaystyle\int x^{-\frac{5}{2}} \, dx$

c $\displaystyle\int \frac{1}{x^{\frac{3}{2}}} \, dx$

d $\displaystyle\int \frac{4}{x^{\frac{1}{2}}} \, dx$

e $\displaystyle\int \frac{x^{-\frac{3}{4}}}{4} \, dx$

f $\displaystyle\int 6x^{-\frac{2}{5}} \, dx$

5 Evaluate these integrals.

a $\displaystyle\int (x^2 - 4x^3) \, dx$

b $\displaystyle\int (3x^2 + 2x^{-2}) \, dx$

c $\displaystyle\int \left(4 - \frac{1}{x^2}\right) dx$

d $\displaystyle\int (5x^4 + 4x^3 + 1) \, dx$

e $\displaystyle\int \left(\frac{1}{2x^2} - \frac{1}{3x^3}\right) dx$

f $\displaystyle\int \left(\frac{4x}{5} + \frac{4}{5}\right) dx$

g $\displaystyle\int \left(\frac{4}{5}x^3 - \frac{3}{4}x^2 + \frac{2}{3}x\right) dx$

h $\displaystyle\int \left(\frac{1}{x^2} - \frac{1}{x^3}\right) dx$

i $\displaystyle\int (ax + bx^2 + cx^3) \, dx$

j $\displaystyle\int \left(\frac{px^2}{q} - \frac{q}{px^2}\right) dx$

6 Evaluate these integrals.

a $\displaystyle\int (3x^{\frac{1}{2}} - 2)\, dx$

b $\displaystyle\int \left(t^2 + \frac{1}{t^2}\right) dt$

c $\displaystyle\int (v^{\frac{5}{2}} - v^{-\frac{5}{2}})\, dv$

d $\displaystyle\int \left(\frac{4}{r^{\frac{1}{2}}} + \frac{5}{r^{\frac{3}{2}}}\right) dr$

e $\displaystyle\int \left(\sqrt{x} + \frac{1}{\sqrt{x}}\right) dx$

f $\displaystyle\int \left(x\sqrt{x} - \frac{3}{x\sqrt{x}}\right) dx$

g $\displaystyle\int (t^2\sqrt{t} - 2t^3\sqrt{t})\, dt$

h $\displaystyle\int \left(\frac{1}{4\sqrt{r}} + \frac{3}{r\sqrt{r}}\right) dr$

7 Integrate each expression with respect to x.

a $x(x-1)$

b $(x+2)^2$

c $2(x^3 - 3)$

d $(3x-1)(2x-3)$

e $x^2(5x+3)$

f $x(2x+3)^2$

g $(x-1)^3$

h $x^3(x^2-4)$

8 Evaluate these integrals.

a $\displaystyle\int \left(\frac{x^2+1}{x^2}\right) dx$

b $\displaystyle\int \left(\frac{\sqrt{t}-2}{t^2}\right) dt$

c $\displaystyle\int \sqrt{x}\,\frac{(1-x)}{2}\, dx$

d $\displaystyle\int \left(\frac{3-t}{t^3} + 3\right) dt$

e $\displaystyle\int \frac{1-t^2}{\sqrt{t}}\, dt$

f $\displaystyle\int \frac{1+r}{r\sqrt{r}}\, dr$

9 Find $\displaystyle\int \left(x - \frac{1}{x^2} + \sqrt[3]{x}\right) dx.$

10 Find $\displaystyle\int \left(\int 3x\, dx\right) dx.$ Your answer will include two constants.

INVESTIGATION

11 A student shows her working as:

$$\int x^{-\frac{3}{2}}\,dx = \frac{x^{-\frac{1}{2}}}{-\frac{1}{2}}$$

$$= -2x^{-\frac{1}{2}}$$

$$= 2x^{\frac{1}{2}}$$

What is wrong with her answer?
What is the correct solution?

12 'If you integrate a linear expression, you get a quadratic expression.'

a   Is this always true?

b   What happens if you integrate a quadratic expression?

c   What happens if you integrate a reciprocal expression?

Think of the different sorts $\frac{1}{x}$, $\frac{1}{x^2}$, etc.

13 Consider the integral equation

$$\int 3(x+k)^2\,dx = x^3 + 9x^2 + 27x + 10$$

Find the value of k that makes this expression true.

8.3 Finding the constant of integration

The constant of integration, c, generates a family of curves.

Consider $\dfrac{dy}{dx} = x^2$

Its integral is $y = \dfrac{x^3}{3}$, or $y = \dfrac{x^3}{3} + 1$, or …

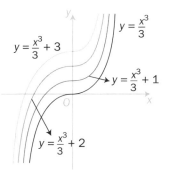

You can find the value of the constant of integration, c, if you are given a point on the curve.

EXAMPLE 1

Given that $f'(x) = x$ and $(-1, -2)$ is a point on the curve represented by $f(x)$, find $f(x)$.

Integrate to find f(x):
$$f(x) = \int f'(x)\, dx$$
$$= \frac{x^2}{2} + c$$

Remember if you integrate f'(x) you get f(x).

Substitute $x = -1$, $y = -2$:
$$-2 = \frac{(-1)^2}{2} + c$$
$$-2 = \frac{1}{2} + c$$

f(x) = -2 at (-1, -2)

Rearrange:
$$c = -\frac{5}{2}$$

Hence the equation of the curve is $f(x) = \dfrac{x^2}{2} - \dfrac{5}{2}$

You can use this method to find $f(x)$ whenever you know $f'(x)$ and a point on the curve.

EXAMPLE 2

The gradient of the curve $y = f(x)$ at any point (x, y) is $\dfrac{4}{x^2}$. Find the equation of the curve if it passes through the point $\left(\dfrac{1}{2}, -1\right)$.

Rewrite:
$$\frac{dy}{dx} = \frac{4}{x^2} = 4x^{-2}$$

Integrate with respect to x:
$$y = \int 4x^{-2}\, dx$$

$$= \frac{4x^{-2+1}}{(-2+1)} + c$$

Simplify:
$$y = -\frac{4}{x} + c$$

At $\left(\dfrac{1}{2}, -1\right)$
$$-1 = -\frac{4}{\frac{1}{2}} + c$$

$$-\frac{4}{\frac{1}{2}} = -4 \times \frac{2}{1} = -8$$

Make c the subject:
$$c = -1 + 8$$
$$= 7$$

Hence the equation of the curve is $y = -\dfrac{4}{x} + 7$

C5

EXAMPLE 3

If $f'(x) = 3x^2 - 2x + 1$, find the equation of the curve $f(x)$, given that $(1, 2)$ lies on the curve.

$$f'(x) = 3x^2 - 2x + 1$$
$$f(x) = \int (3x^2 - 2x + 1)\, dx$$

Integrate:
$$= \frac{3x^3}{3} - \frac{2x^2}{2} + x + c$$

Simplify:
$$= x^3 - x^2 + x + c$$

Find c: At $(1, 2)$ $2 = 1 - 1 + 1 + c$
$$c = 1$$

Hence the equation of the curve is $f(x) = x^3 - x^2 + x + 1$

Exercise 8.3

1 Given $f'(x)$ and a point which lies on each curve find the equation of the curve.

a $f'(x) = 2x - 1$, $(2, 1)$

b $f'(x) = 3x^2 + 2x$, $(1, 2)$

c $f'(x) = x - 4$, $(0, 3)$

d $f'(x) = 2x^2 - x$, $(1, 2)$

e $f'(x) = 4x$, $\left(\frac{2}{3}, 3\right)$

f $f'(x) = \frac{x}{2}$, $(4, 4)$

g $f'(x) = x + \frac{1}{x^2}$, $(2, -3)$

h $f'(x) = \frac{1}{\sqrt{x}}$, $(2, 0)$

i $f'(x) = x^{\frac{3}{2}}$, $(1, -1)$

j $f'(x) = 4x^3 - 3x^2$, $(2, -3)$

2 Find these integrals and find the equation of the curve given that it passes through the given point.

a $\displaystyle\int \frac{2}{x^2}\, dx$, $\left(\frac{1}{2}, -1\right)$

b $\displaystyle\int \frac{x+1}{\sqrt{x}}\, dx$, $(4, -2)$

c $\displaystyle\int \frac{1-x}{x^3}\, dx$, $\left(\frac{2}{3}, 0\right)$

d $\displaystyle\int [x(x-2) + 1]\, dx$, $(2, -1)$

e $\displaystyle\int (x-2)^2\, dx$, $(-1, 2)$

f $\displaystyle\int [x\sqrt{x} - 2]\, dx$, $(4, 5)$

g $\displaystyle\int \frac{1}{x\sqrt{x}}\, dx$, $(2, \sqrt{2})$

h $\displaystyle\int (3x-1)(x+2)\, dx$, $(-2, \sqrt{3})$

i $\displaystyle\int x^2(\sqrt{x} - 1)\, dx$, $(1, 0)$

j $\displaystyle\int (\sqrt{x} - 1)^2\, dx$, $\left(\frac{1}{4}, \frac{1}{4}\right)$

3 The gradient of the curve $y = f(x)$ is given by $f'(x) = ax + b$ where a and b are constants. The curve passes through the points $(1, 0)$, $(2, 3)$ and $(3, 7)$.
Find the equation of the curve.

4 $\dfrac{dy}{dx} = x + \dfrac{1}{x^2}$

   a Use integration to find y in terms of x.

   b Given that $y = \dfrac{1}{2}$ when $x = 2$, find the value of y at $x = 1$.

5 The curve with equation $y = f(x)$ passes through the point $(1, 4)$.

   Given that

   $$f'(x) = 1 + \frac{3x + 2}{x^{\frac{1}{2}}}, x > 0,$$

   find $f(x)$ and simplify your answer.

INVESTIGATION

6 The second derivative of a function is
  $f''(x) = 6x - 2$

   a Given that the gradient of $f(x)$ at the point $(1, 4)$ is 7, find $f'(x)$.

   b Integrate a second time to find the function $f(x)$.

$\underline{\Omega}$

1 Integrate with respect to x.

   a $2x^2$

   b $-5x^4$

   c $0.8x^3$

   d $(2x)^2$

   e $\left(\dfrac{2}{x}\right)^2$

   f $\left(\dfrac{1}{\sqrt{x}}\right)^3$

   g $\sqrt{\sqrt{x}}$

   h $\left(\dfrac{x}{2}\right)^{-3}$

   i $x^{\frac{4}{3}}$

   j $2x^{-0.5}$

   k $\dfrac{3}{4}x^{-\frac{1}{4}}$

   l $-x^{-1.5}$

2 Integrate these expressions.

   a $\displaystyle\int\left(3t^2-\dfrac{1}{t^2}\right)dt$

   b $\displaystyle\int(1-r)^2\,dr$

   c $\displaystyle\int\left(\dfrac{2-x}{x^3}\right)dx$

   d $\displaystyle\int v(6v-1)\,dv$

3 Integrate these expressions

   a $\displaystyle\int(x^2-1)(x-1)\,dx$

   b $\displaystyle\int\dfrac{(t+1)(t-1)}{t^2}\,dt$

   c $\displaystyle\int r^2(\sqrt{r}-3r)\,dr$

   d $\displaystyle\int\dfrac{x\sqrt{x}-5}{x^2}\,dx$

4 Given that $y = 2x - \dfrac{6}{x^3}$, $x \neq 0$, find $\displaystyle\int y\,dx$

5 The curve with equation $y = f(x)$ passes through the point $(1, 8)$.

   Given that $f'(x) = 3 + \dfrac{7x^3+1}{x^{\frac{1}{2}}}$, $x \neq 0$,

   find $f(x)$ and simplify your answer.

6 Find $\displaystyle\int\left(3\sqrt{x}-\dfrac{1}{x^2}\right)dx$

7 Given that $y = x - \dfrac{4}{x^2}$, $x \neq 0$, find $\displaystyle\int y\,dx$

8 **a** Given that $y = 2x^3 - 3x + 7$

   find **i** $\dfrac{dy}{dx}$

   ii $\dfrac{d^2y}{dx^2}$

b Find $\displaystyle\int \left(2 + 2\sqrt{x} - \dfrac{1}{2x^2}\right) dx$

9 Find $\displaystyle\int \left(4x + 3\sqrt{x}\right) dx$

10 The gradient of a curve is given by

$$f'(x) = x^2 + \frac{1}{x^2}, x \neq 0$$

and the curve passes through the point $\left(3, \dfrac{8}{9}\right)$.

Find the equation of the curve and determine the y-coordinate when $x = 1$.

11 Find $\displaystyle\int (2x + 3)^2 dx$

12 If $y = f(x)$ and $f'(x) = \dfrac{x^2 + 2}{x^4}$, find the equation of the curve if it passes through the point $(1, -4)$.

13 **a** If $x = t + 1$ and $y = t^2 + 1$ eliminate t to obtain an equation in the form $y = f(x)$ and show that $f'(x) = 2(x - 1)$

b Given $y = \displaystyle\int 2(x - 1) dx$, find the equation in the form $y = f(x)$, given that the values $x = 3$ and $y = -2$ satisfy the equation.

Exit

Integration Summary

Refer to

○ Integration is the reverse of the differentiation process.
If you integrate $\dfrac{dy}{dx}$ with respect to x you get y.

8.1

○ The general rule for integration is

$$\int ax^n \, dx = \frac{ax^{n+1}}{n+1} + c$$ given that $n \neq -1$

8.1

where c is the constant of integration.

○ To integrate a sum or difference, you integrate each part
separately so $\displaystyle\int f'(x) + g'(x) \, dx = f(x) + g(x) + c$

8.4

○ Given an expression for $\dfrac{dy}{dx}$ together with a point on
the curve, you can integrate the expression and substitute the
coordinates to find the original equation of the curve.

8.5

Links

Integration, along with differentiation, is part of the
branch of mathematics known as calculus.

Many equations that model real-life phenomena contain
derivatives, particularly things that move or change,
such as machines with moving parts.
Engineers need to set up these equations, by working
out what terms should go in them, and then they
can solve the equations by integrating them.
By solving these equations, they can begin to understand
real-world phenomena and make predictions.

1 **a** A sequence is defined by the recurrence relation
$u_{n+1} = u_n + 4$ and $u_1 = 5$.
Write down the first five terms of the sequence.

b The sum of the first n terms of the sequence in part **a** is 945.
Find n.

2 **a** The first term of an arithmetic series is –8 and the common difference is 3.
Write down the first four terms of the series.

b If the nth term of the series in part **a** is 133 what is the value of n?

c Which is the first term in the series that has a value greater than 200?

3 In a recurrence sequence $u_{n+2} = 2u_{n+1} - 3u_n$,
$u_1 = 3$ and $u_2 = 4$.
Find terms u_6 and u_7.

4 John is a season ticket holder at United Football Club.
In his first year he paid £300 for a season ticket.
The following year he paid £350, the next year £400.
Assuming that the cost of a season ticket increases by the same amount each year, how much will he pay for the season ticket in the tenth year?
How much will he have paid in total to watch United over the ten-year period?

5 The equation of a curve is given by $y = x^2 - 3x - 4$

a Write down the equation for $\dfrac{dy}{dx}$.

b Use the result for $\dfrac{dy}{dx}$ to work out the gradient of the curve at the points where it crosses the x-axis.

6 A curve has equation $y = \dfrac{1}{x} + x^2$

a Find the gradient of the curve at the point where $x = 2$.

b Find the equation of the tangent to the curve at the point where $x = 2$.

7 A curve is given by the equation $y = x^2 + 3x - 10$

   a Show that the point A, $(3, 8)$, lies on the curve.

   b A tangent is drawn to the curve at point A, $(3, 8)$. Find the gradient of the tangent and the normal to the curve at this point.

   c Find the equation of the tangent and the normal to the curve at the point A giving the equations in the form $ax + by + c = 0$

8 Find $\displaystyle\int \left(\frac{x+1}{\sqrt{x}} \right) dx$

9 a If $y = f(x)$ and $f'(x) = 2ax + 1$, where a is a constant, show that $y = ax^2 + x + c$

   b The curve $y = f(x)$ passes through the point A, $(2, 7)$, and B, $(-1, -2)$. Find the values of a and c.

10 Given that $y = 2x\sqrt{x} + 3\sqrt{x}$

   Find **a** $\dfrac{dy}{dx}$ **b** $\displaystyle\int y \, dx$

11 The gradient of a curve C is given by $\dfrac{dy}{dx} = (1 - 2x)^2$ and the point $A\left(\dfrac{3}{2}, \dfrac{3}{2}\right)$ lies on the curve.

   a Find the equation of the tangent to the curve at the point A.

   b Find the equation of the curve C in the form $y = f(x)$.

   c The normal at the point A meets the x-axis at the point B. Find the coordinates of B.

12 The curve C has equation $y = x^3 - 4x^2 + 2x + 4$

   The point P has coordinates $(2, 0)$.

   a Show that P lies on C.

   b Find the equation of the tangent to C at P, giving your answer in the form $y = mx + c$, where m and c are constants.

   Another point, Q, also lies on C. The tangent to C at Q is parallel to the tangent to C at P.

   c Find the coordinates of Q.

9

Algebra and functions

This chapter will show you how to
○ perform algebraic long division
○ recall and use the Remainder Theorem
○ recall and use the Factor Theorem
○ factorise cubic functions and other expressions.

Before you start

You should know how to:

1 Perform numerical long division without using a calculator.

e.g. 1081 ÷ 23

$$
\begin{array}{r}
47 \\
23\overline{)1081} \\
92 \\
\overline{161} \\
161 \\
\overline{0}
\end{array}
$$

1081 ÷ 23 = 47 no remainder

2 Manipulate expressions.

e.g. Simplify $-2x - (-3x)$

Apply the rules of signs:

$-2x - (-3x) = -2x + 3x$

$\qquad = x$

3 Evaluate functions.

e.g. If $f(x) = x^2 - 2x + 3$

find the value of f(−2).

$x^2 - 2x + 3 = (-2)^2 - 2(-2) + 3$

$\qquad = 4 + 4 + 3$

$\qquad = 11$

Check in:

1 Work out these long divisions.
   a $780 \div 15$
   b $1428 \div 21$
   c $1332 \div 18$

   These divisions leave remainders

   d $632 \div 14$
   e $1520 \div 27$
   f $1580 \div 32$

2 Simplify
   a $2a - (-2a)$
   b $-a + (-3a)$
   c $-2a - (+3a)$
   d $a - (-2a)$
   e $-4a + (+2a)$

3 a If $f(x) = x^2 - 2x$; find f(1).
   b If $f(x) = x^3 + 3x^2 - 1$; find f(−1).
   c If $f(x) = (x - 2)(2x - 1)$; find f(2).
   d If $f(x) = x^2(3x - 2)$; find f(−2).
   e If $f(x) = 2x^3 - 3x^2 - x$; find f(3).
   f If $f(x) = 1 - 4x^2$; find $f\left(\dfrac{1}{2}\right)$.

You can simplify algebraic fractions by cancelling common factors in the numerator and denominator.

EXAMPLE 1

Simplify the algebraic fraction $\dfrac{12x - 6x^2}{3x^2}$

Factorise the numerator: $\dfrac{12x - 6x^2}{3x^2} = \dfrac{6x(2 - x)}{3x^2}$

$= \dfrac{2 \times 3x \times (2 - x)}{3x \times x}$

Divide top and bottom by $3x$: $= \dfrac{2(2 - x)}{x}$

The simplified fraction is $\dfrac{2(2 - x)}{x}$

You will often need to factorise the numerator and denominator before simplifying the fraction.

EXAMPLE 2

Simplify the fraction $\dfrac{2x^2 + 5x - 3}{2x^2 + 7x + 3}$

Factorise both the numerator and the denominator:

$$\frac{2x^2 + 5x - 3}{2x^2 + 7x + 3} = \frac{(2x - 1)(x + 3)}{(2x + 1)(x + 3)}$$

Cancel by the common factor $(x + 3)$:

The simplified fraction is $\dfrac{2x - 1}{2x + 1}$

Check you have factorised correctly by expanding your brackets.

You can think of an algebraic fraction as a division by a polynomial.

e.g. $\dfrac{x - 2}{x + 3} \equiv (x - 2) \div (x + 3)$

You can use long division to divide a polynomial of degree m by a polynomial of degree n, where $m \geqslant n$.
The degree of the resulting polynomial is $m - n$.

The degree of a polynomial is the highest power it contains.
e.g. $x^2 - x + 1$ has degree 2.

EXAMPLE 3

Work out $(x^3 + 2x^2 - 5x - 6) \div (x - 2)$

$x^3 + 2x^2 - 5x - 6$ is the numerator.
$x - 2$ is the denominator.

You should write each polynomial with the highest x-power on the left and the lowest on the right.

Set out as a long division:

$$x - 2 \overline{)x^3 + 2x^2 - 5x - 6}$$

In $(x - 2)$ the lead term is x.

What must you multiply the lead term, x, by to get the first term, x^3?
Answer, x^2

Write this on the answer line of the division:

$$x - 2 \overline{)\overset{x^2}{x^3 + 2x^2 - 5x - 6}}$$

Write like terms in the same column to help you to organise your working.

Multiply the divisor, $(x - 2)$, by x^2:

$$x - 2 \overline{)\overset{x^2}{x^3 + 2x^2 - 5x - 6}}$$
Subtract: $\dfrac{x^3 - 2x^2}{+4x^2}$

$x^2(x - 2) = x^3 - 2x^2$
$2x^2 - (-2x^2) = 4x^2$

Bring down the next term, $-5x$:

$$x - 2 \overline{)\overset{x^2}{x^3 + 2x^2 - 5x - 6}}$$
$$\underline{x^3 - 2x^2} \downarrow$$
$$+4x^2 - 5x$$

You now multiply the lead term, x, by $4x$ to get the first term, $4x^2$.
Multiply the divisor $(x - 2)$ by $4x$:

$$x - 2 \overline{)\overset{x^2 + 4x}{x^3 + 2x^2 - 5x - 6}}$$
$$\underline{x^3 - 2x^2}$$
$$+4x^2 - 5x$$
$$\underline{4x^2 - 8x} \downarrow$$
Subtract: $\qquad 3x - 6$

$4x(x - 2) = 4x^2 - 8x$

| Remember to bring down the next term, -6.

You multiply the lead term, x, by $+3$ to get the first term, $3x$.

$$x - 2 \overline{)\overset{x^2 + 4x + 3}{x^3 + 2x^2 - 5x - 6}}$$
$$\underline{x^3 - 2x^2}$$
$$+4x^2 - 5x$$
$$\underline{4x^2 - 8x}$$
$$3x - 6$$
Subtract: $\qquad \dfrac{3x - 6}{0}$

$3(x - 2) = 3x - 6$

In this case the remainder is 0.
This means that $x - 2$ is a factor of $x^3 + 2x^2 - 5x - 6$.

So $(x^3 + 2x^2 - 5x - 6) \div (x - 2) = x^2 + 4x + 3$

C2

Sometimes, as with numbers, you will get a remainder.

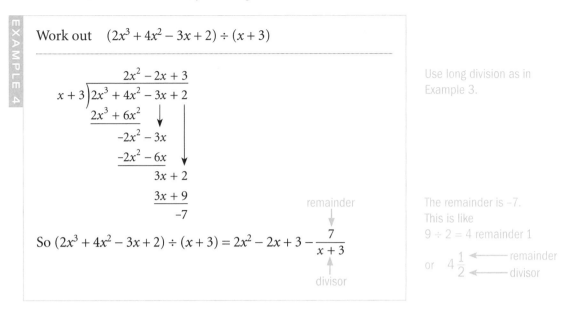

Work out $(2x^3 + 4x^2 - 3x + 2) \div (x + 3)$

Use long division as in Example 3.

$$2x^2 - 2x + 3$$
$$x + 3 \overline{\smash{\big)}\ 2x^3 + 4x^2 - 3x + 2}$$
$$\underline{2x^3 + 6x^2}$$
$$-2x^2 - 3x$$
$$\underline{-2x^2 - 6x}$$
$$3x + 2$$
$$\underline{3x + 9}$$
$$-7 \quad \text{remainder}$$

So $(2x^3 + 4x^2 - 3x + 2) \div (x + 3) = 2x^2 - 2x + 3 - \dfrac{7}{x + 3}$

divisor

The remainder is –7.
This is like
$9 \div 2 = 4$ remainder 1

or $\quad 4\frac{1}{2}$ ⟵ remainder
⟵ divisor

Some cubics do not have an x^2-term.
You should insert a $0x^2$ to help you to organise your working.

e.g. $x^3 + 3x + 2 = x^3 + 0x^2 + 3x + 2$

Similarly you can insert a 0x to show that there is no x-term.

Work out $(x^3 + 3x + 2) \div (x - 1)$

Insert $0x^2$: $\quad x^3 + 3x + 2 = x^3 + 0x^2 + 3x + 2$

$$x^2 + x + 4$$
$$x - 1 \overline{\smash{\big)}\ x^3 + 0x^2 + 3x + 2}$$
$$\underline{x^3 - x^2}$$
$$x^2 + 3x$$
$$\underline{x^2 - x}$$
$$4x + 2$$
$$\underline{4x - 4}$$
$$6$$

So $(x^3 + 3x + 2) \div (x - 1) = x^2 + x + 4 + \dfrac{6}{x - 1}$

Exercise 9.1

1 By factorising each expression where appropriate, simplify these fractions.

a $\dfrac{x^2 + 3x + 2}{x + 2}$

b $\dfrac{x^2 - 2x + 1}{x - 1}$

c $\dfrac{x^2 - x - 6}{x + 2}$

d $\dfrac{x^2 - 2x - 8}{x - 4}$

e $\dfrac{x^3 + 3x^2 + 2x}{x^2 + 3x + 2}$

f $\dfrac{4x^2 - 4x + 1}{2x - 1}$

g $\dfrac{6x^2 - x - 1}{2x^2 + x - 1}$

h $\dfrac{x^2 + 7x + 10}{2x^2 + 11x + 5}$

i $\dfrac{2x^2 - 9x + 9}{2x^2 - 11x + 12}$

C2

2 Use long division to perform each calculation.

a $(x^3 + x^2 - 3x + 1) \div (x - 1)$ **b** $(x^3 + 4x^2 + 2x - 1) \div (x + 1)$

c $(x^3 + 3x^2 + 4x + 4) \div (x + 2)$ **d** $(x^3 - x - 6) \div (x - 2)$

e $(x^3 + 6x^2 + 8x - 3) \div (x + 3)$ **f** $(x^3 - 6x^2 + 7x + 4) \div (x - 4)$

g $(2x^3 - 5x^2 + x + 2) \div (x - 2)$ **h** $(x^3 - 3x^2 - 6x + 8) \div (x + 2)$

i $(6x^3 + 25x^2 + 3x - 4) \div (x + 4)$ **j** $(8x^3 - 30x^2 + 31x - 15) \div (2x - 5)$

3 Perform these long divisions.

a $(x^3 - x + 6) \div (x + 2)$ **b** $(x^3 - 5x + 12) \div (x + 3)$

c $(x^3 - 13x - 12) \div (x - 4)$ **d** $(x^3 + x^2 - 2) \div (x - 1)$

e $(x^3 + 4x^2 - 8) \div (x + 2)$ **f** $(x^4 + 4x^3 + 2x^2 + 1) \div (x + 1)$

g $(2x^4 - 4x^3 + 3x^2 - 8x + 4) \div (x - 2)$ **h** $(3x^4 - 2x^3 - x^2 + 2x - 2) \div (x - 1)$

i $(x^3 - 2x^2 - 4x + 3) \div (x - 3)$ **j** $(x^4 - 4x^3 + 16x - 16) \div (x - 2)$

4 Perform each long division.

a $(x^2 + 3x - 1) \div (x + 1)$ **b** $(x^2 - 2x + 4) \div (x - 2)$

c $(2x^2 - 3x + 5) \div (x - 1)$ **d** $(x^3 + 4x^2 - x + 1) \div (x - 1)$

e $(2x^3 + x - 1) \div (x + 3)$ **f** $(x^3 - 1) \div (x - 1)$

g $(2x^3 - 5) \div (x + 1)$ **h** $(x^4 - 1) \div (x - 1)$

5 Divide each of the cubic expressions by the given quadratic expression.

a $(x^3 + 2x^2 - 8x) \div (x^2 - 2x)$

b $(x^3 - x^2 + 2) \div (x^2 + x + 2)$

c $(x^3 - 1) \div (x^2 - x + 3)$

d $(2x^3 + 5x^2 - 5) \div (x^2 + x - 1)$

INVESTIGATION

6 **a** Use long division to simplify $f(x) = \dfrac{x + 4}{x + 1}$

b Use your answer to find the limit of $f(x)$ as x tends to infinity.

c Express $\dfrac{x^2 + 5x - 6}{x^2 + 4x - 5}$ in the form $A + \dfrac{B}{Cx + D}$

○ The Remainder Theorem states that when f(x) is divided by ($ax - b$), where a and b are real numbers, the remainder is given by $f\left(\dfrac{b}{a}\right)$.

Similarly, when f(x) is divided by ($ax + b$) the remainder is given by $f\left(-\dfrac{b}{a}\right)$.

Consider the polynomial f(x).

Divide f(x) by ($ax - b$), where a and b are real numbers, to give a new function, Q(x), and a remainder, r:

$$\frac{f(x)}{(ax - b)} = Q(x) + \frac{r}{(ax - b)}$$

Multiply both sides by ($ax - b$):

$$f(x) = (ax - b)Q(x) + r$$

Let $x = \dfrac{b}{a}$:

$$f\left(\frac{b}{a}\right) = \left(a\frac{b}{a} - b\right)Q\left(\frac{b}{a}\right) + r$$

$$\Rightarrow \quad f\left(\frac{b}{a}\right) = r$$

EXAMPLE 1

Find the remainder when ($x^2 + 3x - 4$) is divided by ($x + 2$).

Let $\qquad\qquad$ $f(x) = x^2 + 3x - 4$

Substitute $x = -2$: $\quad f(-2) = (-2)^2 + 3(-2) - 4$

$$= 4 - 6 - 4$$

$$= -6$$

The divisor is ($x + 2$) so you evaluate f(-2).

Hence ($x^2 + 3x - 4$) ÷ ($x + 2$) gives remainder –6.

Check your answer using long division:

$$
\begin{array}{r}
x + 1 \\
x + 2\overline{\smash{\big)}\,x^2 + 3x - 4} \\
\underline{x^2 + 2x} \downarrow \\
x - 4 \\
\underline{x + 2} \\
-6
\end{array}
$$

Both methods give the same remainder.

C2

You can use the Remainder Theorem to evaluate the remainder of an algebraic division.

EXAMPLE 2

Use the remainder theorem to find the remainder when
$f(x) = 3x^3 - x^2 - 8x - 3$ is divided by

a $x - 1$

b $3x + 2$

---

a $f(1) = 3(1^3) - (1)^2 - 8(1) - 3$

$\qquad = 3 - 1 - 8 - 3$

$\qquad = -9$

The remainder is –9.

The divisor is $(x - 1)$ so work out f(1).

Remainder $\neq 0$ so $(x - 1)$ is not a factor.

b $f\left(-\dfrac{2}{3}\right) = 3\left(-\dfrac{2}{3}\right)^3 - \left(-\dfrac{2}{3}\right)^2 - 8\left(-\dfrac{2}{3}\right) - 3$

$\qquad = 3\left(-\dfrac{8}{27}\right) - \dfrac{4}{9} + \dfrac{16}{3} - 3$

$\qquad = 1$

The remainder is 1.

The divisor is $(3x + 2)$ so work out $f\left(-\dfrac{2}{3}\right)$.

Remainder $\neq 0$ so $(3x + 2)$ is not a factor.

You can also use the Remainder Theorem to find the value of a missing constant in a given function or expression.

EXAMPLE 3

The function, $x^3 + ax^2 - 2x - 5$, has a remainder of 7 when divided by $(x - 2)$.
Find the value of a.

Let $\quad f(x) = x^3 + ax^2 - 2x - 5$

Substitute $x = 2$: $f(2) = (2)^3 + a(2)^2 - 2(2) - 5$

$\qquad\qquad\qquad = 8 + 4a - 4 - 5$

$\qquad\qquad\qquad = 4a - 1$

The divisor is $(x - 2)$ so you evaluate f(2).

$4a - 1$ is the remainder of the division.

Set up an equation and solve to find a: $4a - 1 = 7$

$\qquad\qquad\qquad\qquad\qquad\qquad\qquad a = 2$

You were told that the remainder is equal to 7.

Hence $a = 2$

You can find a missing constant and the remainder of a division when given an expression and one of its factors.

C2

EXAMPLE 4

The expression, $x^3 + bx^2 - 3x - 1$, is divisible exactly by $(x - 1)$. Find the value of b and the remainder when the expression is divided by $(x + 3)$.

Let $\quad f(x) = x^3 + bx^2 - 3x - 1$

$$f(1) = 0$$

Substitute $x = 1$: $\qquad f(1) = (1)^3 + b(1)^2 - 3(1) - 1$
$$= b - 3$$

This follows since $(x - 1)$ is a factor of f(x).

Equate to 0 and solve for b: $\quad b - 3 = 0$
$$b = 3$$

Substitute $b = 3$ into f(x): $\qquad f(x) = x^3 + 3x^2 - 3x - 1$

Substitute $x = -3$: $\qquad f(-3) = (-3)^3 + 3(-3)^2 - 3(-3) - 1$
$$= -27 + 27 + 9 - 1 = 8$$

The divisor is $x + 3$ so you evaluate f(–3).

Hence the remainder is 8.

Exercise 9.2

1 Find the remainder when each expression is divided by the given linear expression.

a $x^2 + 3x - 1$; $x + 2$

b $x^3 - 2x^2 + 3$; $x - 2$

c $2x^3 - 4x^2 + 3x$; $x - 1$

d $1 - 2x - 3x^2 + x^3$; $x - 3$

e $x^4 - 2x^2 + 4$; $x + 2$

f $8x^2 - 2x - 3$; $2x - 1$

g $6x^2 + 4x - 1$; $2x + 1$

h $4x^2 - 6x + 5$; $2x - 3$

i $9x^3 + 2x^2 - x$; $3x + 4$

j $8x^3 - 8x^2 + x - 2$; $2x - 5$

k $1 - x^4$; $3x - 2$

l $x(2 - x)(3 + x)$; $4x - 3$

m $(2x + 1)(1 - 3x)^2$; $2x + 1$

n $(x + 1)(x + 2)(x + 3)$; $2x + 1$

2 **a** The function $f(x) = x^2 + ax - 2$ has a remainder of 3 when divided by $(x + 2)$. Use this to find the value of a.

b The function $f(x) = ax^2 - 2x + 4$ has a remainder of 2 when divided by the linear expression $(2x - 1)$. Find the value of a.

c Find the value of a given that $x^3 + 2x^2 - ax + 1$ has a remainder of 5 when divided by $(x - 2)$.

d If $(x^3 - 2ax^2 + 4x - 5) \div (x - 3)$ leaves a remainder of –2 find the value of a.

e If $(x^3 + 2ax^2 - ax + 3) \div (x + 2)$ leaves a remainder of –15 find the value of a.

3 a If $(x - a)$ is a factor of $2x^2 + 5x - 3$ use the Remainder Theorem to find the possible values of a.

  b When $f(x) = x^3 - ax^2 + 1$ is divided by $(x + 2)$ the remainder is 13.
  Find the remainder when $f(x)$ is divided by $(x - 2)$.

  c The expression, $x^3 - 4x^2 + px + 3$, is divisible by $(x + 3)$ with no remainder.
  Find

    i the value of p
    ii the remainder

  when the expression is divided by $(x + 1)$.

4 The functions $2x^3 + 3x - 2$ and $x^3 + kx^2 + 2x - 4$, have the same remainder when divided by $(x - 2)$.
What is the value of k?

5 The expression, $2x^3 + ax^2 + b$, has a remainder of 3 when divided by $(x - 1)$ and a remainder of 4 when divided by $(x - 2)$.
Find the values of a and b.

6 Given that $f(x) = x^3 + ax^2 + bx + 2$, $f(1) = -3$ and $f(2) = -4$

  a find the values of a and b

  b use the Remainder Theorem to show that $(x + 2)$ is a factor and hence factorise the expression completely.

7 a Given that $f(x) = px^3 + 23x^2 + qx - 8$ and $f(-1) = 15$ and $f(-2) = 48$

    i find the values of p and q
    ii use the Remainder Theorem to factorise the expression completely.

  b Show that $(x^2 - 9)$ is a factor of $x^4 - x^3 - 15x^2 + 9x + 54$ and factorise the expression completely.

INVESTIGATION

8 For the function $f(x) = x^3 - 4x^2 - 6x + 3$, find the remainder when $f(x)$ is divided by

  a $2x + 1$ **b** $2x - 1$ **c** $3x$.

9.3 The Factor Theorem

If $(ax - b)$ is a factor of the polynomial f(x), then $(ax - b)$ divides f(x) with no remainder and a special case of the Remainder Theorem follows.

- The Factor Theorem states that for the function f(x)

  - if $\left(x - \dfrac{b}{a}\right)$ is a factor then f$\left(\dfrac{b}{a}\right) = 0$

  for all real numbers a and b.

Suppose that $(ax - b)$ is a factor of f(x).
Then $(ax - b)$ divides f(x) exactly and the remainder is equal to zero.
Hence, by the Remainder Theorem,

$$f\left(\dfrac{b}{a}\right) = 0$$

You can use the Factor Theorem to factorise cubic expressions, where this is possible, and to solve cubic equations.

EXAMPLE 1

Determine whether or not $(x - 3)$ is a factor of the expression, $x^3 - 6x^2 + 5x + 12$

Let   f$(x) = x^3 - 6x^2 + 5x + 12$

If $(x - 3)$ is a factor then   f$(3) = 0$

Substitute $x = 3$:
$$f(3) = (3)^3 - 6(3)^2 + 5(3) + 12$$
$$= 27 - 54 + 15 + 12$$
$$= 0$$

f$(3) = 0$
Hence $(x - 3)$ is a factor of f(x).

You can use the Factor Theorem with algebraic long division in order to factorise an expression.

EXAMPLE 2

Show that $(x - 2)$ is a factor of $x^3 - 4x^2 + x + 6$
Hence factorise the expression completely.

Let $f(x) = x^3 - 4x^2 + x + 6$

If $(x - 2)$ is a factor then $\quad f(2) = 0$

Substitute $x = 2$: $\quad f(2) = (2)^3 - 4(2)^2 + (2) + 6$
$$= 8 - 16 + 2 + 6$$
$$= 0$$

$f(2) = 0$
Hence $(x - 2)$ is a factor of $f(x)$.

Divide $x^3 - 4x^2 + x + 6$ by $(x - 2)$:

This will allow you to find the other factors.

$$
\begin{array}{r}
x^2 - 2x - 3 \\
x - 2 \overline{)\, x^3 - 4x^2 + x + 6\,} \\
\underline{x^3 - 2x^2}\;\downarrow \\
-2x^2 + x \\
\underline{-2x^2 + 4x} \\
-3x + 6 \\
\underline{-3x + 6} \\
0
\end{array}
$$

There is no remainder
so $(x - 2)$ is a factor.

$\therefore\ f(x) = (x - 2)(x^2 - 2x - 3)\ = (x - 2)(x + 1)(x - 3)$

$x^2 - 2x - 3 = (x + 1)(x - 3)$

Factorising a cubic expression allows you to sketch its curve.

The solutions of $f(x) = 0$ in Example 2
are $x = 2$, $x = -1$ and $x = 3$.

These correspond to the x-axis crossings of the graph of $f(x)$
and can be used to sketch the curve.

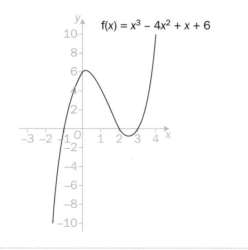

$f(x) = x^3 - 4x^2 + x + 6$

Sometimes you will need to use trial and improvement to find a value of a which gives $f(a) = 0$.
Try to structure your approach.

e.g. First try $a = 1$ followed by $a = -1$ then try $a = 2$ and $a = -2$ and so on.

Factorise the expression $\quad x^3 - 3x^2 - 10x + 24$
Hence solve the equation $\quad x^3 - 3x^2 - 10x + 24 = 0$

Let $\quad f(x) = x^3 - 3x^2 - 10x + 24$

Use trial and improvement to find a which gives $f(a) = 0$:

$f(1) = 1 - 3 - 10 + 24 = 12$

$f(-1) = -1 - 3 + 10 + 24 = 30$

$f(2) = 8 - 12 - 20 + 24 = 0$

$f(1) \neq 0$ so $(x - 1)$ is not a factor of $f(x)$.

$f(-1) \neq 0$ so $(x + 1)$ is not a factor of $f(x)$

$f(2) = 0$ so $(x - 2)$ **is** a factor of $f(x)$.

Divide $f(x)$ by $(x - 2)$ to find the other factors:

$$x - 2 \overline{)\, x^3 - 3x^2 - 10x + 24 \,}$$

$$\begin{array}{r} x^2 - x - 12 \\ \underline{x^3 - 2x^2} \\ -x^2 - 10x \\ \underline{-x^2 + 2x} \\ -12x + 24 \\ \underline{-12x + 24} \\ 0 \end{array}$$

Hence $f(x) = (x - 2)(x^2 - x - 12)$

$\qquad\quad = (x - 2)(x + 3)(x - 4)$

After factorising the quadratic

Hence the solutions of $f(x) = 0$ are $x = -3$, $x = 2$ and $x = 4$.

If $(x - 2)$ is a factor of $\quad f(x) = x^3 - 3x^2 + a$, find the value of a.

$(x - 2)$ is a factor so $f(2) = 8 - 12 + a = 0$

Hence $a = 4$

Take care with the signs.
Remember:
if $(x + a)$ is a factor of $f(x)$ then $x = -a$ is a solution of $f(x) = 0$;
if $(x - a)$ is a factor of $f(x)$ then $x = a$ is a solution of $f(x) = 0$.

Exercise 9.3

1 For each function, $f(x)$, find whether or not the given linear expression is a factor.

a $f(x) = x^2 - x - 6;\ x + 2$

b $f(x) = x^3 + x^2 - x - 1;\ x + 1$

c $f(x) = x^3 + 5x^2 + 8x + 4;\ x + 2$

d $f(x) = x^3 - 6x^2 + 12x - 8;\ x - 2$

e $f(x) = x^3 - 3x^2 - 9x + 27;\ x - 3$

f $f(x) = 4x^3 + 8x^2 + 5x + 1;\ x + 2$

g $f(x) = x^3 + 5x^2 + 5x - 3;\ x + 3$

h $f(x) = 2x^3 - x^2 + 6x - 3;\ 2x - 1$

2 Show that in each case the given linear expression is a factor of f(x). Hence factorise the function, f(x), completely.

a $f(x) = x^3 + 2x^2 - x - 2; x - 1$

b $f(x) = x^3 + 4x^2 + x - 6; x + 2$

c $f(x) = x^3 + 2x^2 - 11x - 12; x - 3$

d $f(x) = 2x^3 + 15x^2 + 31x + 12; x + 3$

e $f(x) = 3x^3 - 13x^2 + 4x; x - 4$

f $f(x) = x^3 - 2x^2 + 3; x + 1$

g $f(x) = x^3 + x^2 + 2x + 8; x + 2$

h $f(x) = 3x^3 + 13x^2 - 16; x + 4$

3 Use the Factor Theorem to factorise each expression fully.

a $x^3 - 4x^2 + x + 6$

b $x^3 + 5x^2 - 2x - 24$

c $x^3 + 7x^2 + 2x - 40$

d $x^3 - 6x^2 + 11x - 6$

e $x^3 - 2x^2 - 23x + 60$

f $2x^3 + 5x^2 - x - 6$

4 By factorising find all the solutions to each equation.

a $4x^3 + 16x^2 + 19x + 6 = 0$

b $4x^3 - 27x + 27 = 0$

c $12x^3 + 25x^2 + x - 2 = 0$

d $6x^3 + 37x^2 + 58x + 24 = 0$

5 a If $(x - 1)$ is a factor of $x^3 + 3x^2 - 4a + 2$, find the value of a.

b Given that $(x + 2)$ is a factor of $x^3 + ax^2 + 2x + 4$, find the value of a.

c If $(x - 3)$ is a factor of $2x^3 - 3x^2 + ax - 6$, find the value of a.

d If $(x + 1)$ and $(x - 2)$ are both factors of $x^3 + bx^2 + ax - 1$, find the values of a and b.

e Given that $(x - 1)$ and $(x + 2)$ are both factors of $x^3 + ax^2 + bx + 3$, find the values of a and b.

f Given that $(x + 1)$, $(x - 1)$ and $(x - 2)$ are all factors of the expression $x^4 + ax^3 + bx^2 + cx + 8$, find, by solving simultaneous equations, the values of the constants a, b and c.

g Show, by using the factor theorem, that $(a + b)$ is a factor of the expression $2a^3 + 7a^2b + 7ab^2 + 2b^3$.
Write the expression as the product of three factors.

INVESTIGATION

6 This is the graph of the function $f(x) = x^3 - 3x^2 + kx + 8$.
Use the graph to find the value of k.
Hence find the values of the other x-intercepts.

1 a Divide $2x^3 + x^2 - 7x - 6$ by $(x+1)$

b Factorise the function, $f(x) = 2x^3 + x^2 - 7x - 6$, completely.

c Hence solve $f(x) = 0$

2 If $(x+a)$ is a factor of $x^2 - 8x + 15$, find the possible values of a.

3 a Show that $(x-2)$ is a factor of
$x^3 - 10x^2 + 31x - 30$

b Factorise completely the expression
$x^3 - 10x^2 + 31x - 30$

c Hence sketch the graph of the cubic.

4 a Use the factor theorem to show that $(x-3)$ is a factor
of $2x^3 + x^2 - 25x + 12$

b Factorise $2x^3 + x^2 - 25x + 12$ completely.

5 The function $f(x) = 2x^3 + 3x^2 - 29x + c$,
where c is a constant.
Given that $f(-3) = 0$

a find the value of c

b factorise $f(x)$ completely

c find the remainder when $f(x)$ is divided by $(x+2)$.

6 The function $f(x) = x^3 + 4x^2 + x - 6$

a Use the factor theorem to show that $(x+2)$ is
a factor of $f(x)$.

b Factorise $f(x)$ completely.

c Write down all the solutions to the
equation $x^3 + 4x^2 + x - 6 = 0$ [(c) Edexcel Limited 2007]

7 The function $f(x) = 2x^3 + 9x^2 + 7x - 6$

a Find the remainder when $f(x)$ is divided by $(x+1)$.

b Use the factor theorem to show that $(x+3)$ is a factor of $f(x)$.

c Factorise $f(x)$ completely.

C2

8 The function $f(x) = x^3 - 2x^2 + ax + b$, where a and b are constants.

$(x - 3)$ is a factor of $f(x)$.
When $f(x)$ is divided by $(x + 1)$, the remainder is 28.

a Find the value of a and the value of b

b Find the remainder when $f(x)$ is divided by $(x - 2)$.

9 **a** Use the factor theorem to show that $(x + 2)$ is a factor of

$$x^3 - x^2 - 10x - 8$$

b Hence find all the solutions of the equation

$$x^3 - x^2 - 10x - 8 = 0$$

10 Show that $(x - y)$ is a factor of the function in x and y given by

$$f(x, y) = x^2(y - 2) + y^2(2 - x) + 4(x - y)$$

Hence, or otherwise, factorise $f(x, y)$ completely.

$f(x, y)$ is a function of both variables x and y.

11 **a** The function $f(x) = 4x^3 + ax^2 + bx + c$,
where a, b and c are constants.

If $f(2) = 0$, $f(1) = 3$ and $f(-1) = -15$, find the values of the constants a, b and c.

b Factorise $f(x)$.

12 Factorise $4a^4 - 5a^2b^2 + b^4$ completely.

C2

Exit

Summary   Refer to

○ You can use algebraic long division to divide a polynomial of degree m
  by a polynomial of degree n, where $m \geqslant n$.   9.1

○ The Remainder Theorem states that
  when the function $f(x)$ is divided by $(ax - b)$

  the remainder is given by $f\left(\dfrac{b}{a}\right)$.   9.2

○ The Factor Theorem states that for the function $f(x)$
  if $(ax - b)$ is a factor then $f\left(\dfrac{b}{a}\right) = 0$.   9.3

Links

Polynomial functions are used by engineers to model
phenomena in the real world.

e.g. Forces on a suspension bridge use wires of varying length each
with different tensile strengths.

Linear functions are rarely sufficient and polynomials
with powers of three, four or even higher are needed
with a variety of unknown co-efficients to be determined.
Although computers are used to determine these
co-efficients, they will be programmed using the
techniques you have learned in this chapter.

C2

10

Coordinate geometry

This chapter will show you how to
- apply the circle theorems to circle problems
- find the distance between two points and calculate the midpoint of a line
- find the equation of a circle
- find the points of intersection of a circle and a line.

Before you start

You should know how to:

1 Find the equation of a straight line.

e.g. Find the equation of the line joining the points $A(2, 5)$ and $B(4, -1)$.

Use $\dfrac{y - y_1}{x - x_1} = \dfrac{y_2 - y_1}{x_2 - x_1}$:

$\dfrac{y - 5}{x - 2} = \dfrac{-1 - 5}{4 - 2}$

$\dfrac{y - 5}{x - 2} = -3$

$3x + y - 11 = 0$

2 Complete the square.

e.g. Complete the square for the quadratic, $x^2 + 3x$

$x^2 + 3x = x^2 + 3x + \dfrac{9}{4} - \dfrac{9}{4}$

$= \left(x + \dfrac{3}{2}\right)^2 - \dfrac{9}{4}$

3 Determine whether a quadratic has two, one or no real solutions.

e.g. $2x^2 - 3x - 4 = 0$

Investigate the discriminant, $b^2 - 4ac$:

$a = 2, b = -3, c = -4$

$b^2 - 4ac = (-3)^2 - 4(2)(-4)$

$\qquad = 9 + 32$

$b^2 - 4ac > 0$

Hence there are two real solutions.

Check in:

1 Find the equation of the line joining the given points A and B. **6**

  a $A(1, 5); B(3, 9)$

  b $A(-2, 3), B(5, -1)$

  c $A(0, 7), B(-3, -3)$

  d $A(4, -2), B(1, -4)$

  e $A(-3, 4), B(2, -4)$

2 Complete the square for each quadratic expression. **3**

  a $x^2 + 4x$

  b $x^2 + 5x$

  c $x^2 - 3x$

  d $x^2 - x$

  e $2x^2 - 4x$

3 How many real solutions are there for each quadratic equation? **3**

  a $x^2 - 2x - 5 = 0$

  b $2x^2 + x - 2 = 0$

  c $x^2 + 4x + 4 = 0$

  d $2x^2 - 3x + 4 = 0$

  e $3x^2 - 10x + 2 = 0$

C2

Coordinate geometry of the circle

Given the coordinates of the ends of a diameter of a circle you can find the coordinates of its centre.

Let the diameter, AB, have coordinates $A(x_1, y_1)$ and $B(x_2, y_2)$ and the centre of the circle be at the point given by $O(x, y)$.

The point O is midway between points A and B.

○ The coordinates of the centre of the circle, O, are

$$x = \frac{x_1 + x_2}{2} \text{ and } y = \frac{y_1 + y_2}{2}$$

This is the mean of the x and y values.

You can then use Pythagoras' theorem to find the radius of the circle.

See Chapter 0 on the CD-ROM for revision on the length and midpoint of a line segment.

EXAMPLE 1

The points $A(3, 4)$ and $B(-1, 6)$ are the end points of a diameter.
a Find the coordinates of the centre of the circle.
b Find the radius of the circle.

a Let the centre of the circle, O, have coordinates (x, y).

$$x = \frac{x_1 + x_2}{2}$$

$$= \frac{3 + (-1)}{2}$$

$$= \frac{2}{2} = 1$$

$A = (3, 4)$ and $B = (-1, 6)$ so $x_1 = 3$ and $x_2 = -1$.

and $$y = \frac{y_1 + y_2}{2}$$

$$= \frac{4 + 6}{2}$$

$$= 5$$

$y_1 = 4$ and $y_2 = 6$.

Hence the centre of the circle has coordinates $(1, 5)$.

b The radius of the circle is the line OA which has end points $O(1, 5)$ and $A(3, 4)$.

Use Pythagoras' theorem to find OA:

$$OA^2 = (x_1 - x)^2 + (y_1 - y)^2$$

$$OA^2 = (3 - 1)^2 + (4 - 5)^2$$

$$= 4 + 1 = 5$$

$$OA = \sqrt{5}$$

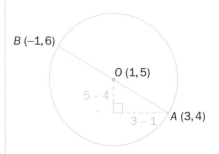

You can find the length of a chord of a circle.

Let $A(x_1, y_1)$ and $B(x_2, y_2)$ be points on the circumference of the circle.

Draw a right-angled triangle ABC as shown in the diagram:

Length of $\quad AC = x_2 - x_1$
and length of $\quad BC = y_2 - y_1$

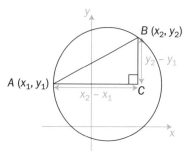

Apply Pythagoras' theorem:

$$AB^2 = AC^2 + BC^2$$
Hence $\quad AB^2 = (x_2 - x_1)^2 + (y_2 - y_1)^2$

Take square roots on both sides:

$$AB = \sqrt{[(x_2 - x_1)^2 + (y_2 - y_1)^2]}$$

You can use this technique in any circle.

EXAMPLE 2

Find the length of chord AB if $A = (-2, 3)$ and $B = (1, 5)$.

$A = (-2, 3) \quad$ so $\quad x_1 = -2 \quad$ and $\quad y_1 = 3$
$B = (1, 5) \quad$ so $\quad x_2 = 1 \quad$ and $\quad y_2 = 5$

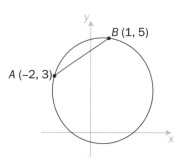

Substitute the values into the formula:

$$AB = \sqrt{[(x_2 - x_1)^2 + (y_2 - y_1)^2]}$$

$$AB = \sqrt{[(1 - -2)^2 + (5 - 3)^2]}$$

$$= \sqrt{[9 + 4]}$$

$$= \sqrt{13}$$

Take care with the signs when substituting.

Hence length of the chord $AB = 3.61$ units correct to 3 s.f.

Consider a circle with centre at the point O.

Let AB be a chord of the circle and M be the midpoint of the chord AB.

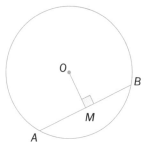

○ The perpendicular bisector of the chord AB, which intersects AB at the midpoint M, passes through the centre of the circle, O.

You can use this information to find the perpendicular distance of the chord AB from the centre O.

EXAMPLE 3

The points $A(3, 4)$ and $B(5, 10)$ are on the circumference of the circle with centre $O(10, 5)$. Find the perpendicular distance of the chord AB from the centre of the circle O.

You may find that a sketch helps you to visualise the problem.

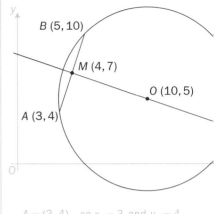

Let $M(x_3, y_3)$ be the midpoint of the chord AB.

Use the formula for the midpoint of a line to find the values of x_3 and y_3:

$$x_3 = \frac{x_1 + x_2}{2} = \frac{3 + 5}{2} = 4$$

$$y_3 = \frac{y_1 + y_2}{2} = \frac{4 + 10}{2} = 7$$

Hence $M = (4, 7)$

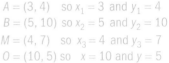

$A = (3, 4)$ so $x_1 = 3$ and $y_1 = 4$
$B = (5, 10)$ so $x_2 = 5$ and $y_2 = 10$
$M = (4, 7)$ so $x_3 = 4$ and $y_3 = 7$
$O = (10, 5)$ so $x = 10$ and $y = 5$

Use the distance formula to calculate the distance OM:

$$OM = \sqrt{[(4 - 10)^2 + (7 - 5)^2]}$$

$$= \sqrt{[36 + 4]}$$

$$= \sqrt{40}$$

$$= 6.32$$

Hence the perpendicular distance from the centre of the circle to the chord is 6.32 units correct to 3 s.f.

You can solve problems involving chords of circles.

EXAMPLE 4

The points $A(p, -2)$ and $B(3, q)$ are the ends of the diameter of a circle with centre $O(2, -4)$. Find the values of p and q.

Use the midpoint formula:

$$A = (p, -2)$$
$$B = (3, q)$$
and $\quad O = (2, -4)$

O is the midpoint of AB.

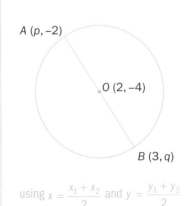

Substitute the known values into the midpoint formula:

$$2 = \frac{p + 3}{2} \qquad -4 = \frac{-2 + q}{2}$$

$$4 = p + 3 \qquad -8 = -2 + q$$

$$p = 1 \qquad q = -6$$

using $x = \frac{x_1 + x_2}{2}$ and $y = \frac{y_1 + y_2}{2}$

Hence the values are $p = 1$ and $q = -6$.

C2

You will often need to recall and use the circle theorems you met at GCSE.

See the bridging chapter for a reminder of the basic circle theorems.

o The angle at the centre of a circle is twice the angle at the circumference from the same arc.

Draw the radius CO and extend it to D:

$$AO = OC$$ (they are both radii)

$$\angle OAC = \angle OCA = x$$ (isosceles triangle)

$$\angle COA = 180° - 2x$$ (angles in a triangle)

$$\angle AOD = 2x$$ (angles on a straight line)

You can use a similar method to show that $\angle DOB = 2y$

Hence $\angle ACB = x + y$

and $\angle AOB = 2x + 2y$ as required.

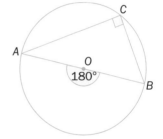

You can use this circle theorem to prove other results.

EXAMPLE 5

Prove that the angle in a semicircle is a right angle.

Angle AOB at the centre $= 180°$

Angle at centre $= 2 \times$ angle at circumference

So angle ACB at circumference $= 90°$

C2

o The angle between a tangent and the radius at the point of contact (where the tangent touches the circle) is a right angle.

o The perpendicular line from the centre of a circle to a chord bisects the chord.

Try to show these results for yourself.

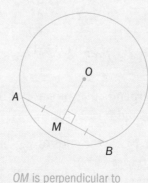

A is the point of contact between the tangent and the circle.
Angle $OAT = 90°$

OM is perpendicular to the chord AB.
$AM = MB$

Exercise 10.1

1 The coordinates of the end points of the diameter, AB, of a circle are given. Find the coordinates of the centre of each circle.

a $A\ (0, 3);\ B\ (4, 3)$

b $A\ (1, 7);\ B\ (2, 5)$

c $A\left(\dfrac{3}{2}, 4\right);\ B\left(\dfrac{7}{2}, 5\right)$

d $A\ (-1, 3);\ B\ (4, 5)$

e $A\left(-\dfrac{7}{2}, -\dfrac{4}{3}\right);\ B\left(-\dfrac{5}{2}, \dfrac{5}{3}\right)$

f $A\left(2, -\dfrac{5}{4}\right);\ B\left(-7, \dfrac{3}{4}\right)$

g $A\ (0.4, 3);\ B\ (-1.5, -2.6)$

h $A\left(2\sqrt{2}, -\sqrt{3}\right);\ B\left(4\sqrt{2}, -2\sqrt{3}\right)$

2 Find the length of the chord joining the points A and B on the circumference of each circle. Give your answers correct to three significant figures.

a $A\ (3, 1);\ B\ (5, 7)$

b $A\ (5, 3);\ B\ (2, 1)$

c $A\ (-2, -3);\ B\ (4, 2)$

d $A\ (2, -3);\ B(-5, 0)$

e $A\ (-2, 5);\ B\ (-2, 7)$

f $A\left(\dfrac{1}{2}, 1\dfrac{1}{2}\right);\ B\left(\dfrac{7}{2}, -2\dfrac{1}{2}\right)$

3 Find the distance of the chord, AB, from the centre, O, of each circle.

a centre $(1, 3)$; chord $A\ (0, 1),\ B\ (4, 3)$

b centre $(4, 7)$; chord $A\ (1, 3),\ B\ (2, 5)$

c centre $(-1, 2)$; chord $A\ (-3, 2),\ B\ (4, -4)$

d centre $(-3, -2)$; chord $A\ (1, 5),\ B\ (3, 9)$

e centre $(2, -4)$; chord $A\ (1, -3),\ B\ (4, 6)$

f centre $\left(1\dfrac{1}{2}, -2\dfrac{1}{2}\right)$; chord $A\left(3, -1\dfrac{1}{2}\right),\ B\left(1\dfrac{1}{2}, 3\right)$

4 The diameter of each circle is AB and the centre is at O. Find the coordinates of point B.

a $A\ (1, 3);\ O\ (3, 5)$

b $A\ (2, 5),\ O\ (-2, 4)$

c $A\ (4, 5);\ O\ (-3, -4)$

d $A\ (-2, 0);\ O\ (4, -5)$

e $A\left(\dfrac{1}{2}, 2\dfrac{1}{2}\right);\ O\ (3, 1)$

f $A\ (0, -3);\ O\ (-2, 3)$

5 a Find the equation of the perpendicular bisector of the chord, AB, where A is $(2, 5)$ and B is $(3, 8)$.

b The points $A(a, 3)$ and $B(4, b)$ are the ends of a diameter of a circle with centre $(1, 5)$. Find the values of the constants a and b.

6 The ends of a diameter, AB, have coordinates $A(1, 5)$ and $B(4, 6)$ and the point $C(2, 7)$ lies on the circumference of the same circle. Show that triangle ABC is a right-angled triangle.

7   The lines, $y = 3x + 2$ and $y = -2x + 3$, are chords of the circle which intersect at the point P.
    Find the distance of P from the centre of the circle $O(1, 2)$.

8   The points $A(2, 3)$, $B(-4, 3)$, and $C(1, 5)$ lie on the circumference of a circle.

    a   Find the equations of the perpendicular bisectors of chords AB and BC.

    b   Hence find the coordinates of the centre of the circle.

9   The points $A(4, 2)$, $B(5, 6)$, and $C(0, 3)$ lie on the circumference of a circle. Show that the angle BAC is a right angle and hence determine the coordinates of the centre of the circle and the radius of the circle.
    Write the radius correct to two decimal places.

10 A circle passes through the points $(0, 0)$, $(0, 5)$ and $(3, 0)$.

    a   Use this information to find the coordinates of the centre of the circle.

    b   Determine the radius of the circle.

11 The line $y + 2x = 3$ crosses the x-axis at the point A and the y-axis at the point B.

    a   If AB is a diameter of a circle find the coordinates of the centre.

    b   Show that the circle passes through the point $(0, 0)$ and give reasons for your conclusion.

12 Two circles intersect at $(5, 8)$.
    The centres of the circles have coordinates $(2, 4)$ and $(7, a)$, where a is a constant.
    The radii drawn from the centres of the circles to this point of intersection are perpendicular to each other.

    a   Determine the value of the constant a.

    b   Using this value of a find the equation of the straight line joining the centres of the two circles.

INVESTIGATION

13 A circle has a chord with end points $A(1, 2)$ and $B(5, 6)$.
    The centre of the circle is $C\left(\frac{1}{2}, 4\right)$.
    Is AB a diameter of the circle?

o The equation of a circle with radius r and centre $C(a, b)$ is
$$(x - a)^2 + (y - b)^2 = r^2$$

Consider a circle of radius, r, with centre $C(a, b)$.

Let point $P(x, y)$ be any point on the circumference of the circle.

Triangle PBC is right-angled, and

$CB = x - a$
$BP = y - b$

Apply Pythagoras' theorem to triangle PBC:

$$CB^2 + BP^2 = CP^2$$
$$(x - a)^2 + (y - b)^2 = r^2$$

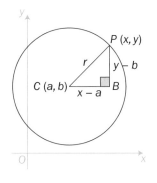

CP is the radius of the circle.

C2

The general equation of a circle centred at $O(0, 0)$ is
$$x^2 + y^2 = r^2$$

Try to show this for yourself.

You can find the radius and centre point of a circle given its equation.

EXAMPLE 1

The equation of a circle is $(x + 2)^2 + (y - 4)^2 = 9$
Find the centre and the radius of the circle.

The equation of the circle is $(x + 2)^2 + (y - 4)^2 = 9$

Compare this with the general equation $(x - a)^2 + (y - b)^2 = r^2$ which has centre (a, b) and radius r.

Hence the centre of the circle is $(-2, 4)$ and the radius is 3.

You can find the equation of a circle given its centre and radius.

EXAMPLE 2

Write down the equation of the circle with centre $(-3, 2)$ and radius 4 cm.

A circle with centre (a, b) and radius r has an equation of the form

$$(x - a)^2 + (y - b)^2 = r^2$$

Substitute $a = -3$, $b = 2$ and $r = 4$:

The equation of the circle is
$(x + 3)^2 + (y - 2)^2 = 16$

Sketching a graph may help you to visualise the problem:

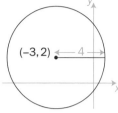

▌Take care with signs.

Sometimes you will need to rearrange the equation of a circle into the standard form before you can find its centre and radius.

EXAMPLE 3

The equation of a circle is given by $x^2 + y^2 - 4y - 5 = 0$
Find the centre of the circle and its radius.

Rewrite:
$$x^2 + y^2 - 4y - 5 = 0$$
$$x^2 + y^2 - 4y = 5$$

There is only one term in x.
This comes from the x-bracket, $(x + 0)^2$

The y-terms must come from a perfect square of the form $(y \pm b)^2$

Complete the square for the y-terms:

$$y^2 - 4y = y^2 - 4y + 4 - 4$$
$$= (y - 2)^2 - 4$$

Rewrite the equation with the brackets:

$$(x + 0)^2 + (y - 2)^2 - 4 = 5$$

Rearrange:
$$(x + 0)^2 + (y - 2)^2 = 9$$

Compare this equation with $(x - a)^2 + (y - b)^2 = r^2$.

Hence the centre of the circle is $(0, 2)$ and the radius is 3.

You need to rewrite the equation in the form
$(x \pm a)^2 + (y \pm b)^2 = r^2$

Coefficient of y: -4
halve it: -2
square it: 4
add/subtract it.

The centre is at (a, b) and the radius is r.

C2

You can solve problems involving circles and lines.
There are three possibilities.

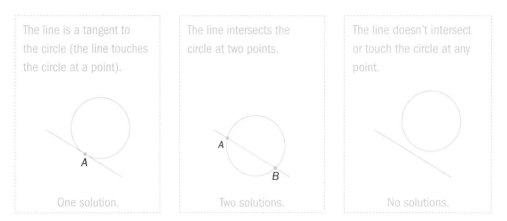

The line is a tangent to the circle (the line touches the circle at a point).

One solution.

The line intersects the circle at two points.

Two solutions.

The line doesn't intersect or touch the circle at any point.

No solutions.

You can find the points of intersection by solving the equations
of the circle and line simultaneously.

EXAMPLE 4

The line $y = x - 1$ intersects the circle $(x + 4)^2 + (y - 1)^2 = 68$
at points A and B.
Find
a the coordinates of A and B
b the length of AB.

a Substitute $y = x - 1$ into the circle equation:

$$(x + 4)^2 + (x - 2)^2 = 68 \qquad x - 1 - 1 = x - 2$$

Expand the brackets and solve for x:

$$x^2 + 8x + 16 + x^2 - 4x + 4 = 68$$

Simplify:
$$2x^2 + 4x - 48 = 0$$
$$2(x^2 + 2x - 24) = 0$$
$$x^2 + 2x - 24 = 0$$

Factorise:
$$(x + 6)(x - 4) = 0$$

The solutions are $x = 4$ and $x = -6$.

$2(x^2 + 2x - 24) = 0$
and since $2 \neq 0$
$x^2 + 2x - 24 = 0$

Substitute the x-values into $y = x - 1$ to find the y-values:
when $x = 4$; $y = 4 - 1 = 3$,
and when $x = -6$; $y = -6 - 1 = -7$.
Hence the points of intersection are $A(4, 3)$ and $B(-6, -7)$.

Make sure that you pair the x- and y-values together correctly.

b Find the length of AB:

$$AB = \sqrt{[(x_2 - x_1)^2 + (y_2 - y_1)^2]} = \sqrt{[(-6 - 4)^2 + (-7 - 3)^2]}$$

$$= \sqrt{[10^2 + 10^2]} = \sqrt{200}$$

$A = (4, 3)$
$B = (-6, -7)$

Take care with the signs.

Hence the length of the chord AB is $\sqrt{200}$ or $10\sqrt{2}$ units.

C2

You can show if a given line touches or intersects a given circle.

EXAMPLE 5

Show that the y-axis is a tangent to the circle $(x-2)^2 + (y+5)^2 = 4$ and find the point of contact.
Show also that the circle does not intersect the x-axis.

The point where a tangent touches a circle is called the point of contact.

The circle $(x-2)^2 + (y+5)^2 = 4$ meets the y-axis where $x = 0$.

Substitute $x = 0$ into the equation: $(0-2)^2 + (y+5)^2 = 4$

Simplify and solve for y:
$$4 + (y+5)^2 = 4$$
$$(y+5)^2 = 0$$

Hence $y = -5$ and, as this is the only solution, the line $x = 0$ must be a tangent to the circle at the point $(0, -5)$.

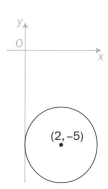

The circle intersects with the x-axis where $y = 0$.

Substitute $y = 0$ into the equation of the circle:

$$(x-2)^2 + (0+5)^2 = 4$$

Expand:
$$x^2 - 4x + 4 + 25 = 4$$
$$x^2 - 4x + 25 = 0$$

Investigate the discriminant, $b^2 - 4ac$:

$a = 1, b = -4, c = 25$

$$b^2 - 4ac = (-4)^2 - 4(1)(25)$$
$$= 16 - 100 = -84$$

■ Take care with the signs.

$b^2 < 4ac$ and so the quadratic has no solutions.

Hence the circle does not intersect the x-axis.

Alternatively, you could have inferred this since the circle has centre $(2, -5)$ and radius 2.

Exercise 10.2

1 In the following examples write down

 i the coordinates of the centre

 ii the radius of the circle.

 a $(x+1)^2 + y^2 = 9$ **b** $(x+2)^2 + (y-1)^2 = 9$

 c $(x-3)^2 + (y-2)^2 = 16$ **d** $(x-\sqrt{2})^2 + (y+\sqrt{3})^2 = 4$

 e $(x-2\sqrt{3})^2 + (y+\sqrt{3})^2 = 3$ **f** $(x^2 - 2x + 1) + (y^2 + 4y + 4) = 4$

2 Given the coordinates of the centre of the circle and its radius write down the equation of each circle.

 a $C(1, 2); r = 2$ **b** $C(-1, 0); r = 1$

 c $C(-2, 2); r = 3$ **d** $C(3, -4); r = \sqrt{2}$

 e $C(-\sqrt{2}, -\sqrt{3}); r = \sqrt{7}$ **f** $C\left(\frac{1}{2}, -\frac{1}{2}\right); r = \frac{1}{4}$

185

3 **a** The equation of a circle is given by $x^2 - 4x + y^2 + 3 = 0$
      Find the coordinates of the centre of the circle and the radius.

    b Show that the centre of the circle with equation
      $x^2 + y^2 + 4x - 2y + 1 = 0$ is at (-2, 1).
      Hence determine the radius of the circle.

4 **a** Show that the point (3, -4) lies on the circle with equation
      $(x - 2)^2 + (y + 3)^2 = 2$

    b Determine whether the point (2, 7) lies on the circumference
      of the circle with equation $(x + 3)^2 + (y - 2)^2 = 50$

    c The point (2, 3) lies on the circumference of the circle
      with equation $(x + 1)^2 + (y - 2)^2 = a^2$, where a is a constant.
      Find the value of a.

5 **a** Find the equation of the circle with centre (3, 2) which
      passes through the point (5, 4).

    b The diameter of a circle has end points at (1, 3) and (7, -5).
      Find the equation of the circle.

    c Determine whether the point (-2, 3) lies inside or outside
      the circle whose equation is $(x + 3)^2 + (y - 1)^2 = 4$

6   The equation of a circle is given by $x^2 + y^2 + 6x - 4y + 4 = 0$
    Prove that the line with equation $y = x + 5$ passes through
    the centre of this circle.

7 **a** Show that the line $2y + x = 18$ is a tangent to the circle
      $(x - 2)^2 + (y - 3)^2 = 20$
      Determine the coordinates of the point of contact.

    b Show that the line $2y + x = 11$ is a tangent to the circle with
      equation $(x + 2)^2 + (y - 4)^2 = 5$ and find the coordinates of
      the point of contact.

8 **a** The line $y = 2x + 1$ intersects the circle $(x - 2)^2 + (y - 1)^2 = 16$
      at the points A and B. Find the coordinates of A and B.

    b The line $y = x - 3$ touches the circle $(x + 3)^2 + (y + 2)^2 = 8$
      at point A. Find the coordinates of A.

    c Show that the line $y + x = 1$ intersects the circle
      $(x - 4)^2 + (y + 3)^2 = 2$ at the points A and B and hence determine
      the coordinates of these two points.

    d The line $y = x + 2$ and the circle $(x - 1)^2 + (y + 4)^2 = 25$ intersect at
      the points P and Q. Find the coordinates of P and Q.

9 The line, $y = x + 3$, intersects the circle with equation $(x - 2)^2 + (y - 5)^2 = 18$ at the points A and B.
Find the coordinates of A and B. Show that the line AB is a diameter.

10 The line, $y = x + a$, where a is a constant, is a tangent to the circle $(x - 4)^2 + (y - 1)^2 = 16$
Find the two possible values of a, writing your values correct to two decimal places.

11 **a** The circle $(x + 3)^2 + (y - 4)^2 = 17$ intersects the x-axis at the points A and B. Find the length of AB.

b Find the coordinates of the points where the circle $x^2 + y^2 - 10x - 9y = 0$ intersects the x-and y-axes.
Determine the coordinates of the centre of the circle.

c The circle $(x + 4)^2 + (y + 4)^2 = 20$ crosses the x-axis at the points A and B and the y-axis at points C and D.
Find the area of the quadrilateral $ABCD$.

d The circle $(x - 1)^2 + (y + 4)^2 = 10$ intersects with the y-axis at points A and B. Given that point O is the centre of the circle show that lines OA and OB are equally inclined to the x-axis.

e The line $y = 0$ is a tangent to the circle $(x + 3)^2 + (y - 3)^2 = 9$ at the point P.
Show that $x = 0$ is also a tangent to the circle at a point Q.
If O is the centre of the circle determine the area of the triangle OPQ.

INVESTIGATION

12 Box A shows equations of different circles.
Box B gives their corresponding centres.

a Match each equation with its centre.

b Give an example of a circle to match the extra centre.

A

$x^2 - 6x + y^2 - 4y - 10 = 0$
$x^2 - 6x + y^2 + 4y - 24 = 0$
$x^2 - 4x + y^2 + 8y - 4 = 0$
$x^2 + 4x + y^2 - 8y + 3 = 0$

B

$(3, -2)$
$(2, 3)$
$(2, -4)$
$(3, 2)$
$(-2, 4)$

C2

1 GCSE exam question

P, Q, R and S are points on a circumference of a circle, centre O.
PR is a diameter of the circle.
Angle $PSQ = 56°$.

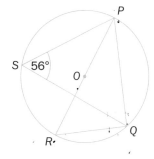

a Find the size of angle PQR.
Give a reason for your answer.

b Find the size of angle PRQ.
Give a reason for your answer.

c Find the size of angle POQ.
Give a reason for your answer.

[(c) Edexcel Limited 2003]

2 The points A $(3, 0)$ and B $(8, 5)$ lie on the circumference of a circle.
Find the equation of the perpendicular bisector of the chord AB.

3 A circle has centre at O $(3, -2)$
Point A $(-2, 5)$ lies on the circumference of the circle.
Determine the radius of the circle and find the coordinates
of B, the other end of the diameter AOB.

4 Write down the equation of the circle which has centre
$(-2, 5)$ and radius 5.
Show that the circle crosses the y-axis at two points and
that the x-axis is a tangent to the circle.

5 The line $y = x - 2$ intersects the circle $(x + 1)^2 + (y + 3)^2 = 8$ at the
points A and B. Find the coordinates of A and B. Draw a diagram.

6 A circle has centre (a, b) and radius 4. $b > 0$
The circle crosses the x-axis at the points $(-2, 0)$ and $(2, 0)$.
Find the equation of the circle.
Find the coordinates of the points where the circle crosses
the y-axis, giving your answers in a simplified surd form.

7 The circle, C, with centre A, has equation $x^2 + y^2 - 8y + 12 = 0$
Find

a the coordinates of A

b the radius of C.

c Show that C does not intersect or touch the x-axis.

d Find the coordinates of the points at which the circle crosses
the y-axis.

Given that the line, L, with gradient $\frac{1}{2}$ passes through A

e find the equation of the line L.

8 The line $y = 3x - 4$ is a tangent to the circle, C, touching C at the point P, $(2, 2)$, as shown in the figure.
The point Q is the centre of C.

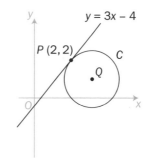

a Find the equation of the straight line through P and Q.

Given that Q lies on the line, $y = 1$
b   show that the x-coordinate of Q is 5

c   find an equation for C.

[(c) Edexcel Limited 2006]

9 In the figure, $A(3, 0)$, and $B(1, 6)$, are the end points of a diameter of the circle C.
Find

a   the exact length of AB

b   the coordinates of the midpoint, P, of AB

c   an equation for the circle C.

10 The circle, C, has centre $(4, 5)$ and passes through the point $(2, -1)$.
Find an equation for C.

11 The points A and B have coordinates $(3, -2)$ and $(9, 6)$ respectively.

a   Find the coordinates of the midpoint of AB.

Given that AB is a diameter of the circle C
b   find an equation for C.

12 The circle $x^2 + y^2 + 8x - 6y + 16 = 0$ has centre at the point (p, q).
Find the value of p and the value of q.
Show that the line $y = 2x + 11$ is a diameter of the circle.
Find the radius of the circle.
Determine the x-coordinates of the ends of the diameter, giving your answer correct to two decimal places.

13 The equation of a circle is $x^2 + y^2 + 2gx + 2fy + c = 0$ where g, f and c are constants.
Show that the centre of the circle is at the point $(-g, -f)$ and find an expression for the radius in terms of g, f and c.
Hence, or otherwise, find the coordinates of the centre of the circle, and the exact radius, of the circle with equation
$2x^2 + 2y^2 + 6x - 3y - 2 = 0$

C2

Summary   Refer to

○ The midpoint of the line joining the points $A(x_1, y_1)$ and $B(x_2, y_2)$
  has coordinates given by $x = \dfrac{x_1 + x_2}{2}$ and $y = \dfrac{y_1 + y_2}{2}$ 10.1

○ The distance between the two points $A\,(x_1, y_1)$ and $B\,(x_2, y_2)$
  is found by applying Pythagoras' theorem to produce the formula

  $AB = \sqrt{[(x_2 - x_1)^2 + (y_2 - y_1)^2]}$ 10.1

○ You can use circle theorems to solve problems involving
  circles and tangents.   10.1

○ The equation of a circle with radius r and centre at the point
  (a, b) is given by $(x - a)^2 + (y - b)^2 = r^2$ 10.2

○ You can find the points of intersection of a circle and a line by
  solving their equations simultaneously.   10.2

C2

Links

The motion of planets is known to be elliptical in shape.
To simplify the theory, mathematicians can model their
motion in terms of a circle. Using knowledge of straight
lines, they can then gain an understanding of shooting
stars or meteorites 'intersecting' or colliding with the
trajectory of a planet.

In particular, by using knowledge of the discriminant
and the number of roots it has, mathematicians can
make predictions on when a meteorite will or will not
come near to the earth. Similarly, we can gain an
understanding of the trajectory of orbiting satellites that
are required to maintain the same distance above the
earth at all times, yet never crossing each other's paths.

Exponentials and logarithms

This chapter will show you how to
- evaluate and sketch the graph of an exponential function
- apply the laws of logarithms to simplifying expressions
- use logarithms to find solutions to exponential equations.

Before you start

You should know how to:

1   Solve quadratic equations.

e.g. Solve $x^2 - x - 12 = 0$

Factorise:

$(x + 3)(x - 4) = 0$

Either $x + 3 = 0$ or $x - 4 = 0$

so $x = -3$ or $x = 4$

2   Simplify expressions with indices.

e.g. Simplify $2a^3 \times (3a)^2$

Square the bracket: $2a^3 \times 9a^2$

Apply the rule of indices:

$a^3 \times a^2 = a^5$

So $2a^3 \times (3a)^2 = 18a^5$

3   Recognise an asymptote.

e.g. Sketch the graph of

the equation $y = 1 + \dfrac{1}{x}$

You should know the graph of $y = \dfrac{1}{x}$

Translate 1 unit up the y-axis

noting the asymptotes at $y = 1$ and $x = 0$.

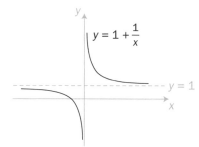

Check in:

1   Solve

   a $x(2x - 1) = 0$

   b $x^2 - 4x + 4 = 0$

   c $2x^2 - 5x - 3 = 0$

   d $3x^2 - x - 2 = 0$

   e $10x^2 - 11x - 6 = 0$

   f $4x^3 - 12x^2 + 9x = 0$

2   Simplify

   a $3a \times (4a)^3$ **b** $7a \div 2a^{-1}$

   c $(a^2)^{\frac{3}{2}}$ **d** $(2a)^3 \times (3a)^{-2}$

   e $(2\sqrt{a})^2 \times a^2$ **f** $(4a)^{\frac{1}{2}} \div 3\sqrt{a}$

3   Sketch the curves and identify their asymptotes.

   a $y = \dfrac{2}{x}$

   b $y = 2 + \dfrac{1}{x}$

   c $y = \dfrac{1}{2x}$

   d $y = -\dfrac{1}{x}$

C2

Exponential graphs

The general equation of an **exponential function** is
$y = a^x$, where a is a positive constant $(a > 0)$

e.g. $y = 2^x$

You can investigate the graph of $y = a^x$

$f(x) = e^x$ is a special exponential function. This is covered in C3.

EXAMPLE 1

Sketch the graph of **a** $y = 2^x$ **b** $y = 2^{-x}$ for $-5 \leqslant x \leqslant 5$

Make a table of values:

x	-5	-4	-3	-2	-1	0	1	2	3	4	5
2^x	0.03	0.06	0.13	0.25	0.5	1	2	4	8	16	32
2^{-x}	32	16	8	4	2	1	0.5	0.25	0.13	0.06	0.03

The x-axis is an asymptote to both curves.

Since $2^0 = 1$ the curves cross the y-axis at $(0, 1)$.

a

b

For large positive values of x the graph of $y = 2^x$ rises very steeply.

For large negative values of x the graph of $y = 2^x$ approaches the x-axis but never meets or crosses it.

The graph of $y = 2^{-x}$ is a reflection of $y = 2^x$ in the y-axis.

- The graph of the function $y = a^{-x}$ is a reflection in the y-axis of the graph of the function $y = a^x$.

Consider the graphs of the functions $y = 2^x$, $y = 3^x$ and $y = 4^x$ drawn on the same diagram:

For larger positive values of x each curve rises very steeply.

Each curve crosses the y-axis at $(0, 1)$.

The x-axis is an asymptote to each curve.

Graphs of the type $y = a^x$ with $a > 0$
- are of a similar shape with the x-axis as an asymptote
- pass through the point $(0, 1)$.

Since $a^0 = 1$ for all $a > 0$.

C2

Exercise 11.1

1 If the equation of the curve is $y = a^x$, sketch the curve of the equation $y = a^{-x}$

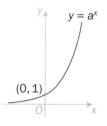

2 **a** Plot the graph of the equation $y = (1.5)^x$ taking values of x from -3 to $+3$.

   b Plot the graph of $y = 4^x$ and, on the same axes, the graph of $y = \left(\frac{1}{4}\right)^x$ taking values of x from -2 to $+2$.

   c Plot the graph of $y = (0.5)^x$ for $-4 \leqslant x \leqslant 4$.

3 Plot the graphs of $y = 5^x$ and $y = (0.2)^x$ on the same axes for the interval $-2 \leqslant x \leqslant 2$.

4 Plot the graph of the equation $y = 3^{-x}$ for $-3 \leqslant x \leqslant 3$.

5 **a** Plot the graphs of $y = 2^x$ and the straight line $y = 6$ from $x = 0$ to $x = 3$.
   Write down an estimate of the coordinates of the point where the line and the curve intersect.
   Hence, deduce an approximate solution to the equation $2^x = 6$.

   b Plot the graphs of $y = 2^{-x}$ and the straight line $y = 10$ from $x = -4$ to $x = 0$.
   Hence find, from the graph, an approximate solution to the equation $2^{-x} = 10$.

6 Plot the graphs of $y = 3^x$ and the straight line $y = x + 3$ from $x = 0$ to $x = 2$.
   From your graph find an approximate solution to the equation $3^x = x + 3$ in the given range.

7 **a** Plot the graphs of $y = 2^x$ and $y = x^2$ in the interval $0 \leqslant x \leqslant 3$.
   Hence show that there is a solution to the equation $x^2 = 2^x$ in the given interval.

   b By extending the interval of values of x show that there are two solutions to the equation $x^2 = 2^x$ and use your graph to estimate the other solution.

INVESTIGATIONS

8 **a** Compare the values of 2^{2x} and 4^x for $-2 \leqslant x \leqslant 5$.
   What do you notice?

   b Deduce the relationship between the graphs of 27^x and 3^{3x}

9 Look at this table of values for an exponential function.
   Can you deduce the equation of the function?

x	0	1	2	3
$f(x)$	$\frac{1}{2}$	1	2	4

C2

11.2 Logarithms

Consider the exponential equation $x = a^y$

You say that y is the logarithm of x to the base a.

You write this as $y = \log_a x$

○ $x = a^y \Leftrightarrow y = \log_a x$

$\Leftrightarrow$ means 'if and only if'.

The logarithm of x to base a is the power to which a must be raised to give x.

You can write expressions involving indices as logarithms.

EXAMPLE 1

Write in logarithmic form

a $2^7 = 128$ **b** $3^4 = 81$ **c** $10^5 = 100\,000$

---

a $\qquad\qquad 2^7 = 128$

$\qquad$ so $\log_2 128 = 7$

b $\qquad\qquad 3^4 = 81$

$\qquad$ so $\log_3 81 = 4$

c $\qquad\qquad 10^5 = 100\,000$

$\qquad$ so $\log_{10} 100000 = 5$

You can reverse the process.

EXAMPLE 2

Find the value of each logarithm.

a **i** $\log_{10} 100$ **ii** $\log_{10} 1000$

b **i** $\log_4 64$ **ii** $\log_2 64$

---

a **i** $\log_{10} 100$

$\qquad 10^2 = 100 \quad$ so $\log_{10} 100 = 2$

ii $\log_{10} 1000$

$\qquad 10^3 = 1000 \quad$ so $\log_{10} 1000 = 3$

b **i** $\log_4 64$

$\qquad 4^3 = 64 \quad$ so $\log_4 64 = 3$

ii $\log_2 64$

$\qquad 2^6 = 64 \quad$ so $\log_2 64 = 6$

o Generally $\log_a a = 1$
              $\log_a 1 = 0$
   for all $a > 0$.

Since $a^1 = a$ for all $a > 0$.
Since $a^0 = 1$ for all $a > 0$.

EXAMPLE 3

Find the value of

a $\log_7 7$ b $\log_7 1$

a $7^1 = 7$ b $7^0 = 1$
   so $\log_7 7 = 1$ so $\log_7 1 = 0$

Your calculator can work with logarithms to the base 10.
You should be able to do calculations involving logarithms using
your calculator.

Your calculator can also work with
logarithms to the base e, known
as natural logarithms (ln). These
are covered in C3.

EXAMPLE 4

Work out the values of the following on your calculator,
giving the answers correct to three significant figures.

a $\log_{10} 5$ b $\log_{10} 0.05$ c $\log_{10} \pi$

a $\log_{10} 5 = 0.699$

b $\log_{10} 0.05 = -1.30$

c $\log_{10} \pi = 0.497$

Use the [log] key.

$10^{0.699...} = 5$

C2

You can take logarithms to find missing powers when working in
base 10 using your calculator.

EXAMPLE 5

Find the value of x such that $10^x = 2900$

Write in logarithmic form: $\log_{10} 2900 = x$

Use your calculator: $x = 3.46$ to 3 s.f.

Exercise 11.2

1 Write each of the following expressions in logarithmic form.

   a $2^9 = 512$ b $3^7 = 2187$

   c $10^5 = 100\,000$ d $(0.5)^4 = 0.0625$

   e $(5)^{-2} = 0.04$ f $20^1 = 20$

2 Work out the value of each logarithm.

    a $\log_{10} 1000$ **b** $\log_2 64$

    c $\log_3 81$ **d** $\log_5 \left(\frac{1}{5}\right)$

    e $\log_6 216$ **f** $\log_4 \left(\frac{1}{64}\right)$

3 Use your calculator to find these values.
   Write your answers to three significant figures.

    a $\log_{10} 8$ **b** $\log_{10} 27$

    c $\log_{10} 515$ **d** $\log_{10} 3756$

    e $\log_{10} \left(\frac{1}{2}\right)$ **f** $\log_{10} \sqrt{5}$

    g $\log_{10} \frac{(\sqrt{3})}{2}$ **h** $\log_{10} 0.0001$

    i $\log_{10} \frac{1}{(\sqrt{2})}$ **j** $\log_{10} \frac{9}{11}$

4 Rewrite each of the following in index form, $a^x = n$, and
   then find the value of n.
   Give your answers correct to three significant figures
   where appropriate.

    a $\log_2 n = 8$ **b** $\log_2 n = 4$
    c $\log_3 n = 3$ **d** $\log_3 n = 1$
    e $\log_{10} n = -1$ **f** $\log_{10} n = -2$
    g $\log_4 n = 0.5$ **h** $\log_5 n = -3$
    i $\log_7 n = 0.25$ **j** $\log_2 n = -9$

5 Find the base a of each of the given logarithms.

    a $\log_a 4 = 2$ **b** $\log_a 27 = 3$
    c $\log_a 1000 = 3$ **d** $\log_a 64 = 6$
    e $\log_a 64 = 2$ **f** $\log_a 243 = 5$
    g $\log_a 81 = 4$ **h** $\log_a 10 = 1$

INVESTIGATIONS

6 **a** Choose a number from the box for the base of
each of these logarithms.

$\log_{...} 16 = 2$

$\log_{...} 64 = 3$

$\log_{...} 25 = 2$

$\log_{...} 1 = 0$

$\log_{...} \frac{1}{9} = -2$

$\log_{...} 100 = 2$

$\log_{...} \frac{1}{2} = -1$

4	0
5	6
1	8
3	9
10	16
2	

b For each number not used in part **a** write a new
logarithmic expression which uses this number
as the base.

7 Calculations are simple if log equations have integer
solutions.

For example, if you are given $\log \frac{1}{25}$ then choose
the base 5 to give the integer solution –2.

$\log_5 \frac{1}{25} = -2$

Choose bases for the following logarithms so that
their solutions have integer values.

a $\log \frac{1}{16}$

b $\log 125$

c $\log \frac{1}{81}$

d $\log 64$

8 **a** Use the mathematical symbols +, –, ×, ÷ and = to
make each logarithmic equation true.

  i $\log_{10} 10 \;\square\; \log_{10} 100 \;\square\; \log_{10} 1000$

  ii $\log_{10} 5 \;\square\; \log_{10} 3 \;\square\; \log_{10} 15$

  iii $\log_{10} 1000 \;\square\; \log_{10} 100 \;\square\; \log_{10} 10$

  iv $\log_{10} 8 \;\square\; \log_{10} 2 \;\square\; \log_{10} 4$

Hence deduce the value, without using a calculator, of

b $\log_{10} 20 + \log_{10} 5$

c $\log_{10} 20 - \log_{10} 2$

C2

If $p = \log_a x$ and $q = \log_a y$
then $a^p = x$ and $a^q = y$

$p = \log_a x$ $q = \log_a y$
$a^p = x$ $a^q = y$

From the laws of indices it follows that
$xy = a^p \times a^q$
$ = a^{(p+q)}$
and so $\log_a(xy) = p + q$

Hence the general rule

   o $\log_a(xy) = \log_a x + \log_a y$

You can use this rule to write the sum of two logarithms of the same base as a single logarithm.

EXAMPLE 1

Write $\log_2 4 + \log_2 3$ as a single logarithm.

Use the law for addition of logarithms:

$\log_2 4 + \log_2 3 = \log_2(4 \times 3)$
$ = \log_2 12$

Again let $p = \log_a x$ and $q = \log_a y$
so that $a^p = x$ and $a^q = y$

From the laws of indices it follows that
$\dfrac{x}{y} = \dfrac{a^p}{a^q}$
$\phantom{\dfrac{x}{y}} = a^{(p-q)}$
and so $\log_a\left(\dfrac{x}{y}\right) = p - q$

Hence the general rule

   o $\log_a\left(\dfrac{x}{y}\right) = \log_a x - \log_a y$

You can use this rule to rewrite logarithms in a required form.

C2

EXAMPLE 2

Write each logarithm as the difference between two logarithms.

a $\log_5 \left(\dfrac{7}{2}\right)$ **b** $\log_3 \left(\dfrac{4}{3}\right)$

Use the law for subtracting logarithms in reverse in each case:

a $\log_5 \left(\dfrac{7}{2}\right) = \log_5 7 - \log_5 2$

b $\log_3 \left(\dfrac{4}{3}\right) = \log_3 4 - \log_3 3$

$\qquad\qquad = \log_3 4 - 1$ $\quad \log_a a = 1$ for all $a > 0$.

Now consider $p = \log_a x$
so that $a^p = x$

The laws of indices imply that
$x^n = a^{pn}$

and so $\log_a (x^n) = pn$

Hence the general rule

○ $\log_a (x^n) = n \log_a x$

A special case of this rule is $\log_a \left(\dfrac{1}{p}\right)$

Since $\dfrac{1}{p} = p^{-1}$

it follows that $\log_a \left(\dfrac{1}{p}\right) = \log_a p^{-1}$

Apply the rule $\log_a (x^n) = n \log_a x$:

$\qquad\qquad \log_a \left(\dfrac{1}{p}\right) = -1 \times \log_a p$

○ $\log_a \left(\dfrac{1}{x}\right) = -\log_a x$

You can use the rules of logarithms to simplify expressions.

C2

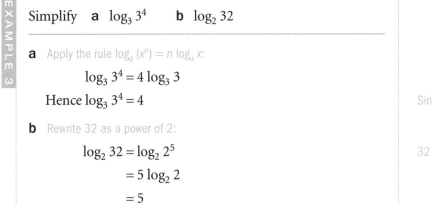

EXAMPLE 3

Simplify   **a** $\log_3 3^4$ **b** $\log_2 32$

a Apply the rule $\log_a (x^n) = n \log_a x$:

$$\log_3 3^4 = 4 \log_3 3$$

Hence $\log_3 3^4 = 4$ *Since $\log_3 3 = 1$*

b Rewrite 32 as a power of 2:

$$\log_2 32 = \log_2 2^5$$ *$32 = 2^5$*

$$= 5 \log_2 2$$

$$= 5$$

You can combine the rules of logarithms to simplify more complicated expressions.

EXAMPLE 4

Simplify   **a** $4 \log_2 3 + 2 \log_2 5$

   b $\log_3 45 - \log_3 5$

a Use the rule $\log_a (x^n) = n \log_a x$:

$$4 \log_2 3 + 2 \log_2 5 = \log_2 3^4 + \log_2 5^2$$

$$= \log_2 (3^4 \times 5^2)$$ *$\log_a x + \log_a y = \log_a xy$*

$$= \log_2 (81 \times 25)$$

$$= \log_2 2025$$

b Use the rule $\log_a \left(\dfrac{x}{y}\right) = \log_a x - \log_a y$:

$$\log_3 45 - \log_3 5 = \log_3 \left(\frac{45}{5}\right)$$

$$= \log_3 9$$

$$= \log_3 3^2$$

$$= 2 \log_3 3$$ *$\log_a (x^n) = n \log_a x$*

$$= 2$$ *Since $\log_3 3 = 1$*

You can also rewrite a single logarithm as a sum or difference of several logarithms.

C2

EXAMPLE 5

Express each of the following in terms of log a, log b and log c.

a $\log (ab^3c^2)$ **b** $\log \left(\dfrac{2ab^2}{c}\right)$ **c** $2\log \left(\dfrac{a\sqrt{3}}{b\sqrt{c}}\right)$

The base of the logarithm does not always need to be defined. In this case it is assumed that all of the logs are to the same base.

---

a $\log ab^3c^2 = \log a + \log b^3 + \log c^2$
$\qquad\qquad = \log a + 3\log b + 2\log c$

Separate the logarithms and then simplify each logarithm individually.

b $\log \left(\dfrac{2ab^2}{c}\right) = \log 2ab^2 - \log c$
$\qquad\qquad\quad = \log 2 + \log a + \log b^2 - \log c$
$\qquad\qquad\quad = \log 2 + \log a + 2\log b - \log c$

c $2\log \left(\dfrac{a\sqrt{3}}{b\sqrt{c}}\right) = \log \left(\dfrac{a\sqrt{3}}{b\sqrt{c}}\right)^2$

Writing down each step of your working will help you to keep track of multi-step calculations.

$\qquad\qquad\quad = \log \left(\dfrac{3a^2}{b^2c}\right)$

$\qquad\qquad\quad = \log 3a^2 - \log b^2c$
$\qquad\qquad\quad = \log 3 + \log a^2 - (\log b^2 + \log c)$
$\qquad\qquad\quad = \log 3 + 2\log a - 2\log b - \log c$

C2

Exercise 11.3

1 Simplify these expressions.

a $\log_2 8$ **b** $\log_5 125$

c $\log_4 16$ **d** $\log_3 81$

e $\log_2 512$ **f** $\log_6 216$

g $\log_4 256$ **h** $\log_{10} 1000000$

2 Write each expression as a simplified single logarithm or an integer.

a $\log_2 5 + \log_2 7$ **b** $\log_3 4 - \log_3 \left(\dfrac{1}{2}\right)$

c $\log_3 10 - \log_3 5 + \log_3 2$ **d** $2\log_2 4 - \log_2 8$

e $3\log_5 4 + 2\log_5 3$ **f** $2\log_{20} 5 - 2\log_{20} \left(\dfrac{1}{4}\right)$

g $\log_2 \left(\dfrac{5}{2}\right) + \log_2 \left(\dfrac{4}{3}\right) - \log_2 \left(\dfrac{5}{3}\right)$ **h** $\dfrac{1}{2}\log_3 \left(\dfrac{4}{9}\right) - 2\log_3 \left(\dfrac{9}{4}\right)$

i $2\log_5 1 + \log_5 2$ **j** $\dfrac{1}{3}\log_4 \left(\dfrac{8}{27}\right) + \dfrac{1}{2}\log_4 \left(\dfrac{4}{9}\right)$

3 Simplify and write the final answer as a single logarithm.
You may assume that the logarithms are of the same base.

a $2 \log 5 + 2 \log 3$

b $3 \log 3 - 2 \log 3$

c $2 \log 4 + \log 3 - \log 12$

d $3 \log 2 - 2 \log 3 + \log 18$

e $4 \log 3 + 2 \log 2 - 2 \log 6$

f $2 \log 5 - \log 15 + 2 \log 3$

g $\log 20 - 2 \log 2 - 3 \log 2$

h $\log 2\sqrt{3} + 2 \log 2 - 3 \log \sqrt{3}$

i $3 \log 5 - \log 3 - 2 \log \sqrt{5}$

j $\frac{1}{2} \log 9 + 2 \log 9 - \frac{1}{2} \log 81$

k $\frac{2}{3} \log 27 - \frac{1}{4} \log 81$

l $\frac{3}{4} \log 16 + \frac{1}{3} \log 27 - \frac{1}{2} \log 144$

4 Write in terms of $\log a$, $\log b$ and $\log c$.
You may assume that the logarithms are written to the same base.

a $\log a^2 b$

b $\log\left(\dfrac{a}{b}\right)$

c $2 \log a\sqrt{c}$

d $\frac{1}{2} \log ab^2$

e $2 \log\left(\dfrac{c}{a}\right)$

f $\log a\sqrt{b}$

g $\log\left(\dfrac{a^3 b^2}{\sqrt{c}}\right)$

h $\log \sqrt{abc}$

i $\log\left(\dfrac{\sqrt[3]{a}}{b}\right)$

j $2 \log\left(\dfrac{a\sqrt{b}}{\sqrt{c}}\right)$

5 Given that $\log 2 = 0.301$ and $\log 3 = 0.477$, and without using a calculator, find the value of each of the following.

a $\log 12$ **b** $\log 18$

c $\log 36$ **d** $\log 1.5$

INVESTIGATIONS

6 Assuming the following logarithms are of the same base, which simplify to give $\log 24$?

$3 \log 2 + \log 3$
$24 \log 1$
$\log 2 + \log 6 + \log 2$
$\log 2 + \log 12$
$\log 125 - \log 5 - \log 1$
$\log 8 - \log 3$
$\log 32 - \log 8$
$4 \log 2 + \log 3 - \log 2$

7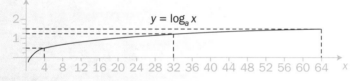

Use the information in the graph to deduce the value of a.

8 **a** Copy and complete the table.

x	$\dfrac{1}{100}$	$\dfrac{1}{10}$	1	10	100
$\log_{10} x$					

b Hence sketch the graph of $y = \log_{10} x$

c Sketch the graph of $y = 10^x$ on the same axes.

Change of base

You can express a logarithm of x to the base a as a logarithm to a different base, b.

Let $y = \log_a x$
so that $x = a^y$

Take $\log_b$ on both sides: $\quad \log_b x = \log_b a^y$

$$\log_b x = y \log_b a$$

$$y = \frac{\log_b x}{\log_b a}$$

giving the general result

$$\log_a x = \frac{\log_b x}{\log_b a}$$

Now substitute $x = b$: $\quad \log_a b = \dfrac{\log_b b}{\log_b a}$

which gives the special case of this rule

$$\log_a b = \frac{1}{\log_b a}$$

Since $\log_b b = 1$.

You can use these rules to convert an expression to a logarithm with base 10. This will then allow you to evaluate the expression using your calculator.

EXAMPLE 1

Find the values of   **a** $\log_2 5$ **b** $\log_3 4$

Give your answers to three significant figures.

Use the change of base rule to express each logarithm in base 10:

a $\log_2 5$

$$\log_2 5 = \frac{\log_{10} 5}{\log_{10} 2}$$

$$= \frac{0.69897}{0.30103}$$

$$= 2.3219$$

b $\log_3 4$

$$\log_3 4 = \frac{\log_{10} 4}{\log_{10} 3}$$

$$= \frac{0.60206}{0.47712}$$

$$= 1.2618$$

Hence $\log_2 5 = 2.32$ and $\log_3 4 = 1.26$ to 3 s.f.

Solving exponential equations

You can use logarithms to solve equations of the form $a^x = n$

EXAMPLE 2

Find the value of x when $2^x = 3$

Give your answer correct to three significant figures.

Take logarithms to base 10 on both sides of the equation:

$$\log_{10} 2^x = \log_{10} 3$$

Rewrite using $\log a^n = n \log a$:

$$x \log_{10} 2 = \log_{10} 3$$

Rearrange:
$$x = \frac{\log_{10} 3}{\log_{10} 2}$$

$$x = \frac{0.47712\ldots}{0.30103}$$

$$x = 1.58 \quad \text{correct to 3 s.f.}$$

> Using base 10 allows you to input the values into your calculator.

> $\log_{10} 3$ and $\log_{10} 2$ are constants so you can divide one by the other.

You can use logarithms to solve more complicated problems.

EXAMPLE 3

Solve the equation $3^{x+1} = 2^{x-1}$

Give the value of x correct to three significant figures.

$$3^{x+1} = 2^{x-1}$$

Take logarithms of both sides to base 10:
$$\log_{10} 3^{x+1} = \log_{10} 2^{x-1}$$

Rewrite using $\log a^n = n \log a$:
$$(x + 1) \log_{10} 3 = (x - 1) \log_{10} 2$$

Evaluate the logarithms: $(x + 1)0.47712\ldots = (x - 1)0.30103\ldots$

Expand and rearrange: $0.47712x + 0.47712 = 0.30103x - 0.30103$

Simplify: $$0.17609x = -0.77815$$

$$x = -\frac{0.77815}{0.17609}$$

Hence $$x = -4.42 \text{ (to 3 s.f.)}$$

> Do not round during your working. Write down enough decimal places so that you can round to 3 s.f in your final answer.

C2

You can use the fact that $a^{2x} = (a^x)^2$ to solve equations involving a^{2x}.

EXAMPLE 4

Find the values of x which satisfy each equation.

a $2^{2x} + 4(2^x) - 5 = 0$

b $3^{2x} - 5(3^x) + 6 = 0$

Give your answers to three significant figures.

a
$$2^{2x} + 4(2^x) - 5 = 0$$

Rewrite the equation: $(2^x)^2 + 4(2^x) - 5 = 0$ This is a quadratic in 2^x.

Substitute $y = 2^x$: $y^2 + 4y - 5 = 0$

Factorise: $(y - 1)(y + 5) = 0$

Either $y - 1 = 0$ or $y + 5 = 0$

hence $y = 1$ or $y = -5$

and so $2^x = 1$ or $2^x = -5$

Since $a^0 = 1$ for all values of a the only possible solution is $x = 0$.

This gives no solution since no value of x could give a negative answer.

Hence the solution is $x = 0$

b
$$3^{2x} - 5(3^x) + 6 = 0$$

Rewrite the equation: $(3^x)^2 - 5(3^x) + 6 = 0$ $3^{2x} = (3^x)^2$

Substitute $y = 3^x$: $y^2 - 5y + 6 = 0$

Factorise: $(y - 2)(y - 3) = 0$

Either $y - 2 = 0$ or $y - 3 = 0$
hence $y = 2$ or $y = 3$

so $3^x = 2$ (1)   or $3^x = 3$ (2)

Take logarithms to base 10 in both cases:

(1) gives $\log_{10} 3^x = \log_{10} 2$ (2) gives $\log_{10} 3^x = \log_{10} 3$

$x \log_{10} 3 = \log_{10} 2$ $x \log_{10} 3 = \log_{10} 3$

$x = \dfrac{\log_{10} 2}{\log_{10} 3}$ $x = \dfrac{\log_{10} 3}{\log_{10} 3}$

$x = 1$

You could have inferred this directly from the general result $a^1 = a$ for all a.

$x = \dfrac{0.30103}{0.47712}$

$x = 0.6309$

Hence the solutions are $x = 0.631$ or $x = 1$ (correct to 3 s.f.)

You can use the change of base rule to solve an equation involving more than one logarithmic base.

EXAMPLE 5

Solve the equation $\log_3 x + 8 \log_x 3 = 6$

$$\log_3 x + 8 \log_x 3 = 6$$

Rewrite using $\log_a b = \dfrac{1}{\log_b a}$: $\quad \log_3 x + \dfrac{8}{\log_3 x} = 6$

$\qquad\qquad\qquad\qquad\qquad\qquad\qquad\qquad\quad \log_x 3 = \dfrac{1}{\log_3 x}$

Let $y = \log_3 x$:

$$y + \frac{8}{y} = 6$$
$$y^2 + 8 = 6y$$
$$y^2 - 6y + 8 = 0$$

Factorise:
$$(y - 4)(y - 2) = 0$$

Hence $\qquad\qquad y = 4 \qquad$ or $\qquad y = 2$

so $\qquad\qquad \log_3 x = 4 \qquad$ or $\quad \log_3 x = 2$

$\qquad\qquad\qquad\quad x = 3^4 \qquad$ or $\qquad x = 3^2$

$\qquad\qquad\qquad\quad x = 81 \qquad$ or $\qquad x = 9$

C2

EXAMPLE 6

Solve for x the equation $\log_4 x^2 + 6 \log_x 4 = 8$

$$\log_4 x^2 + 6 \log_x 4 = 8$$

Rewrite: $\quad 2 \log_4 x + 6 \log_x 4 = 8$

Let $y = \log_4 x$:

$$2y + \frac{6}{y} = 8$$
$$2y^2 + 6 = 8y$$
$$2y^2 - 8y + 6 = 0$$

$\qquad\qquad\qquad\qquad\qquad\qquad\qquad \log_x 4 = \dfrac{1}{\log_4 x}$

Factorise:
$$(2y - 2)(y - 3) = 0$$

Hence $\quad y = 1 \qquad$ or $\qquad y = 3$

so $\quad \log_4 x = 1 \qquad$ or $\quad \log_4 x = 3$

$\qquad\qquad x = 4^1 \qquad$ or $\qquad x = 4^3$

$\qquad\qquad x = 4 \qquad$ or $\qquad x = 64$

Exercise 11.4

Write all your answers correct to three significant figures where appropriate.

1 Use the change of base rule to evaluate these expressions.

a $\log_2 7$

b $\log_3 2$

c $\log_5 4$

d $\log_2 20$

e $\log_4 712$

f $\log_2 0.3$

g $\log_5 0.01$

h $\log_{12}\left(\dfrac{9}{100}\right)$

i $\log_{0.5} 0.2$

j $\log_{100} 2$

2 Find the value of x by taking $\log_{10}$.

a $3^x = 4$ b $2^x = 9$ c $5^x = 2$ d $4^x = 1$

e $9^x = 38$ f $2^{2x} = 7$ g $3^{2x} = 14$ h $2^{3x} = 79$

i $7^{4x} = 512$ j $12^x = \dfrac{1}{5}$

3 Find the value of x by taking $\log_{10}$.

a $2^{x+1} = 5$

b $2^{x-1} = 19$

c $3^{x+2} = 53$

d $3^{2x-1} = 107$

e $4^{2x+3} = 715$

f $2^{x+1} = 3^{2x}$

g $3^{2x-1} = 2^x$

h $7^{2x} = 4^{x+4}$

i $5^{3x-1} = 2^{x+3}$

j $3^{5x+4} = 4^{2x-3}$

4 Find the value of x which satisfies each equation.

a $2^x(2^x - 1) = 0$

b $3^{2x} - 9(3^x) = 0$

c $2^{2x} - 2(2^x) + 1 = 0$

d $3^{2x} - 4(3^x) + 4 = 0$

e $2^{2x} - 6(2^x) + 9 = 0$

f $5^{2x} - 8(5^x) + 16 = 0$

g $2(7^x) - 7^{2x} = 1$

h $4(3^{2x}) - 4(3^x) + 1 = 0$

5 Find the values of x which satisfies each equation.

a $2^{2x} - 2^{x+1} + 1 = 0$

b $3^{2x} - 3^x = 0$

c $2^{2x} - 5(2^x) + 6 = 0$

d $2(3^{2x}) - 9(3^x) + 4 = 0$

e $6(5^{2x}) - 11(5^x) - 10 = 0$

f $2^{2x+1} - 13(2^x) + 20 = 0$

g $3^{2x+2} - 4(3^{x+2}) + 35 = 0$

h $5(2^{2x+2}) - 23(2^x) + 6 = 0$

i $2^{2x+1} = 13(2^x) - 20$

j $3^{2x+1} + 4(3^x) = 4$

6 Find the value of x.

  a $\log_{10} x = 0.321$ **b** $\log_{10} x = 2.175$

  c $\log_2 x = 1.5$ **d** $\log_3 x = 2.78$

  e $\log_5 x = 1.72$ **f** $\log_7 x = 2.83$

  g $\log_4 x^2 = 0.923$ **h** $\log_5 x^3 = 3.47$

  i $\log_2 (x + 2) = 1.76$ **j** $\log_3 (x - 1) = 3.24$

7 Solve for x.

  a $\log_2 x + \log_3 x = 1$ **b** $\log_5 x + \log_2 x = 1.2$

  c $2 \log_5 x - \log_7 x = 2.34$ **d** $\log_8 x - \log_9 x = 1$

  e $\log_2 x^2 + \log_4 x = 1.5$ **f** $\log_5 (x + 1) + \log_4 (x + 1) = 3$

  g $(\log_7 x)^2 = 17$

8 **a** If $\log_4 a = b$ show that $2b \log_a 2 = 1$

  b Find the possible value of x if $2 \log_x 3 = \log_3 x$

9 **a** Solve the simultaneous equations, where the logarithms are written in base 10.
  $$\log x + \log y = 3$$
  $$\log x - \log y = 2$$

  b Show that $\dfrac{1}{\log_2 a^2} = \log_a \sqrt{2}$

  c Find the possible values of a^x which satisfy the equation
  $$a^x + 1 = 2a^{-x}$$
  and deduce that the only value of x which is possible is $x = 0$.

INVESTIGATION

10 You want to solve the equation below.
   The beginning of two methods are shown:

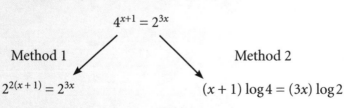

$$4^{x+1} = 2^{3x}$$

Method 1   Method 2

$2^{2(x+1)} = 2^{3x}$ $(x + 1) \log 4 = (3x) \log 2$

  a **i** Use both methods to find x.

    ii Which method do you prefer? Justify your answer.

  b Which method would you use to solve
    $32^{x+4} = 2^{3x}$ and why?

Review 11

Give your answers correct to three significant figures where appropriate.

1 Use your calculator to evaluate the following.

  a 5^7 b $(-2)^5$ c 8^{-3}

  d $(0.2)^5$ e $\left(\dfrac{4}{3}\right)^{-4}$ f $(3)^{0.4}$

  g $(5.2)^{1.6}$ h 7^{-4} i $(0.3)^{0.3}$

2 Sketch the graphs of these equations.

  a $y = 4^x$, taking values of x in the range -2 to $+2$

  b $y = \left(\dfrac{1}{3}\right)^x$, for values of x from -3 to $+3$

  c $y = 5^{-x}$, for values of x in the range -2 to $+2$

  d $y = (0.7)^{-x}$, in the interval $-5 \leqslant x \leqslant 5$

3 Without using your calculator, evaluate the following. Show your working.

  a $\log_2 128$ b $\log_3 27$ c $\log_4 64$

  d $\log_2 \left(\dfrac{1}{4}\right)$ e $\log_3 \left(\dfrac{1}{9}\right)$ f $\log_5 625$

4 Find the base a of each logarithm.

  a $\log_a 8 = 3$ b $\log_a 81 = 4$

  c $\log_a 64 = 6$ d $\log_a \left(\dfrac{1}{4}\right) = -2$

5 Rewrite in index form and find the value of n.

  a $\log_3 n = 2$ b $\log_5 n = 3$

  c $\log_2 n = 8$ d $\log_7 n = 3$

6 Use logarithms to find the value of x.

  a $2^x = 7$ b $3^x = 15$

  c $5^x = 100$ d $12^x = 7$

  e $2^{4x} = 1.5$ f $5^{3x} = 0.2$

  g $6^{x+1} = 3$ h $10^{2x} = 5$

7 Find the value of x which satisfies each equation.

a $\quad 7(4^x) = 3(5^x)$

b $\quad 3(2^x) = 4(3^x)$

c $\quad 2(5^{2x}) = 3(4^{2x})$

d $\quad 2^{2x+1} = 3^x$

e $\quad 3^{x-1} = 5^x$

f $\quad 5^{2x} = 3^{2x+1}$

8 Solve

a $\quad 3^x = 5$, giving your answer to three significant figures

b $\quad \log_3 (x+1) - \log_3 x = \log_3 5$

9 Find, giving your answer to three significant figures where appropriate, the value of x for which

a $\quad 2^x = 5$

b $\quad \log_3 (2x - 1) - \log_3 x = 2$

10 Find the values of x which satisfy each equation.

a $\quad 5^{2x} - 11(5^x) + 15 = 0$

b $\quad 3(7^{2x}) - 7(7^x) + 2 = 0$

c $\quad 4(2^{2x}) + 3(2^x) - 1 = 0$

d $\quad 3^x - 5 + 4(3^{-x}) = 0$

11 a Write in terms of $\log a$, $\log b$ and $\log c$.
You may assume that the logarithms are to the same base

i $\quad \log (b\sqrt{c})$

ii $\quad \log \left(\dfrac{1}{ab}\right)$

iii $\quad 2 \log \left(\dfrac{a}{b}\right)$

b Write as a single logarithm of the form $\log N$.

i $\quad \log a + \log b - \log c$

ii $\quad 2 \log a - \dfrac{1}{2} \log c$

iii $\quad \log a - 3 \log b + 2 \log c$

12 Given that $\log 5 = 0.69897$ and $\log 2 = 0.30103$ find, without using your calculator, the value of

a $\quad \log 20$

b $\quad \log 2.5$

c $\quad \log 62.5$

C2

11 Exit

Summary

Refer to

- The graph of an exponential function of the form $f(x) = a^x$ looks like

  11.1

- $x = a^y \Leftrightarrow y = \log_a x$

  11.2

- $\log_a a = 1$
  $\log_a 1 = 0$ for all $a > 0$

  11.2

- The laws of logarithms are

  $$\log_a (xy) = \log_a x + \log_a y$$

  $$\log_a \left(\frac{x}{y}\right) = \log_a x - \log_a y$$

  $$\log_a (x^n) = n \log_a x$$

  and the special case $\log_a \left(\frac{1}{p}\right) = -\log_a p$

  11.3

- The change of base rule is

  $$\log_a b = \frac{\log_c b}{\log_c a}$$

  11.4

- You can use your calculator to solve equations involving indices by taking logarithms.

  11.4

$y = a^x$

$(0, 1)$

C2

Links

Logarithms have many applications in the real world. They are used to design certain measurement scales. Many of the uses of logarithms have been programmed into machines and so aren't immediately obvious. Base 2 is used in information theory and computing and base 10 is used by chemists to measure the acidity, or pH, of a liquid.

The exponential function $y = a^x$ can be used to model many real-life situations such as population growth. The fact that $y = a^x$ is equivalent to $\log_a y = x$ means that logs are equally important.

12 Trigonometry

This chapter will show you how to

- apply trigonometric ratios and rules to solving problems
- evaluate arc length and find areas of sectors and segments of circles
- understand and use radian measures
- solve trigonometric equations and sketch trigonometric graphs
- transform trigonometric graphs
- use trigonometric identities.

Before you start

You should know how to:

1 Solve quadratic equations.

e.g. Solve $x^2 + 3x - 2 = 0$

Use $x = \dfrac{-b \pm \sqrt{(b^2 - 4ac)}}{2a}$:

$x = \dfrac{-3 \pm \sqrt{(9 + 8)}}{2}$

$x = \dfrac{-3 \pm \sqrt{17}}{2} = \dfrac{-3 \pm 4.123}{2}$

$x = -3.56$ or 0.56

2 Understand the bearing of an object from a fixed point.

e.g. From a fixed point, A, a car, B, is seen on a bearing of $215°$.
Draw a diagram to show this.

3 Change the subject of an equation.

e.g. Make x the subject of the equation

$3x - a = 4ax - 5$

Rearrange: $3x - 4ax = a - 5$

Factorise: $x(3 - 4a) = a - 5$

Divide both sides by $(3 - 4a)$:

$x = \dfrac{a - 5}{3 - 4a}$

Check in:

1 Solve these quadratic equations (giving your answers correct to one decimal place where appropriate).

a $x^2 - 2x - 3 = 0$
b $x^2 + x - 3 = 0$
c $2x^2 - x - 1 = 0$
d $x^2 + 4x + 1 = 0$
e $3x^2 + 5x + 1 = 0$

2 Draw diagrams to show the position of point B given its bearing from a fixed point A.

a $075°$
b $300°$
c $130°$
d $042°$
e $205°$
f $090°$

3 Rewrite each equation with x as the subject.

a $a(x + 1) = b(x + 2)$
b $\dfrac{4x}{3} = \dfrac{5a}{6}$
c $\dfrac{2x + a}{2} = \dfrac{3x + b}{2}$
d $ax - 2 = bx + 3$

The sine rule

You can use the sine rule to find angles and sides in triangles which are not right-angled.

Let the vertical height of triangle ABC be h

in $\triangle ABD$ $\sin A = \dfrac{h}{c}$ in $\triangle BCD$ $\sin C = \dfrac{h}{a}$

$h = c \sin A$ $h = a \sin C$

Equate: $a \sin C = c \sin A$

Rearrange: $\dfrac{a}{\sin A} = \dfrac{c}{\sin C}$

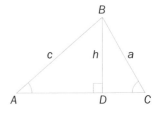

○ The sine rule states that for triangle ABC

$$\frac{a}{\sin A} = \frac{b}{\sin B} = \frac{c}{\sin C} \quad \text{or} \quad \frac{\sin A}{a} = \frac{\sin B}{b} = \frac{\sin C}{c}$$

You can use the sine rule to find the length of a side of when two of the angles and one of the opposite sides are known.

In $\triangle ABC$, angle $A = 35°$, angle $B = 76°$ and side $b = 9\,\text{cm}$. Find the length of side a.

Use the sine rule: $\dfrac{a}{\sin A} = \dfrac{b}{\sin B}$

$\dfrac{a}{\sin 35°} = \dfrac{9}{\sin 76°}$

Rearrange: $a = \dfrac{9 \times \sin 35°}{\sin 76°}$

$a = \dfrac{9 \times 0.5736}{0.9703}$

$a = 5.320$

Hence $a = 5.32\,\text{cm}$ (correct to 3 s.f.)

Drawing a diagram will help you to visualise the problem.

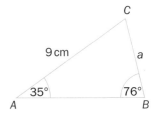

Remember not to round during the working. You can write down rounded numbers, but always use exact figures in your calculations.

You can also use the sine rule to find a missing angle when two of the sides and one of the opposite angles are known.

C2

EXAMPLE 2

In $\triangle ABC$, $a = 11$ cm, $c = 8$ cm and angle $A = 63°$
Find angles C and B.

Use the sine rule $\dfrac{\sin C}{c} = \dfrac{\sin A}{a}$:

$$\frac{\sin C}{8} = \frac{\sin 63°}{11}$$

Rearrange: $\quad \sin C = \dfrac{8 \times \sin 63°}{11}$

$$\text{angle } C = 40.39°$$

Hence $\quad$ angle $C = 40.4°$ (3 s.f.)

Use the angle sum of a triangle to find B:

$$B = 180° - (63° + 40.4°) = 76.6°$$

Hence $C = 40.4°$ and $B = 76.6°$

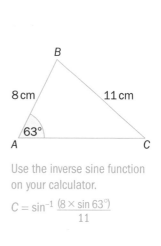

Use the inverse sine function on your calculator.

$C = \sin^{-1} \dfrac{(8 \times \sin 63°)}{11}$

There are sometimes two answers when you find an angle using the sine rule.
This is known as the ambiguous case.

When the angle you are looking for is bigger than the given angle there are two possible solutions.
This is because the information you are given can lead to two different triangles, as in the following example.

This follows since generally

○ $\sin(180° - x) = \sin x$

You will study the graph of $\sin x$ in more detail later in this chapter.

 EXAMPLE 3

In $\triangle ABC$, angle $A = 38°$, $AB = 9$ cm, and $BC = 7$ cm
Find angle C.

Since 7 cm < 9 cm this length could be either BC_1 or BC_2 as shown in the diagram.
Hence there are two possible triangles, ABC_1 or ABC_2.

Use the sine rule in $\triangle ABC$ $\dfrac{\sin C}{c} = \dfrac{\sin A}{a}$:

$$\frac{\sin C}{9} = \frac{\sin 38°}{7}$$

Rearrange: $\quad \sin C = \dfrac{9 \times \sin 38°}{7}$

$$C = 52.3°$$

Alternatively $\quad C = 180° - 52.3° = 127.7°$

Hence the possible solutions are $C = 52.3°$ or $C = 127.7°$

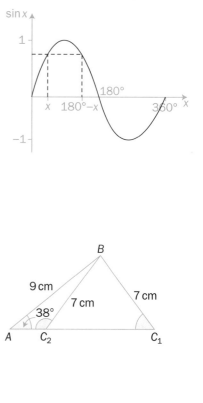

Sometimes you will be asked to find more than one missing angle and side in a given triangle.

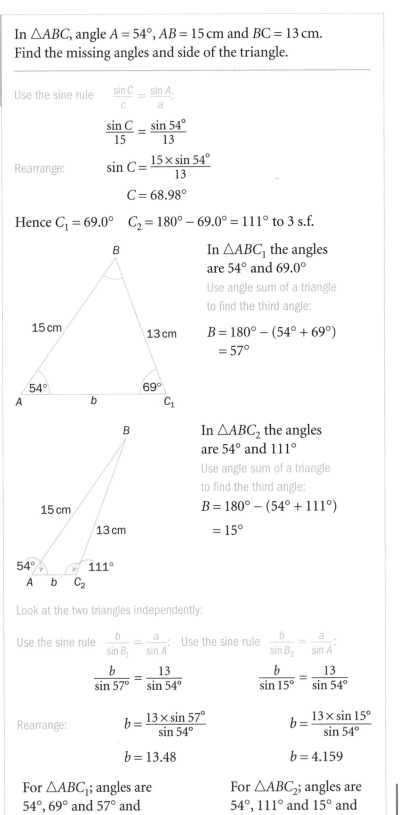

EXAMPLE 4

In $\triangle ABC$, angle $A = 54°$, $AB = 15$ cm and $BC = 13$ cm.
Find the missing angles and side of the triangle.

Use the sine rule $\dfrac{\sin C}{c} = \dfrac{\sin A}{a}$:

$$\frac{\sin C}{15} = \frac{\sin 54°}{13}$$

Rearrange: $\sin C = \dfrac{15 \times \sin 54°}{13}$

$$C = 68.98°$$

Hence $C_1 = 69.0°$ $C_2 = 180° - 69.0° = 111°$ to 3 s.f.

$BC < AB$ means that there will be two possible solutions.

In $\triangle ABC_1$ the angles are $54°$ and $69.0°$

Use angle sum of a triangle to find the third angle:

$$B = 180° - (54° + 69°)$$
$$= 57°$$

In $\triangle ABC_2$ the angles are $54°$ and $111°$

Use angle sum of a triangle to find the third angle:

$$B = 180° - (54° + 111°)$$
$$= 15°$$

Look at the two triangles independently:

Use the sine rule $\dfrac{b}{\sin B_1} = \dfrac{a}{\sin A}$:   Use the sine rule $\dfrac{b}{\sin B_2} = \dfrac{a}{\sin A}$:

$$\frac{b}{\sin 57°} = \frac{13}{\sin 54°} \qquad \frac{b}{\sin 15°} = \frac{13}{\sin 54°}$$

Rearrange: $b = \dfrac{13 \times \sin 57°}{\sin 54°} \qquad b = \dfrac{13 \times \sin 15°}{\sin 54°}$

$$b = 13.48 \qquad\qquad b = 4.159$$

For $\triangle ABC_1$; angles are $54°$, $69°$ and $57°$ and base is 13.5 cm

For $\triangle ABC_2$; angles are $54°$, $111°$ and $15°$ and base is 4.16 cm

Use your diagrams to check your final answers. Do they make sense?

C2

Exercise 12.1

Give angles correct to the nearest 0.1° and sides correct to 3 s.f.

1   Find the requested missing side or angle in each triangle.

   a If $a = 5$ cm, $b = 4$ cm and $A = 49°$ find B.

   b If $a = 6$ cm, $A = 39°$ and $B = 53°$ find b.

   c Find a when $A = 76°$, $B = 38°$ and $b = 5.5$ cm.

   d Find C when $A = 63°$, $c = 14$ cm and $a = 15$ cm.

   e Given that $b = 9.5$ cm and $c = 7.8$ cm and that $B = 54°$ find the size of C.

   f Given that $C = 37°$, $B = 103°$ and $b = 21$ cm find c.

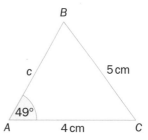

This is the triangle for **1a**.
You should draw diagrams for the other questions.

2   In each triangle find all the missing sides and angles.

   a In triangle ABC, $A = 58°$, $B = 47°$ and $AB = 14$ cm.

   b Triangle RST has angles $R = 105°$ and $S = 27°$ and side $ST = 9.3$ cm.

   c In triangle XYZ, angle $Y = 53°$ and exterior angle $Z = 112°$ The side YZ measures 24 cm.

3   Find the two missing angles and the third side of each triangle PQR giving the two possible sets of solutions.

   a $P = 31°$, $r = 18$ cm, $p = 13$ cm   **b** $P = 70°$, $r = 36$ cm, $p = 34$ cm

   c $P = 25°$, $r = 18$ cm, $p = 15$ cm   **d** $P = 65°$, $r = 8$ cm, $p = 7.5$ cm

4   In the diagram, $AB = 4$ cm, $BC = 5$ cm, angle $BAD = 31°$ and angle $BDC = 81°$ Find the angles x and y.

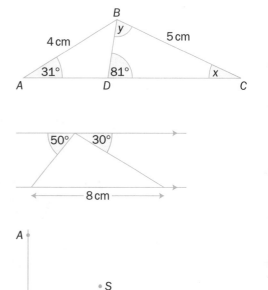

INVESTIGATIONS

5   The diagram shows a triangle bounded by two parallel lines.

   Find the lengths of the two unlabelled sides.

6   The points A and B represent two lighthouses on the coast.

   A ship is at the point S. The ship is on a bearing of 130° from A and 020° from B. Given that the distance from S to A is 5 km, calculate the distance between the two lighthouses.

The cosine rule

You can also use the cosine rule to find missing angles and sides in non-right-angled triangles.

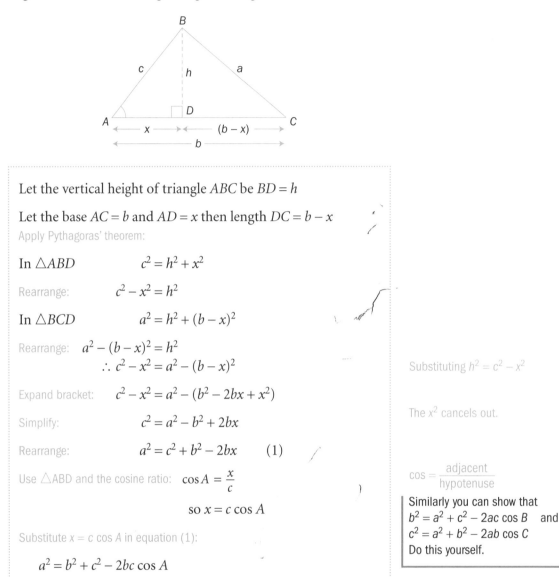

Let the vertical height of triangle ABC be $BD = h$

Let the base $AC = b$ and $AD = x$ then length $DC = b - x$

Apply Pythagoras' theorem:

In $\triangle ABD$ $\qquad c^2 = h^2 + x^2$

Rearrange: $\qquad c^2 - x^2 = h^2$

In $\triangle BCD$ $\qquad a^2 = h^2 + (b - x)^2$

Rearrange: $a^2 - (b - x)^2 = h^2$

$\qquad \therefore c^2 - x^2 = a^2 - (b - x)^2$ — Substituting $h^2 = c^2 - x^2$

Expand bracket: $\quad c^2 - x^2 = a^2 - (b^2 - 2bx + x^2)$

Simplify: $\qquad c^2 = a^2 - b^2 + 2bx$ — The x^2 cancels out.

Rearrange: $\qquad a^2 = c^2 + b^2 - 2bx \qquad (1)$

Use $\triangle ABD$ and the cosine ratio: $\quad \cos A = \dfrac{x}{c}$ — $\cos = \dfrac{\text{adjacent}}{\text{hypotenuse}}$

$\qquad\qquad\qquad so\ x = c \cos A$

Substitute $x = c \cos A$ in equation (1):

$\quad a^2 = b^2 + c^2 - 2bc \cos A$

Similarly you can show that
$b^2 = a^2 + c^2 - 2ac \cos B$ and
$c^2 = a^2 + b^2 - 2ab \cos C$
Do this yourself.

○ The cosine rule states that for triangle ABC

$$a^2 = b^2 + c^2 - 2bc \cos A \quad \text{or} \quad \cos A = \frac{b^2 + c^2 - a^2}{2bc}$$

and $\quad b^2 = a^2 + c^2 - 2ac \cos B \quad \text{or} \quad \cos B = \dfrac{a^2 + c^2 - b^2}{2ac}$

and $\quad c^2 = a^2 + b^2 - 2ab \cos C \quad \text{or} \quad \cos C = \dfrac{a^2 + b^2 - c^2}{2ab}$

You can use the cosine rule to find the length of a side when the two other sides and the included angle are known.

In triangle ABC, $AB = 5$ cm, $AC = 7$ cm and angle $A = 63°$
Find BC.

Write down the three sides a, b and c:
$a = BC$, $b = AC = 7$ cm and $c = AB = 5$ cm

Use the cosine rule $a^2 = b^2 + c^2 - 2bc \cos A$:

$$a^2 = 7^2 + 5^2 - 2(7)(5)(\cos 63°)$$
$$= 49 + 25 - (70\cos 63°)$$
$$= 49 + 25 - (70 \times 0.4539)$$
$$= 49 + 25 - 31.779\ldots$$
$$= 42.22\ldots$$

Take square roots: $a = 6.4977\ldots$

Hence $BC = 6.50$ cm   (to 3 s.f.)

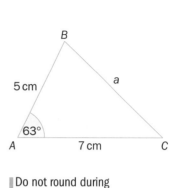

Do not round during your working.

The cosine of an acute angle is positive while the cosine of an obtuse angle is negative.

e.g. $\cos 60° = 0.5$
$\cos (180° - 60°) = \cos 120° = -0.5$

○ $\cos (180° - A) = -\cos A$

You can also use the cosine rule to find a missing angle when you know all three sides of a triangle.

You will study the graphs of the cosine and sine functions in more detail later in this chapter.

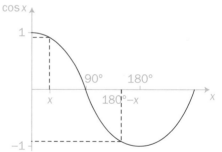

C2

The sides of the $\triangle ABC$ are $a = 4$ cm, $b = 5$ cm and $c = 7$ cm
Find the size of the largest angle in the triangle.

Use the cosine rule $\cos C = \dfrac{a^2 + b^2 - c^2}{2ab}$:

$$\cos C = \frac{4^2 + 5^2 - 7^2}{2 \times 4 \times 5}$$
$$= \frac{16 + 25 - 49}{40}$$
$$= \frac{41 - 49}{40} = -\frac{8}{40} = -0.2$$

so $C = 101.5°$

Hence   angle $C = 102°$ (to 3 s.f.)

The largest angle is opposite the longest side so you are looking for angle C.

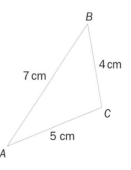

The negative sign tells you that the angle is obtuse.

You can use trigonometry to solve real-life problems.

From an observation point, *C*, the bearings of a radar beacon, *B*, and a watch-tower, *A*, are 310° and 022° respectively. The distance of the observation point from the radar beacon is 3 km and from the watch-tower, 4 km. Find the distance from the radar beacon to the watch-tower.

Draw a clear diagram:

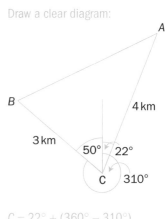

Use the cosine rule $c^2 = a^2 + b^2 - 2ab \cos C$:

$a = 3, b = 4, C = 72°$: $c^2 = 3^2 + 4^2 - (2 \times 3 \times 4 \times \cos 72°)$

$$= 9 + 16 - (24 \times \cos 72°)$$

$$= 9 + 16 - 7.416 = 17.58$$

$$c = \sqrt{17.58} = 4.193$$

Distance from radar beacon to watch-tower = 4.19 km   (to 3 s.f.)

$C = 22° + (360° - 310°)$

Sometimes you will need to use both the sine rule and the cosine rule to solve a problem.

If the triangle is right-angled you can use Pythagoras which is simpler. Always check this first.

C2

Solve the triangle in which $AB = 8.5$ cm, $BC = 9.3$ cm and $AC = 7.5$ cm

'Solve the triangle' means find all of the missing sides and angles.

You know that $a = BC = 9.3$, $b = AC = 7.5$ and $c = AB = 8.5$

Find angle *A* using the cosine rule $\cos A = \dfrac{b^2 + c^2 - a^2}{2bc}$:

A is the largest angle (it is opposite the longest side). Finding the largest angle first is a good approach.

$$\cos A = \frac{7.5^2 + 8.5^2 - 9.3^2}{2 \times 7.5 \times 8.5}$$

$$= \frac{56.25 + 72.25 - 86.49}{127.5} = \frac{42.01}{127.5}$$

so $A = 70.76°$

Find a second angle using the sine rule $\dfrac{\sin B}{b} = \dfrac{\sin A}{a}$:

The sine rule is simpler to use than the cosine rule.

$$\frac{\sin B}{7.5} = \frac{\sin 70.76°}{9.3}$$

Re-arrange: $\sin B = \dfrac{7.5 \sin 70.76°}{9.3}$

$$= \frac{7.081}{9.3} = 0.7614$$

so $B = 49.59°$

Use angle sum of triangle to find *C*:

$$C = 180° - (70.76° + 49.59°) = 59.65°$$

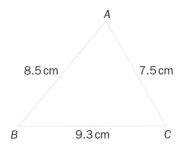

Hence the angles of the triangle are
$A = 70.8°$, $B = 49.6°$ and $C = 59.7°$

Exercise 12.2

Throughout the exercise give your final answers correct to 3 s.f.

1 **a** In triangle ABC, angle $A = 60°$, $AB = 5$ cm and $AC = 8$ cm. Find BC.

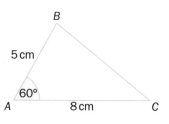

b For $\triangle ABC$, angle $C = 53°$, $AC = 7.8$ cm and $BC = 9.2$ cm. What is the length of side AB?

c In triangle ABC, angle $A = 7°$, $AB = 23$ cm and $AC = 37$ cm. Find the length of side BC.

This is the triangle for 1a. You should draw diagrams for the other questions.

d In $\triangle ABC$, $AB = 5$ cm, $BC = 6$ cm and $AC = 6$ cm. Find the size of angle A.

e For triangle ABC, $a = 12$ cm, $b = 9$ cm and $c = 13$ cm. Find angle B.

f In $\triangle ABC$, $a = 24$ cm, $b = 19$ cm and $c = 21$ cm. What size is the smallest angle in the triangle?

2 In the following triangles use the sine rule, cosine rule or a combination of both to solve the triangles fully.

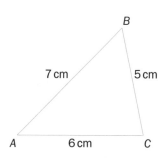

a $a = 5$ cm, $b = 6$ cm and $c = 7$ cm

b $a = 9.4$ cm, $c = 8.2$ cm and angle $B = 54°$

c $AB = 12$ cm, angle $A = 49°$ and angle $B = 76°$

d $AB = 23$ cm, $AC = 25$ cm and angle $A = 102°$

This is the triangle for 2a. Draw diagrams for the other questions.

3 **a** A trapezium, as shown in the diagram, has sides $AB = 9$ cm, $BC = 6$ cm, $CD = 13$ cm and $AD = 5$ cm. The angle $ADC = 82°$.

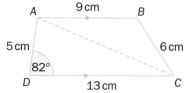

Find **i** the length of the diagonal AC

ii the size of the angle ABC.

b A field is in the shape of a parallelogram and has sides of lengths 350 m and 180 m. The longest diagonal across the field measures 470 m. Find the angles between the sides of the field.

c The edges of a triangular plot of land are of lengths 23 m, 37 m and 45 m. Find the angles at the corners of the plot.

4 From an observation point, A, a marker buoy is on a bearing of 058° at a distance of 450 m and from an observation point, B, the marker buoy is on a bearing of 023° and at a distance of 320 m. A is due west of B.

What is the distance between A and B?

5 A lighthouse and a coastguard station are 15 km apart with the lighthouse due west of the coastguard station. A freighter is sighted by the lighthouse keeper on a bearing of 050°; the coastguard records the position of the freighter as being 12 km from the station.

Draw a diagram to show the two possible positions of the freighter and find the distance between these positions.

12.3 Area of a triangle

○ The area of a triangle is given by

$$\text{area} = \frac{1}{2}\text{base} \times \text{height}$$

The 'height' is the vertical height of the triangle.

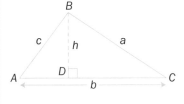

For the triangle ABC, area $= \frac{1}{2}b \times h$ (1)

Use the sine ratio in $\triangle ABD$: $\sin A = \dfrac{h}{c}$

Rearrange: $h = c \sin A$

Substitute $h = c \sin A$ in equation (1):

$$\text{area of triangle} = \frac{1}{2}bc \sin A$$

Now show similar results for included angles B and C by taking the other two vertical heights.

○ The area of a triangle ABC is given by

$$\text{area} = \frac{1}{2}bc \sin A = \frac{1}{2}ab \sin C = \frac{1}{2}ac \sin B$$

EXAMPLE 1

Find the area of triangle ABC if $a = 8\,\text{cm}$, $b = 5\,\text{cm}$ and $C = 38°$

Use the formula   area $= \frac{1}{2}ab \sin C$:

$$\text{area} = \frac{1}{2} \times 8 \times 5 \times \sin 38° = 12.313\ldots$$

Hence the area of the triangle is $12.3\,\text{cm}^2$ (to 3 s.f.)

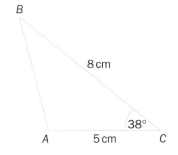

Sometimes you will need to find the included angle before you can calculate the area.

EXAMPLE 2

Find the area of triangle ABC if $a = 9.8\,\text{cm}$, $b = 6.7\,\text{cm}$ and $A = 52°$

Use the sine rule: $\dfrac{\sin B}{6.7} = \dfrac{\sin 52°}{9.8}$

Rearrange: $\sin B = \dfrac{6.7 \times \sin 52°}{9.8}$

$$\sin B = \frac{6.7 \times 0.7880}{9.8} = \frac{5.2796}{9.8} = 0.5387$$

Hence $B = 32.6°$ (to 3 s.f.)

Use angle sum of a triangle: $C = 180° - (52° + 32.6°) = 95.4°$

Now find the area: area $= \frac{1}{2}ab \sin C$

$$= \frac{1}{2} \times 9.8 \times 6.7 \times \sin 95.4°$$

Hence the area of the triangle is $32.7\,\text{cm}^2$ (to 3 s.f.)

Angle C is the required included angle. First find angle B using the sine rule and then find angle C using the angle sum of a triangle.

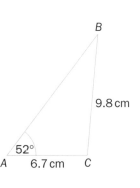

Exercise 12.3

1 Find the area of each triangle ABC.

   a $c = 8.2$ cm, $b = 14$ cm, $A = 102°$

   b $A = 36°$, $B = 78°$, $a = 11.42$ cm, $b = 19$ cm

   c $A = 54°$, $a = 37$ cm, $b = 43$ cm

2 **a** In $\triangle ABC$, $a = 7$ cm, $b = 10$ cm and the area of the
      triangle is 28 cm^2 Find angle C.

   b Triangle ABC has an area of 53 cm^2 $a = 7.5$ cm and $B = 38°$
      Find the length of side c.

   c In triangle ABC, $b = 4$ cm, $a = 9$ cm and the area of the
      triangle is 14 cm^2. Find the size of angle A.

   d In an isosceles triangle two sides are of length 7 cm
      and the area is 20 cm^2
      Find the size of the included angle.

3 **a** In triangle ABC, $AB = \sqrt{2}$ cm and $BC = \sqrt{3}$ cm
      The angle between these two sides is $60°$

      Given that $\cos 60° = 0.5$, show that the area of the
      triangle is $\dfrac{3\sqrt{2}}{4}$ cm^2

   b The sides of triangle ABC are $a = 3x$, $b = (x + 2)$ and $\cos 60° = 0.5$ and $\sin 60° = \dfrac{\sqrt{3}}{2}$
      $c = (2x + 1)$ and angle A is $60°$
      Use the cosine rule to find the value of x and show that
      the triangle is equilateral.
      Show, also, that the area of the triangle is given by $\dfrac{9\sqrt{3}}{4}$

   c In triangle ABC, $a = (x + 1)$, $c = (2x + 1)$ and $B = 30°$ $\cos 30° = \dfrac{\sqrt{3}}{2}$ and $\sin 30° = 0.5$
      If the area of the triangle is 0.75 m^2 what is the value of x?

INVESTIGATION

4 Put these four triangles in order of size of area, from smallest to largest.
  Show your working.

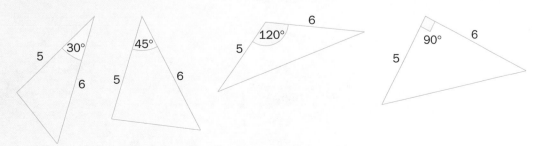

Radian measure

Until now you have measured angles in degrees.
There is, however, another angle measure known as radians.

For a circle of radius r, the angle at the centre,
which subtends a part of the circumference of
length r, is equal to one radian.

As the circumference of the circle is $2\pi \times r$
then the total angle at the centre is 2π radians
which is also $360°$ (a complete circle).

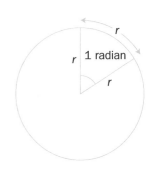

Hence

  ◦ 2π radians $= 360°$ or π radians $= 180°$

Learn this relationship.

From this you can deduce that

  ◦ 1 radian $= \dfrac{180}{\pi}$ degrees   and   1 degree $= \dfrac{\pi}{180}$ radians

You can use this information to convert between degrees
and radians.

EXAMPLE 1

a Change $50°$ to radians.

b Convert 1.5 radians to degrees.

c Change $315°$ to radians leaving your answer in term of π.

d Convert $\dfrac{4\pi}{5}$ radians to degrees.

---

a Use $1° = \dfrac{\pi}{180}$ radians:

$$50° = \dfrac{\pi}{180} \times 50$$

so $50° = 0.873$ radians

b Use 1 radian $= \dfrac{180}{\pi}$:

$$1.5 \text{ radians} = \dfrac{180}{\pi} \times 1.5$$

so 1.5 radians $= 85.9°$

c Use $1° = \dfrac{\pi}{180}$ radians:

$$315° = \dfrac{\pi}{180} \times 315$$

so $315° = \dfrac{7\pi}{4}$ radians

d Use 1 radian $= \dfrac{180}{\pi}$ degrees:

$$\dfrac{4\pi}{5} \text{ radians} = \dfrac{180}{\pi} \times \dfrac{4\pi}{5}$$

so $\dfrac{4\pi}{5}$ radians $= 144°$

Arc length

Consider a circle of radius r with an angle of θ ("theta") radians which is subtended by an arc of length s.

Consider the length of s as a proportion of the circumference:

$$\text{arc length, } s = \frac{\text{angle in sector}}{\text{total angle at centre of circle}} \times \text{circumference}$$

Substitute the values: $s = \dfrac{\theta}{2\pi} \times 2\pi r$

Cancel: $s = \theta r$

A sector is part of a circle bounded by two radii and an arc.

Angle at centre
$360° = 2\pi$ radians

θ is in radians.

The length, s, of an arc which subtends an angle θ radians at the centre of a circle, radius r, is given by

$$s = r\theta$$

C2

EXAMPLE 2

A sector of a circle of radius 3.5 cm contains an angle of 60°. Find the length of the arc to three significant figures.

Remember that θ must be in radians.

Convert 60° to radians: $60° = \dfrac{\pi}{3} = 1.047$ radians

Use the formula arc length $s = r\theta$:

$$s = 3.5 \times 1.047$$
$$= 3.665 \text{ cm}$$

Hence length of arc $= 3.67$ cm (to 3 s.f.)

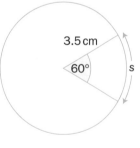

You can apply this formula to real-life problems.

EXAMPLE 3

A logo consists of a circle of radius 12 cm with a sector removed. The angle of the sector is 45°. Find the perimeter of the logo correct to three significant figures.

The reflex angle is
$360° - 45° = 315°$

Use $1° = \dfrac{\pi}{180}$ radians to convert 315° to radians:

$$315° = \frac{\pi}{180} \times 315$$
$$= 5.498 \text{ radians}$$

Use the formula for arc length: $s = r\theta = 12 \times 5.498$
$$= 65.976 \text{ cm}$$

Hence the perimeter of the logo $= 12 + 12 + 65.976$

The perimeter is 90.0 cm (to 3 s.f.)

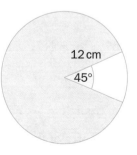

Perimeter of logo
= arc length + two radii lengths

Area of a sector

You can derive a formula for the area of a sector.

Consider the area of the sector as a proportion of the area of the circle:

$$\text{area of sector, } A = \frac{\text{angle in sector}}{\text{total angle at centre of circle}} \times \text{area of circle}$$

Substitute the values: $A = \frac{\theta}{2\pi} \times \pi r^2$

Cancel: $A = \frac{\theta r^2}{2}$

Total angle at centre of circle is $360° = 2\pi$ radians

○ The area of a sector with angle θ radians in a circle radius r is given by $A = \frac{1}{2}r^2\theta$

EXAMPLE 4

Find the area of the minor sector of a circle of radius 12.5 cm when the angle contained in the sector is 40°

Convert 40° to radians: $40° = \frac{\pi \times 40}{180}$ radians

Use the formula for area of a sector:

$$A = \frac{1}{2} \times 12.5^2 \times \frac{\pi \times 40}{180} = 54.54 \text{ cm}^2$$

Area of sector $= 54.5 \text{ cm}^2$ correct to 3 s.f.

You can also find the area of a segment.

A segment is part of a circle bounded by an arc and a chord.

EXAMPLE 5

The chord AB of a circle of radius 7 cm subtends an angle of 54° at the centre. Find the area of the shaded segment.

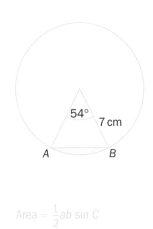

You can see from the diagram that
area of segment = area of sector − area of triangle

Change 54° to radians: $54° = 54 \times \frac{\pi}{180}$ radians

Find area of sector using $A = \frac{1}{2}r^2\theta$:

$$\text{Area of sector} = \frac{1}{2}(7)^2 \times 54 \times \frac{\pi}{180} = 23.091 \text{ cm}^2$$

Find area of triangle using $A = \frac{1}{2}ab \sin C$:

$$\text{Area of triangle} = \frac{1}{2} \times 7 \times 7 \times \sin 54° = 19.821 \text{ cm}^2$$

$\text{Area} = \frac{1}{2}ab \sin C$

Hence the area of the segment
= area of sector − area of triangle
$= 23.091 - 19.821 = 3.27 \text{ cm}^2$ (to 3 s.f.)

C2

Exercise 12.4

1 Convert each angle from degrees to radians.
   Give your answers correct to 3 s.f.

   a 20°   **b** 108°   **c** 525°

2 Convert each angle from radians to degrees.
   Give your answers correct to 3 s.f.

   a 4.75 radians   **b** 5 radians   **c** 3.2 radians

3 Change each angle to radians.
   Give your answer as a multiple of π.

   a 40°   **b** 270°   **c** 25°

   d 450°   **e** 225°   **f** 600°

4 Change each angle from radians to degrees.

   a $\dfrac{\pi}{5}$ **b** 7π **c** $\dfrac{7\pi}{8}$

5 Find these ratios.

   a $\cos\dfrac{\pi}{3}$ **b** $\sin\dfrac{\pi}{2}$ **c** $\tan\dfrac{\pi}{4}$ Your calculator must be in radian mode.

   d $\cos\pi$ **e** $\sin\dfrac{\pi}{6}$ **f** $\tan\dfrac{\pi}{3}$

6 Find the arc length of sectors with radii and angles as follows.
   Give your answers correct to 3 s.f.

   a $r = 16$ cm, $\theta = 1.98$ radians   **b** $r = 4.3$ m, $\theta = 35°$

   c $r = 5.23$ m, $\theta = 300°$ **d** $r = 0.03$ m, $\theta = \dfrac{3\pi}{8}$ radians

7 Find the areas of the sectors with the following radii and
   subtended angles, correct to 3 s.f.

   a $r = 4$ cm, $\theta = 2$ radians   **b** $r = 3.2$ cm, $\theta = \dfrac{\pi}{2}$ radians

   c $r = 0.5$ m, $\theta = 1.5$ radians   **d** $r = 4.8$ cm, $\theta = 72°$

   e $r = 17$ cm, $\theta = 124°$ **f** $r = 0.03$ m, $\theta = 14°$

8 **a** The arc length of a sector of a circle of radius 8.5 cm is 3 cm.
Find the angle at the centre of the sector, in degrees, correct to 3 s.f.

b Two points, A and B, are on the circumference of a circle of radius 4.8 cm.
The angle AOB is 1.3 radians, where O is the centre of the circle.
Find the length of the major arc of the circle, correct to 3 s.f.

Remember to use radians.

c A chord, AB, of a circle of radius 5 cm subtends an angle at the centre of 60°
as shown in the diagram.
Find the perimeter of the segment, bound by the minor arc AB, correct to 3 s.f.

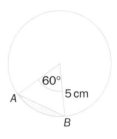

9 Give your answers correct to 3 s.f.

Draw diagrams and remember to work in radians.

a The area of a sector of a circle is 24 cm² and the angle contained in the sector is 60°. Find the radius of the sector.

b A sector contains an angle of $\frac{\pi}{5}$ radians and the area of the sector is 30 cm².
What is the radius of the circle?

c A sector of area 12 cm² has a radius of 4.2 cm.
Find the size of the angle at the centre in degrees.

d The area of a sector of a circle is 45 cm² and its radius is 13.4 cm. Find the perimeter of the sector.

e The arc length of a sector is 8.7 cm and its radius is 9.2 cm. Find the area of the sector.

f A circle of radius 5 cm has a chord AB subtending an angle of 72° at the centre as shown in the diagram. Find the area of the minor segment AB.

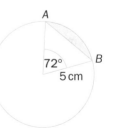

g The area of a segment is 20 cm² and the angle subtended by the chord forming the segment is 1.3 radians.
What is the radius of the circle?

C2

10 A sector of a circle has centre C and an arc AB. The arc PQ of a smaller circle, centre C, cuts off the shaded area in the sector, as shown in the diagram.

If $PC = CQ = 4$ cm, $AP = BQ = x$ cm and angle $\theta = \dfrac{\pi}{3}$, show that the area of shape $ABQP$ is given by

$$\frac{\pi x}{6}(x+8)\,\text{cm}^2$$

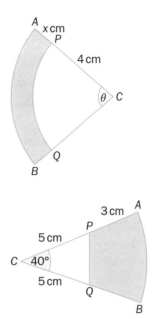

11 A sector of a circle has centre C and arc AB. There is a point, P, on the radius AC, where $AP = 3$ cm and $PC = 5$ cm. There is a point, Q, on radius BC such that $BQ = 3$ cm and $QC = 5$ cm. Angle $ACB = 40°$. Find the area of $APQB$.

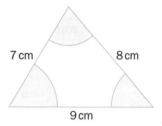

12 A circle, centre C, is divided into two sectors by the radii CA and CB. The ratio of the area of the minor sector to that of the major sector is $1 : p$ and the angle contained in the minor sector is θ radians.

Show that $\quad \theta = \dfrac{2\pi}{p+1}$

13 At each of the vertices of a triangle a sector of radius 2 cm is cut out. If the sides of the triangle are 7 cm, 8 cm and 9 cm, what area is left after the sectors have been removed?

14 The points A and B lie on the circumference of a circle, centre C. Tangents are drawn to the circle at A and B and intersect at the point P. The radius of the circle is 8 cm and the angle at the centre subtended by AB is 135°. Find the area of the shaded shape ABP.

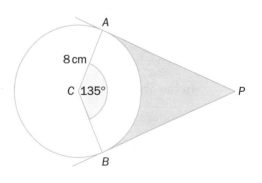

You can find the sine, cosine and tangent of an angle in the range $0 \leqslant \theta \leqslant 90°$ using your calculator.

o The trigonometric ratios are

$$\sin \theta = \frac{\text{opposite}}{\text{hypotenuse}} \quad \cos \theta = \frac{\text{adjacent}}{\text{hypotenuse}} \quad \tan \theta = \frac{\text{opposite}}{\text{adjacent}}$$

See Chapter 0 for a reminder of basic trigonometry.

Notice that

$$\frac{\sin \theta}{\cos \theta} = \sin \theta \div \cos \theta$$

$$= \frac{O}{H} \div \frac{A}{H}$$

$$= \frac{O}{H} \times \frac{H}{A}$$

$$= \frac{O}{A} = \tan \theta$$

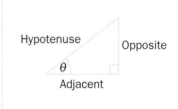

o $\tan \theta \equiv \dfrac{\sin \theta}{\cos \theta}$

You can use this relationship between $\sin \theta$, $\cos \theta$ and $\tan \theta$ to solve trigonometric problems.

You can find the trigonometric ratios of angles greater than 90° by considering a circle with centre O and radius, OP, of 1 unit.

The circle is divided into four quadrants.

Let P have coordinates (x, y).
As OP moves round the circle it forms an angle, θ, which increases from 0 to 360°

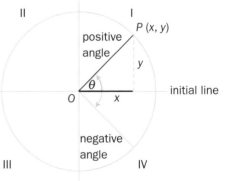

Positive angles are measured in an anticlockwise direction.
Negative angles are measured in a clockwise direction.

In the first quadrant, $0 < \theta < 90°$

In the second quadrant, $90° < \theta < 180°$

In the third quadrant, $180° < \theta < 270°$

In the fourth quadrant, $270° < \theta < 360°$

Consider the ratios:

$$\sin \theta = \frac{y}{OP} = \frac{y}{1} = y$$

$$\cos \theta = \frac{x}{OP} = \frac{x}{1} = x$$

and $\quad \tan \theta = \frac{\sin \theta}{\cos \theta} = \frac{y}{x}$

$OP = 1$ unit

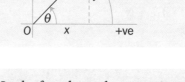

- In the second quadrant $x < 0$ and $y > 0$ so $\sin \theta > 0$ and $\cos \theta$ and $\tan \theta$ are negative.

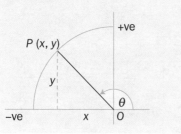

- In the first quadrant $x > 0$ and $y > 0$ so $\sin \theta$, $\cos \theta$ and $\tan \theta$ are positive.

- In the third quadrant $x < 0$ and $y < 0$ so $\sin \theta < 0$, $\cos \theta < 0$ and $\tan \theta > 0$.

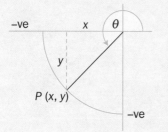

- In the fourth quadrant $x > 0$ and $y < 0$ so $\sin \theta < 0$, $\cos \theta > 0$ and $\tan \theta < 0$.

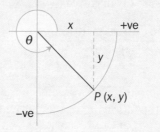

Learn in which quadrant each ratio is positive or negative.

- 1st quadrant   All ratios are positive
- 2nd quadrant   Sin θ is positive
                        $\cos \theta$ and $\tan \theta$ are negative
- 3rd quadrant   Tan θ is positive
                        $\sin \theta$ and $\cos \theta$ are negative
- 4th quadrant   Cos θ is positive
                        $\sin \theta$ and $\tan \theta$ are negative

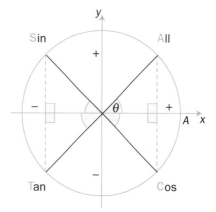

The hypotenuse is always positive.

You may find a memory aid or phrase useful. e.g. "CAST"

C2

EXAMPLE 1

Draw a diagram to show the position of each angle in a quadrant and state whether the trigonometric ratio is positive or negative.

a sin 153°

b cos (−125°)

a 153° is in the second quadrant.
sine is positive in second quadrant.
Hence sin 153° is positive.

b −125° is in the third quadrant.
cosine is negative in third quadrant.
Hence cos (−125°) is negative.

EXAMPLE 2

Write down the sign of the trigonometric ratios for each of these angles.

a tan 124°

b sin (−35°)

c cos 305°

a 124° is in the second quadrant.
Hence tan 124° is negative.

b −35° is in the fourth quadrant.
Hence sin (−35°) is negative.

c 305° is in the fourth quadrant.
Hence cos 305° is positive.

C2

You can derive the following results by again considering the sign of each ratio in each of the four quadrants.

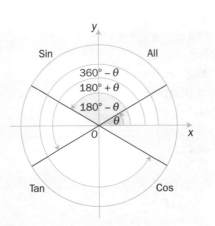

- $\sin (180° − \theta) = \sin \theta$
  $\sin (180° + \theta) = -\sin \theta$
  $\sin (360° − \theta) = -\sin \theta$

- $\cos (180° − \theta) = -\cos \theta$
  $\cos (180° + \theta) = -\cos \theta$
  $\cos (360° − \theta) = \cos \theta$

- $\tan (180° − \theta) = -\tan \theta$
  $\tan (180° + \theta) = \tan \theta$
  $\tan (360° − \theta) = -\tan \theta$

The same results hold for angles measured in radians with 180° replaced by π and 360° replaced by 2π. e.g $\sin (\pi − \theta) = \sin \theta$

You can use these results to simplify expressions.

Simplify   **a** $2 \sin (180° − \theta) + \sin (180° + \theta)$
            b $3 \tan (\pi + \theta) − \tan (2\pi − \theta)$

----

a Use the general results: $\sin (180° − \theta) = \sin \theta$
              and $\sin (180° + \theta) = −\sin \theta$

$$2 \sin (180° − \theta) + \sin (180° + \theta) = 2 \sin \theta + (−\sin \theta)$$
$$= \sin \theta$$

b Use the general results: $\tan (\pi + \theta) = \tan \theta$
              and $\tan (2\pi − \theta) = −\tan \theta$

$$3 \tan (\pi + \theta) − \tan (2\pi − \theta) = 3 \tan \theta − (−\tan \theta)$$
$$= 4 \tan \theta$$

You can rewrite trigonometric ratios to express them in terms of acute angles.

Write these trigonometric ratios in terms of acute angles

a $\cos 200°$ **b** $\tan 518°$ **c** $\sin \left(−\dfrac{4\pi}{3}\right)$

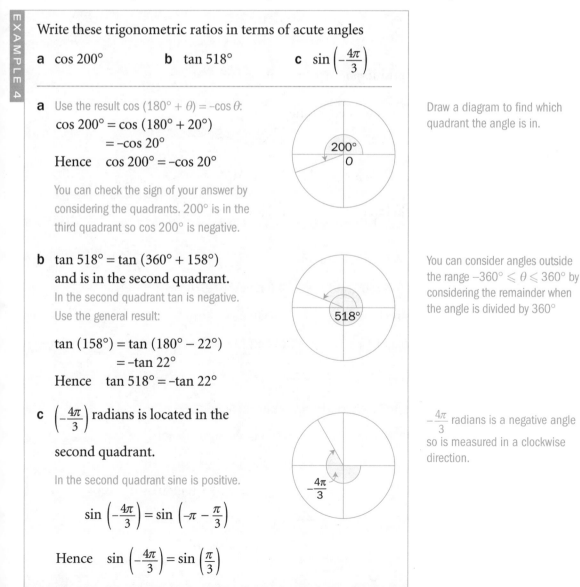

a Use the result $\cos (180° + \theta) = −\cos \theta$:
$$\cos 200° = \cos (180° + 20°)$$
$$= −\cos 20°$$
Hence $\cos 200° = −\cos 20°$

You can check the sign of your answer by considering the quadrants. 200° is in the third quadrant so cos 200° is negative.

Draw a diagram to find which quadrant the angle is in.

b $\tan 518° = \tan (360° + 158°)$
and is in the second quadrant.

In the second quadrant tan is negative.
Use the general result:

$$\tan (158°) = \tan (180° − 22°)$$
$$= −\tan 22°$$
Hence $\tan 518° = −\tan 22°$

You can consider angles outside the range $−360° \leqslant \theta \leqslant 360°$ by considering the remainder when the angle is divided by 360°

c $\left(−\dfrac{4\pi}{3}\right)$ radians is located in the

second quadrant.

In the second quadrant sine is positive.

$$\sin \left(−\frac{4\pi}{3}\right) = \sin \left(−\pi − \frac{\pi}{3}\right)$$

Hence $\sin \left(−\dfrac{4\pi}{3}\right) = \sin \left(\dfrac{\pi}{3}\right)$

$−\dfrac{4\pi}{3}$ radians is a negative angle so is measured in a clockwise direction.

Exercise 12.5

1 Draw diagrams to show the quadrant in which each of the following angles is located.

    a 250°   **b** −120°   **c** 580°

    d −780°   **e** $\dfrac{5\pi}{3}$ **f** $-\dfrac{\pi}{5}$

    g $\dfrac{3\pi}{5}$ **h** $-\dfrac{5\pi}{3}$ **i** $\dfrac{9\pi}{4}$

2 For each of the following angles write down the quadrant in which it is located and the equivalent acute angle made with the x-axis.

    a 305°   **b** −210°   **c** −300°

    d 500°   **e** $\dfrac{3\pi}{4}$ **f** $\dfrac{7\pi}{3}$

    g $-\dfrac{5\pi}{6}$ **h** $-\dfrac{6\pi}{5}$ **i** $\dfrac{13\pi}{3}$

3 Draw a diagram to show the position of each angle in one of the four quadrants.
Hence deduce the sign of the trigonometric ratio.

    a $\sin 210°$ **b** $\cos 108°$ **c** $\sin (-80°)$

    d $\sin 410°$ **e** $\tan (-380°)$ **f** $\cos 315°$

    g $\tan (-315°)$ **h** $\sin \left(\dfrac{8\pi}{3}\right)$ **i** $\cos \left(\dfrac{7\pi}{6}\right)$

4 Simplify the following where θ is an acute angle.

    a $\sin (180° + \theta)$ **b** $\cos (180° - \theta)$ **c** $\tan (180° + \theta)$

    d $\cos (2\pi - \theta)$ **e** $\sin (2\pi + \theta)$ **f** $\tan (2\pi + \theta)$

    g $\cos (3\pi - \theta)$ **h** $\cos (4\pi + \theta)$ **i** $\tan (3\pi + \theta)$

    j $\sin (4\pi - \theta)$

5 Simplify the following expressions where θ is an acute angle.

    a $\sin (180° + \theta) - 2 \sin (180° - \theta)$ **b** $3 \tan (180° - \theta) + 1$

    c $4 \cos (360° + \theta) + 2 \cos (360° - \theta)$ **d** $\sin (180° + \theta)\sin (180° - \theta)$

    e $\tan (180° - \theta) + 3 \tan (180° + \theta)$ **f** $2 \sin \theta + 3 \sin (360° + \theta)$

    g $\tan (\pi + \theta) - 4 \tan (\pi - \theta)$ **h** $\cos (2\pi + \theta) \cos (2\pi - \theta)$

    i $\cos (\pi - \theta)\sin (\pi - \theta)$ **j** $[\tan (3\pi + \theta)]^2$

C2

INVESTIGATIONS

6 Each of the following expressions simplify to
$\sin x$, $\cos x$, $-\sin x$ or $-\cos x$.
Write down each expression and its simplified result.

$\sin (360° + x)$ $\qquad$ $\sin (180° + x)$

$\cos (360° + x)$ $\qquad$ $\cos (180° + x)$

$\sin (180° - x)$ $\qquad$ $\cos (360° - x)$

$\cos (180° - x)$

7 Decide, without using a calculator, if the
following trigonometric expressions give positive
or negative values.

$\sin 460°$ $\qquad$ $\tan -190°$

$\tan -325°$ $\qquad$ $\cos 730°$

$\sin 570°$ $\qquad$ $\sin -580°$

$\cos 510°$ $\qquad$ $\sin 1000°$

8 **a** $\sin(360° + x)$ has the same value as $\sin x$.
By looking at the other quadrants, which other
angle has the same value as $\sin x$?

b Similarly, which other angles have the same values
as $\cos x$ and $\tan x$?

c Use this information to give other angles in the
interval $0° < x < 360°$ that give

  i $\sin 30° = \frac{1}{2}$

  ii $\cos 60° = \frac{1}{2}$

  iii $\tan 45° = 1$

You need to learn the values of some specific trigonometric ratios.

- For the sine and cosine ratios:
  $\sin 0° = 0$
  $\sin 90° = 1$
  $\sin 180° = 0$
  $\sin 270° = -1$
  $\sin 360° = 0$

  You can check these values on your calculator.

  You will study these graphs in more detail in section 12.7.

  $\cos 0° = 1$
  $\cos 90° = 0$
  $\cos 180° = -1$
  $\cos 270° = 0$
  $\cos 360° = 1$

- You can calculate some values for the tangent ratio:
  $\tan 0° = 0$
  $\tan 180° = 0$
  $\tan 360° = 0$

  The graph of $\tan \theta$ has asymptotes at $\theta = 90°$ and $\theta = 270°$

  What happens when you try to input $\tan 90°$ and $\tan 270°$ into your calculator? Do any other values give this result?

Now look at the values of these ratios for the angle 45°.

Consider an isosceles right-angled triangle ABC.

Let sides AB and BC be of unit length.

Use Pythagoras' theorem: $\quad AC^2 = AB^2 + BC^2 = 1^2 + 1^2 = 2$

Take square roots: $\quad AC = \sqrt{2}$

From the diagram, evaluate the trigonometric ratios:

$$\sin A = \frac{BC}{AC} \qquad \cos A = \frac{AB}{AC} \qquad \tan A = \frac{BC}{AB}$$

Hence $\sin 45° = \dfrac{1}{\sqrt{2}} = \dfrac{\sqrt{2}}{2}$

$\cos 45° = \dfrac{1}{\sqrt{2}} = \dfrac{\sqrt{2}}{2}$

$\tan 45° = \dfrac{1}{1} = 1$

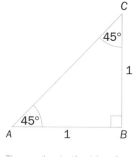

The angles in the triangle are 45°, 45° and 90°.

C2

○ The trigonometric ratios for 45° are

$$\sin 45° = \frac{1}{\sqrt{2}} = \frac{\sqrt{2}}{2} \qquad \cos 45° = \frac{1}{\sqrt{2}} = \frac{\sqrt{2}}{2} \qquad \tan 45° = \frac{1}{1} = 1$$

You can use a similar approach to obtain the values of the trigonometric ratios for the angles 30° and 60°.

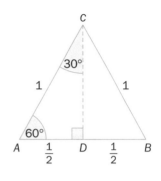

Consider an equilateral triangle ABC.

Let all the sides be of unit length and let CD be a perpendicular from C to the side AB.

Then $AD = DB = \frac{1}{2}$

Use Pythagoras' theorem: $\quad CD^2 = AC^2 - AD^2$

Substitute values: $\qquad = 1^2 - \left(\frac{1}{2}\right)^2 = 1 - \frac{1}{4} = \frac{3}{4}$

Take square roots: $\qquad CD = \frac{\sqrt{3}}{2}$

Angle $CAD = 60°$ and angle $ACD = 30°$

From the diagram, evaluate the trigonometric ratios:

$$\sin CAD = \frac{CD}{AC} \qquad \cos CAD = \frac{AD}{AC} \qquad \tan CAD = \frac{CD}{AD}$$

$$\sin 60° = \frac{\left(\frac{\sqrt{3}}{2}\right)}{1} = \frac{\sqrt{3}}{2} \qquad \cos 60° = \frac{\frac{1}{2}}{1} = \frac{1}{2} \qquad \tan 60° = \frac{\frac{\sqrt{3}}{2}}{\frac{1}{2}} = \sqrt{3}$$

Consider angle ACD to show these results for 30°:

$$\sin 30° = \frac{1}{2}$$

$$\cos 30° = \frac{\sqrt{3}}{2}$$

$$\tan 30° = \frac{1}{\sqrt{3}} = \frac{\sqrt{3}}{3}$$

○ The trigonometric ratios for 30° and 60° are

$$\sin 30° = \frac{1}{2} \qquad \cos 30° = \frac{\sqrt{3}}{2} \qquad \tan 30° = \frac{\sqrt{3}}{3}$$

and $\quad \sin 60° = \frac{\sqrt{3}}{2} \qquad \cos 60° = \frac{1}{2} \qquad \tan 60° = \sqrt{3}$

Learn the trigonometric ratios for 0°, 30°, 45°, 60° and 90° and how to prove the results for 30°, 45° and 60°.

You may find it useful to record these values in a table.

	0°	30°	45°	60°	90°
sin θ	0	$\frac{1}{2}$	$\frac{\sqrt{2}}{2}$	$\frac{\sqrt{3}}{2}$	1
cos θ	1	$\frac{\sqrt{3}}{2}$	$\frac{\sqrt{2}}{2}$	$\frac{1}{2}$	0
tan θ	0	$\frac{\sqrt{3}}{3}$	1	$\sqrt{3}$	$\pm\infty$

You can see these results by comparing the graphs of cos θ and sin θ for $0° \leqslant \theta \leqslant 90°$.

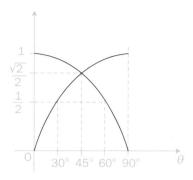

You can use these results to evaluate trigonometric ratios by first expressing them in terms of acute angles and then writing them in surd form.

The values for tan θ can be deduced from the identity

$\tan \theta = \dfrac{\sin \theta}{\cos \theta}$

EXAMPLE 1

C2

Write the following in surd form

a cos 330°

b $\sin\left(\dfrac{2\pi}{3}\right)$

You learned about surds in C1.

---

a cos 330°

b $\sin\left(\dfrac{2\pi}{3}\right)$

You may find it helpful to draw diagrams.

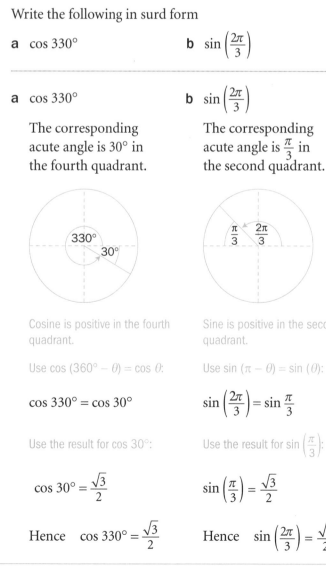

The corresponding acute angle is 30° in the fourth quadrant.

The corresponding acute angle is $\dfrac{\pi}{3}$ in the second quadrant.

Cosine is positive in the fourth quadrant.

Sine is positive in the second quadrant.

Use cos $(360° - \theta) =$ cos θ:

Use sin $(\pi - \theta) =$ sin (θ):

cos 330° = cos 30°

$\sin\left(\dfrac{2\pi}{3}\right) = \sin \dfrac{\pi}{3}$

Use the result for cos 30°:

Use the result for sin $\left(\dfrac{\pi}{3}\right)$:

$\cos 30° = \dfrac{\sqrt{3}}{2}$

$\sin\left(\dfrac{\pi}{3}\right) = \dfrac{\sqrt{3}}{2}$

$\dfrac{\pi}{3}$ radians = 60°

Hence $\cos 330° = \dfrac{\sqrt{3}}{2}$

Hence $\sin\left(\dfrac{2\pi}{3}\right) = \dfrac{\sqrt{3}}{2}$

You can solve problems involving Pythagoras and trigonometric ratios.

EXAMPLE 2

Using the right-angled triangle ABC, where $AB = 5$, $BC = 12$ and angle $B = 90°$, work out the exact value of

a $\cos A$, where A is an obtuse angle

b $\tan C$, for $\frac{3\pi}{2} < C < 2\pi$

C is a reflex angle.

Use Pythagoras' theorem to find the value of AC:

$$AC^2 = AB^2 + BC^2$$
$$= 5^2 + 12^2$$
$$= 25 + 144 = 169$$

Take square roots: $AC = 13$

a $\cos A = \dfrac{AB}{AC} = \dfrac{5}{13}$

Angle A is obtuse, so A is in the 2nd quadrant: $\cos A$ is negative.

Hence $\cos A = -\dfrac{5}{13}$

b $\tan C = \dfrac{AB}{BC} = \dfrac{5}{12}$

Angle C is reflex, so C is in the 3rd quadrant: $\tan C$ is positive.

Hence $\tan C = \dfrac{5}{12}$

reflex angle C

12

obtuse angle A

A   5   B

You will often be asked to give your answer as an exact value.

For an exact value leave your answer in surd form.

EXAMPLE 3

Given that $\tan x = -\dfrac{2}{\sqrt{3}}$ find the exact values of $\cos x$ and $\sin x$ when the angle x is obtuse.

Use the information to draw a diagram of the right-angled triangle ABC:

$$\tan x = \frac{\text{opp}}{\text{adj}} = \frac{BC}{AB} = \frac{2}{\sqrt{3}}$$

Apply Pythagoras' theorem: $AC^2 = AB^2 + BC^2$
$$= \left(\sqrt{3}\right)^2 + 2^2$$
$$= 3 + 4$$
$$= 7$$

Take square roots: $AC = \sqrt{7}$

Angle x is obtuse, so x is in the second quadrant

so $\sin x$ is positive   and $\cos x$ is negative

hence $\sin x = \dfrac{BC}{AC}$ and $\cos x = -\dfrac{AB}{AC}$

$\sin x = \dfrac{2}{\sqrt{7}}$ $\cos x = -\dfrac{\sqrt{3}}{\sqrt{7}}$

C

2

x

A   √3   B

$\tan x = \dfrac{\sin x}{\cos x} = \dfrac{+ve}{-ve} = -ve$

as required.

Check: $\tan x = \dfrac{\sin x}{\cos x} = \dfrac{\frac{2}{\sqrt{7}}}{\frac{\sqrt{3}}{\sqrt{7}}} = -\dfrac{2}{\sqrt{3}}$

Sometimes you will be asked to solve an equation involving a trigonometric ratio to find θ. You should be aware that there may be more than one possible answer.

EXAMPLE 4

Find all the values of the angle θ in the given range.

$$\sin\theta = \frac{\sqrt{3}}{2}, \quad [0° < \theta < 720°]$$

You know that one solution is $\theta = 60°$ since $\sin 60° = \frac{\sqrt{3}}{2}$

Use $\sin(180° - \theta) = \sin\theta$ to find a solution in the 2nd quadrant:
$180° - 60° = 120°$, so $\theta = 120°$ is also a solution.

Consider the next cycle, $360° < \theta < 720°$:

The equivalent values are

$$\theta = 360° + 60° = 420° \quad \text{and} \quad \theta = 540° - 60° = 480°$$

Hence the solutions are $\theta = 60°, 120°, 420°$ and $480°$.

This is the acute angle in the first quadrant.

Sine is also positive in the second quadrant.

$360° + 180° = 540°$

Exercise 12.6

1   Rewrite each of the following in terms of an acute angle.

    a $\sin 150°$ **b** $\cos 210°$ **c** $\tan 135°$ **d** $\sin 240°$

    e $\cos(-135°)$ **f** $\sin(-240°)$ **g** $\cos 390°$ **h** $\sin(-480°)$

2   Write the answers to the following, in surd form where appropriate.

    a $\sin 60°$ **b** $\cos 90°$ **c** $\tan 120°$ **d** $\tan 300°$

    e $\sin 210°$ **f** $\cos(-30°)$ **g** $\sin(-150°)$ **h** $\tan(-60°)$

3   Write the answers to the following in surd form where appropriate.

    a $\sin\frac{\pi}{2}$ **b** $\cos\frac{3\pi}{2}$ **c** $\tan\frac{\pi}{4}$ **d** $\tan\frac{2\pi}{3}$ *These angles are in radians.*

    e $\cos\left(-\frac{\pi}{6}\right)$ **f** $\tan\left(-\frac{\pi}{2}\right)$ **g** $\sin\frac{7\pi}{6}$ **h** $\sin\frac{5\pi}{3}$

4   Use the right-angled triangle ABC, where $AB = 4$ units, $BC = 3$ units and $AC = 5$ units, to work out the value of each ratio, given the information about the angle.

    a $\sin A$, A is acute   **b** $\cos C$, C is acute

    c $\sin A$, A is reflex   **d** $\tan C$, C is reflex

    e $\cos C$, C is reflex   **f** $\sin A$, $270° < A < 360°$

    g $\tan A$, $\frac{3\pi}{2} < A < 2\pi$ **h** $\cos A$, A is obtuse

    i $\sin A$, $360° < A < 450°$ **j** $\cos(-C)$, C is acute

5   Use Pythagoras' theorem and your knowledge of the quadrants
    and associated acute angles to answer these questions.

a Given that $\sin A = \frac{1}{3}$ and A is acute, find the exact values of $\cos A$ and $\tan A$.

b If $\sin A = -\frac{2}{3}$ and $180° < A < 270°$ find the exact values of $\cos A$ and $\tan A$.

c When $\tan x = \frac{1}{\sqrt{2}}$ and $\pi < x < \frac{3\pi}{2}$ find the exact values of $\sin x$ and $\cos x$.

d Given that $\cos B = -\frac{1}{2}$ and B is an obtuse angle find the exact values of $\sin B$ and $\tan B$.

e When $\tan x = -\sqrt{2}$ and x is an obtuse angle find the exact values of $\sin x$ and $\cos x$.

f If $\tan \theta = \frac{5}{12}$ and θ is a reflex angle find the exact values of $\sin \theta$ and $\cos \theta$.

6   Find all the values of the angle θ in the given range.

a $\sin \theta = \frac{1}{2}$, $[0° < \theta < 180°]$ **b** $\cos \theta = \frac{\sqrt{3}}{2}$, $[0° < \theta < 180°]$

c $\tan \theta = 1$, $[0° < \theta < 180°]$ **d** $\cos \theta = \frac{1}{2}$, $[90° < \theta < 270°]$

e $\sin \theta = -\frac{\sqrt{2}}{2}$, $[180° < \theta < 360°]$ **f** $\cos \theta = -1$, $[0° < \theta < 360°]$

g $\sin \theta = -\frac{1}{2}$, $[180° < \theta < 360°]$ **h** $\tan \theta = -\frac{\sqrt{3}}{3}$, $[0° < \theta < 180°]$

7   Find all the values of the angle x, in radian measure, in the given range.

a $\sin x = \frac{1}{2}$, $[0 < x < \pi]$ **b** $\cos x = 0$, $[0 < x < 2\pi]$

c $\sin x = \frac{\sqrt{3}}{2}$, $[\pi < x < 2\pi]$ **d** $\tan x = \sqrt{3}$, $[0 < x < 2\pi]$

e $\cos x = -\frac{1}{2}$, $[\pi < x < 2\pi]$ **f** $\tan x = -\frac{\sqrt{3}}{3}$, $[\pi < x < 2\pi]$

g $\sin x = 1.5$, $[0 < x < 2\pi]$ **h** $\cos x = \frac{1}{2}$, $[0 < x < 4\pi]$

INVESTIGATION

8   **a** Find the unknown length in this triangle.

    b Find $\sin 30°$ as an exact fraction and find
           similar expressions for $\cos 30°$ and $\tan 30°$.

    c Hence prove $(\sin 30°)^2 + (\cos 30°)^2 = 1$

    d Prove $\sin A \cos A \tan A + \sin B \cos B \tan B = 1$
           where $A = 30°$ and $B = 60°$.

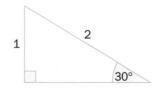

Trigonometric graphs

You can use your knowledge of the sine function to draw the graph of $y = \sin \theta$.

You can draw trigonometric graphs by hand or use graphing software on a graphic calculator or a computer.

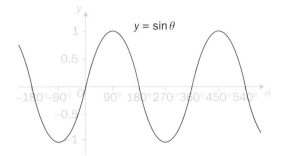

You can extend this graph in both the positive and negative directions to show the value of $\sin \theta$ for any θ.

○ The sine curve is a periodic function.
It has a period of 360° or 2π radians.

$$\sin (\theta + 360°) = \sin \theta \quad \text{and} \quad \sin (\theta - 360°) = \sin \theta$$

Periodic functions repeat themselves after a given interval. This interval is called the period of the function.

○ The graph of $y = \sin \theta$ has symmetry about the line $\theta = 90°$.

$$\sin (90° + \theta) = \sin (90° - \theta)$$

Similarly $y = \sin \theta$ has symmetry about the line $\theta = 450°$ and so on.

Similarly you can draw the graph of $y = \cos \theta$.

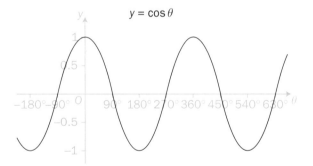

You can extend this graph in both the positive and negative directions to show the value of $\cos \theta$ for any θ.

The cosine curve is the same as the sine curve after a translation of –90°.

○ The cosine function is periodic.
It has a period of 360° or 2π radians.

$$\cos (\theta + 360°) = \cos \theta \quad \text{and} \quad \cos (\theta - 360°) = \cos \theta$$

○ The graph of $y = \cos \theta$ has symmetry about the line $\theta = 0°$.
$$\cos (-\theta) = \cos \theta$$

You can also draw a graph of $y = \tan\theta$.

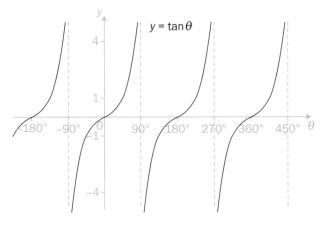

You can extend this graph in both the positive and negative directions to show the value of tan x for any x.

The lines, $\theta = -90°, 90°, 270°...$, are asymptotes to the curve. $y = \tan\theta$ approaches but never meets them.

As you can see the graph of $y = \tan\theta$ behaves quite differently from the graphs of $y = \sin\theta$ and $y = \cos\theta$. However, $y = \tan\theta$ is also periodic.

- The tangent function is periodic.
  It has a period of 180° or π radians.
  $$\tan(\theta + 180°) = \tan\theta \quad \text{and} \quad \tan(\theta - 180°) = \tan\theta$$

- The tangent curve has asymptotes at $(2n + 1)90°$ where n is an integer.

e.g. There is an asymptote at
$\theta = (2 \times 2 + 1) \times 90°$
$\quad = 5 \times 90° = 450°$

You can see from the graph that the curve approaches the asymptotes but never reaches them.
You can show this by writing $\tan\theta \rightarrow \pm\infty$ for these values.

Exercise 12.7

1 **a** Sketch the graph of $y = \cos x$, where x is in radian measure, for values of x from $-\pi$ to $+\pi$

  b Sketch the graph of $y = \sin\theta$, where θ is in radian measure, for values of θ from -2π to $+2\pi$.

  c Sketch the graph of $y = \tan x$, where x is measured in radians, for values of x from $-\pi$ to $+\pi$.

  d i On the same axes sketch the graphs of $y = \sin x$ and $y = \cos x$, where x is measured in radians, for values of x from 0 to 2π.

  ii Show that these two curves intersect at two points only and find the values of sin x and cos x where this occurs.

  iii Find the solutions to the equation $\sin x - \cos x = 0$

INVESTIGATION

2 Use the graphs of sin x and cos x to explain why there are no solutions to the equations

  a $\sin x = 3$ **b** $\cos x = -2$

C2

Transformations of trigonometric graphs

You can transform graphs of trigonometric functions in the same way that you transform graphs of general curves.

You studied transformations of general curves in Chapter 4.

You can sketch the graphs of $y = n \sin x$, $y = n \cos x$ and $y = n \tan x$ where n is a constant.

You can use graphing software to plot trigonometric graphs.

EXAMPLE 1

Sketch the graph of $y = 2 \sin x$ for $0° \leqslant x \leqslant 360°$.

Use a plot of the graph of $y = \sin x$ to sketch the graph of $y = 2 \sin x$:

$y = 2 \sin x = 2 \times \sin x$, so in this case the y-values will be double the values given by $y = \sin x$.

e.g. $\sin 0° = 0$ $\Rightarrow$ $2 \sin 0° = 0$
       $\sin 90° = 1$ $\Rightarrow$ $2 \sin 90° = 2$

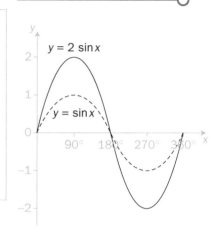

The graph of $y = 2 \sin x$ is the same as the graph of $y = \sin x$ after a stretch parallel to the y-axis by scale factor 2.

○ Generally, the graph $y = n \sin x$ is the graph of $y = \sin x$ after being stretched parallel to the y-axis by a scale factor of n.

You can test this by substituting different values of n and sketching the resulting graphs.

Similar results are true for the graphs of
   $y = n \cos x$ and $y = n \tan x$

Now consider the function $y = n \sin x$ when $n = -1$

Investigate the functions $y = n \cos x$ and $y = n \tan x$ and their graphs for yourself.

EXAMPLE 2

Sketch the graph of $y = -\sin x$ for $0° \leqslant x \leqslant 360°$.

Use a plot of the graph of $y = \sin x$ to sketch the graph of $y = -\sin x$:

$y = -\sin x = -1 \times \sin x$

e.g. $\sin 0° = 0$ $\Rightarrow$ $-\sin 0° = 0$
       $\sin 90° = 1$ $\Rightarrow$ $-\sin 90° = -1$

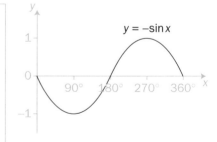

The sine curve has been reflected in the x-axis.

○ Generally, the graph of $y = -\sin x$ is the graph of $y = \sin x$ after a reflection in the x-axis.

Similar results are true for $y = -\cos x$ and $y = -\tan x$. Draw these graphs yourself.

C2

You can also sketch the graphs for equations of the type $y = n + \sin x$

EXAMPLE 3

Sketch the graph of $y = 2 + \sin x$ for $-2\pi \leqslant x \leqslant 2\pi$.

Use a plot the graph of $y = \sin x$ to sketch
the graph of $y = 2 + \sin x$:

Add 2 to every $y = \sin x$ value.

The sine curve has been translated by
+2 units parallel to the y-axis.

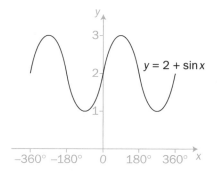

EXAMPLE 4

Sketch the graph of the equation $y = -1 + \cos x$
for $-2\pi \leqslant x \leqslant 2\pi$.

Use a plot of the graph of $y = \cos x$ to sketch
the graph of $y = -1 + \cos x$:

Subtract 1 from every $y = \cos x$ value.

The cosine curve has been translated by
-1 unit parallel to the y-axis.

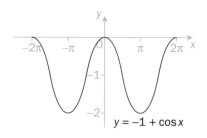

C2

- Generally the graph of $y = \pm k + \sin x$ is a translation of
  the graph of $y = \sin x$ by $\pm k$ parallel to the y-axis.

Similar results follow for the graphs of $y = \cos x$ and $y = \tan x$.
Now look at the effect of adding a constant to the angle in the ratio.

EXAMPLE 5

Sketch the graph of $y = \sin (x + 90°)$ for $0° \leqslant x \leqslant 360°$.

Use a plot of the graph of $y = \sin x$ to sketch
the graph of $y = \sin (x + 90°)$:

The graph of $y = \sin (x + 90°)$ looks like the graph of $y = \cos x$.

The sine curve has been translated by
-90° parallel to the x-axis.

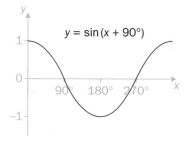

EXAMPLE 6

Sketch the curve $y = \tan (x - 45°)$ for $0 \leqslant x \leqslant 360°$.

Use a plot of the graph of $y = \tan x$ to sketch
the graph of $y = \tan (x - 45°)$:

The tangent curve has been translated by
+45° parallel to the x-axis.

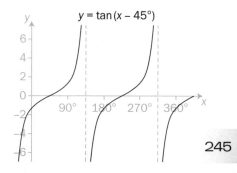

245

Generally

o $y = \sin (x + \theta)$ is a translation of $y = \sin x$ by $-\theta$ parallel to the x-axis

The graphs of $y = \cos (x + \theta)$ and $y = \tan (x + \theta)$ behave in a similar way.

The curves given by $y = \sin (kx)$, $y = \cos (kx)$ and $y = \tan (kx)$ are also related to the curves of $y = \sin x$, $y = \cos x$ and $y = \tan x$ respectively.

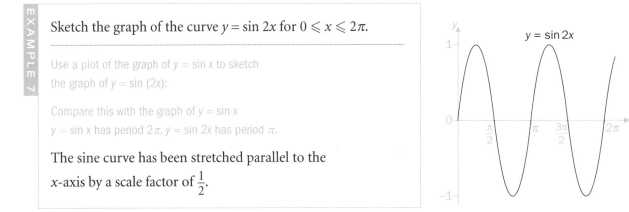

EXAMPLE 7

Sketch the graph of the curve $y = \sin 2x$ for $0 \leqslant x \leqslant 2\pi$.

Use a plot of the graph of $y = \sin x$ to sketch the graph of $y = \sin (2x)$:

Compare this with the graph of $y = \sin x$
$y = \sin x$ has period 2π. $y = \sin 2x$ has period π.

The sine curve has been stretched parallel to the x-axis by a scale factor of $\frac{1}{2}$.

Generally

o The graph of $y = \sin (kx)$ is the graph of $y = \sin x$ after a stretch parallel to the x-axis by a scale factor of $\frac{1}{k}$.

Similar results are true for the graphs of $y = \cos (kx)$ and $y = \tan (kx)$.

Exercise 12.8

1 Sketch each pair of graphs on the same diagram for $0° \leqslant x \leqslant 360°$.
   Label the axes to show the key features of each curve.

   a $y = \sin x$ and $y = 3 \sin x$ **b** $y = \cos x$ and $y = -2 \cos x$ **c** $y = \tan x$ and $y = -\tan x$

2 Sketch these graphs on separate diagrams for $-2\pi \leqslant x \leqslant 2\pi$.
   Include labels to show the key features of each curve.

   a $y = -1 + \sin x$ **b** $y = 3 + \cos x$ **c** $y = -2 + \tan x$

3 Sketch these graphs on separate diagrams for $0° \leqslant x \leqslant 360°$.
   Give the coordinates of the x-axis crossings.

   a $y = \sin (x + 45°)$ **b** $y = \cos (x - 90°)$ **c** $y = \tan (x - 45°)$

C2

4 Sketch these graphs on separate diagrams for $0° \leqslant x \leqslant 360°$.
Give the coordinates of the x-axis crossings.

  a $y = \sin(-x)$ **b** $y = \cos 2x$ **c** $y = \tan\left(\dfrac{x}{2}\right)$

5 Use transformations of the graphs of $\sin x$ and $\cos x$ to show that
the following equations are true.

  a $\sin(x + 180°) = -\sin x$ **b** $\sin(90° - x) = \cos x$

  c $\cos(90° - x) = \sin x$ **d** $\cos(180° - x) = -\cos x$

6 Use transformations of the graphs of $\sin x$ and $\cos x$ to show that
the following equations are true.

  a $\sin x = -\sin(-x)$ **b** $\cos x = \cos(-x)$ **c** $\tan x = -\tan(-x)$

7 Sketch each function and write down its period.

  a $y = \sin\left(\dfrac{\theta}{2}\right)$ **b** $y = \cos(\pi + \theta)$

  c $y = \tan 4\theta$ **d** $y = \cos(-\theta)$

C2

INVESTIGATION

8 Find the equation of each graph.

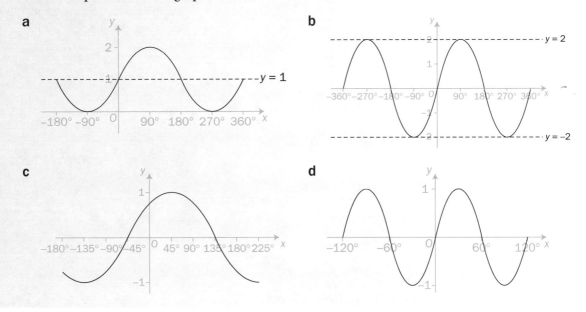

  a   **b**

  c   **d**

Trigonometric identities

The sine, cosine and tangent ratios are related to each other by the trigonometric identities.

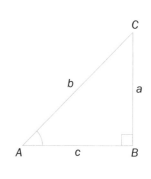

Apply Pythagoras in triangle ABC: $c^2 + a^2 = b^2$

Divide each term by b^2: $\dfrac{c^2}{b^2} + \dfrac{a^2}{b^2} = \dfrac{b^2}{b^2}$

$$\left(\frac{c}{b}\right)^2 + \left(\frac{a}{b}\right)^2 = 1 \qquad (1)$$

For angle A: $\cos A = \dfrac{c}{b}$ and $\sin A = \dfrac{a}{b}$

Substitute these values into (1): $\cos^2 A + \sin^2 A \equiv 1$

○ **Generally, for all θ, $\cos^2 \theta + \sin^2 \theta \equiv 1$**

$\equiv$ means "is equivalent to".

Consider angle A in the right-angled triangle ABC:

$$\tan A = \frac{\text{opposite}}{\text{adjacent}} = \frac{a}{c}$$

Divide both the top and bottom by b: $\tan A = \dfrac{a \div b}{c \div b}$

Substitute $\sin A = \dfrac{a}{b}$ and $\cos A = \dfrac{c}{b}$: $\tan A = \dfrac{\sin A}{\cos A}$

Dividing both top and bottom by the same quantity has no effect on the value of the fraction.

○ **Generally, for all θ, $\tan \theta \equiv \dfrac{\sin \theta}{\cos \theta}$**

You can use these identities to simplify expressions.

Simplify the expression $(1 - \cos^2 A) + 2 \sin^2 A$

Use $\cos^2 A + \sin^2 A \equiv 1$:
Rearrange: $\sin^2 A \equiv 1 - \cos^2 A$

Substitute $\sin^2 A$ for $(1 - \cos^2 A)$ in the expression:

$$(1 - \cos^2 A) + 2 \sin^2 A \equiv \sin^2 A + 2 \sin^2 A$$
$$\equiv 3 \sin^2 A$$

You can also use the identities to prove relationships.

EXAMPLE 2

Prove that $(\sin x + \cos x)^2 \equiv 1 + 2 \sin x \cos x$

Work with the left-hand side (LHS) of the equation:

$$\text{LHS} \equiv (\sin x + \cos x)^2$$

Expand: $\equiv \sin^2 x + 2 \sin x \cos x + \cos^2 x$

$\equiv 1 + 2 \sin x \cos x$

$\text{LHS} \equiv \text{RHS}$ as required.

> You need to transform one side of the equation so that it is the same as the other side. Work with either the LHS or the RHS.
>
> Using $\sin^2 x + \cos^2 x \equiv 1$

Exercise 12.9

> Choose either the LHS or the RHS to work with.

1 Simplify the following expressions.

a $\cos^2 2x + \sin^2 2x$

b $\cos^2 3x - 1$

c $\sqrt{(1 - \sin^2 4\theta)}$

d $\sqrt{\dfrac{1 - \cos^2 2\theta}{1 - \sin^2 2\theta}}$

e $(\cos A - \sin A)^2$

f $\dfrac{\tan x}{\sin x}$

g $\sin^2 x(1 - \cos^2 x)$

h $\cos^2 x + (1 - \sin x)^2$

i $\dfrac{\sqrt{(1 - \sin^2 \theta)}}{\sin \theta}$

2 Prove the following results.

a $1 + \dfrac{1}{\tan^2 A} \equiv \dfrac{1}{\sin^2 A}$

b $\tan^2 \theta + 1 \equiv \dfrac{1}{\cos^2 \theta}$

c $\dfrac{2 \sin x + 3 \cos x}{\cos x} \equiv 2 \tan x + 3$

d $\dfrac{2 \sin x \cos x}{1 - \sin^2 x} \equiv 2 \tan x$

e $\dfrac{1 - \cos^2 A}{\cos^2 A} \equiv \tan^2 A$

f $\sin x - \dfrac{1}{\sin x} \equiv -\dfrac{\cos x}{\tan x}$

g $(\cos x - \sin x)^2 + 2 \sin x \cos x \equiv 1$

h $\tan^2 \theta - \dfrac{1}{\tan^2 \theta} \equiv \dfrac{1 - 2 \cos^2 \theta}{\cos^2 \theta(1 - \cos^2 \theta)}$

i $2 + \tan^2 \theta + \dfrac{1}{\tan^2 \theta} \equiv \dfrac{1}{\sin^2 \theta \cos^2 \theta}$

3 If $x = r \cos \theta$ and $y = r \sin \theta$, where r is a constant, show that $x^2 + y^2 = r^2$

4 If $x = 2 \cos \theta$ and $y = 3 \sin \theta$, find an equation in terms of x and y only. Without sketching the graph deduce the maximum and minimum values of x and y.

INVESTIGATION

5 An alternate proof of $\sin^2 x + \cos^2 x \equiv 1$ begins as follows.

$a = c \cos x$

$b = \ldots$

Complete the proof.

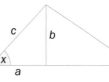

Solving trigonometric equations

You can use your knowledge of trigonometric ratios to solve trigonometric equations.
You first find an associated acute angle to give you the first solution. You can then find further solutions by considering the relevant trigonometric graph.

A trigonometric equation involves a trigonometric ratio and an unknown
e.g. tan x = 1

EXAMPLE 1

Solve the equation $\sin x = \dfrac{\sqrt{2}}{2}$ for $-360° \leqslant x \leqslant 360°$.

Find an associated acute angle:

$$\sin x = \frac{\sqrt{2}}{2}$$

$$x = 45°$$

You should recognise this ratio as a standard result.

Consider the graph of $y = \sin x$ to find the other solutions in the given interval.

Sketch the graph of $y = \sin x$ and the line $y = \dfrac{\sqrt{2}}{2}$ on the same axes:

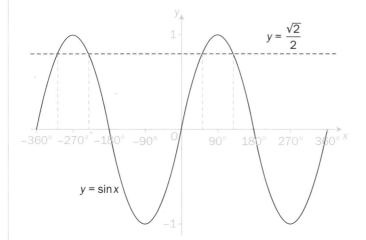

The curve and the line intersect four times in the given interval so there are four solutions.

Use the graph of the sine curve to find the other solutions:

The graph of $y = \sin x$ is symmetric about the line $x = 90°$.
so $x = 90° + 45° = 135°$ is a solution.

Symmetry about 90°:
  $\sin (90° - x) = \sin (90° + x)$

$y = \sin x$ is periodic with period 360°
so $x = 45° - 360° = -315°$ is a solution.

$y = \sin x$ has period 360°:
  $\sin (x) = \sin (x \pm 360°)$

The graph of $y = \sin x$ is symmetric about the line $x = -270°$
so $x = 45° - 270° = -225°$ is a solution.

Compare your solutions to your sketch graph to decide if they are feasible.

Hence the solutions are $x = -315°, -225°, 45°$ and $135°$.

C2

You can use a similar approach to solve equations involving the cosine function and equations when the given value of the trigonometric ratio is negative.

You can find solutions to equations involving multiple angles.

To solve an equation of the form $f(n\theta) = k$
let $x = n\theta$ and solve for x,
then find the corresponding values of θ.

e.g. To solve $\sin 3\theta = \dfrac{1}{2}$

First let $x = 3\theta$ and solve $\sin x = \dfrac{1}{2}$

Then use $\theta = \dfrac{x}{3}$ to find θ.

EXAMPLE 2

Find the values of θ which satisfy the equation $\tan 2\theta = 1$ for $0° \leqslant \theta \leqslant 180°$.

Let $x = 2\theta$

Find an associated acute angle:

$$\tan x = 1$$
$$x = 45°$$

Consider the graph of $y = \tan x$ to find the other solutions.

$x = 2\theta$ so use $0° \leqslant x \leqslant 360°$ for your sketch.

Sketch the graph of $y = \tan x$ and the line $y = 1$ on the same axes:

The curve and the line intersect twice in the given range, so there are two solutions.

Use your knowledge of the tangent curve to find the value of the other solution:

$y = \tan x$ is periodic with period $180°$
so $x = 180° + 45° = 225°$ is a solution.

Hence the solutions are $x = 45°$ and $x = 225°$.

In terms of θ, the solutions are $\theta = 22.5°$ and $\theta = 112.5°$.

You should recognise this ratio as a standard result.

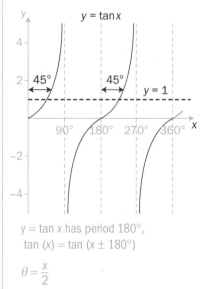

$y = \tan x$ has period $180°$,
$\tan (x) = \tan (x \pm 180°)$

$\theta = \dfrac{x}{2}$

C2

Similarly you can solve trigonometric equations in which the angle is a sum or difference.

To solve equations of this kind:
first let $x = \theta \pm B$ and solve for x
then find the corresponding values for θ.

e.g. $\cos (\theta + 90°) = \dfrac{\sqrt{2}}{2}$

First let $x = \theta + 90°$ and

solve $\cos x = \dfrac{\sqrt{2}}{2}$

Then use $\theta = x - 90°$ to find θ.

EXAMPLE 3

Find the solutions to the equation sin $(A - 30°) = -0.4$ for $0° \leqslant A \leqslant 360°$.

Let $x = A - 30°$ and solve sin $x = -0.4$ for $-30° \leqslant x \leqslant 330°$.

$0° \leqslant A \leqslant 360°$ so
$-30° \leqslant A - 30° \leqslant 330°$
Hence $-30° \leqslant x \leqslant 330°$

Use your calculator to find an associated acute angle:

$$\sin x = -0.4$$
$$x = -23.58° \quad \text{(to 4 s.f.)}$$

Consider the graph of $y = \sin x$ to find the other solutions for $-30° \leqslant x \leqslant 330°$.

Sketch the graph of $y = \sin x$ and the line $y = -0.4$ on the same axes:

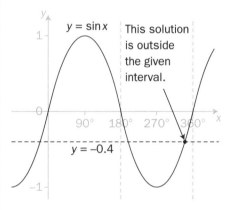

The curve and the line intersect twice in the given interval so there are two solutions.

Use your knowledge of the sine curve to find the value of the other solution:

$\sin (180° - x) = \sin x$,
$$\text{so } x = 180° - (-23.58°)$$
$$= 203.58° \text{ is a solution.}$$

Hence the solutions are $x = -23.58°$ and $x = 203.58°$.

$A = x + 30°$

In terms of A the solutions are
$$A = -23.58° + 30° = 6.42° \text{ and}$$
$$A = 203.58° + 30° = 233.58°$$
$$= 234° \text{ (to 3 s.f.)}$$

You can check your solutions by
○ comparing your results with your graph
○ using your calculator.

C2

You can use a similar method to solve equations in which the sine, cosine or tangent is raised to a power.

EXAMPLE 4

Solve the equation $4\sin^2\theta = 1$ for $-\pi \leqslant \theta \leqslant \pi$ radians.

$$4\sin^2\theta = 1$$

Rearrange: $\quad\sin^2\theta = \dfrac{1}{4}$

Take square roots: $\quad\sin\theta = \pm\dfrac{1}{2}$

Use the standard results to find the associated acute angles:

$\sin\theta = \dfrac{1}{2}$ gives the first value, $\theta = \dfrac{\pi}{6}$

and $\sin\theta = -\dfrac{1}{2}$ gives the first value $\theta = -\dfrac{\pi}{6}$

Consider the graph of $y = \sin\theta$ to find the other solutions in the interval $-\pi \leqslant \theta \leqslant \pi$.

Sketch the graph of $y = \sin\theta$ and the lines

$y = \dfrac{1}{2}$ and $y = -\dfrac{1}{2}$ on the same axes:

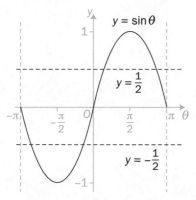

The curve intersects the line $y = \dfrac{1}{2}$ twice in the given interval.

The curve intersects the line $y = -\dfrac{1}{2}$ twice in the given interval, so there are four solutions in total.

Use your knowledge of the sine curve to find the values of the other solutions:

The solutions are $\quad\theta = \dfrac{\pi}{6}, \pi - \dfrac{\pi}{6}$ and $\theta = -\dfrac{\pi}{6}, -\pi + \dfrac{\pi}{6}$

Hence the solutions are $\quad\theta = -\dfrac{5\pi}{6}, \theta = -\dfrac{\pi}{6}, \theta = \dfrac{\pi}{6}$ and $\theta = \dfrac{5\pi}{6}$

$\sin^2\theta \equiv (\sin\theta)^2$ so the square root of the LHS is $\sin\theta$.

$\sqrt{\dfrac{1}{4}} = \pm\dfrac{1}{2}$. Remember to include both of these solutions.

Use the radian mode on your calculator to check these results.

C2

Sometimes you need to rearrange a trigonometric equation before you can solve it.

You can apply the rules of algebra to trigonometric equations.

EXAMPLE 5

Solve the equation $2 \sin^2 \theta = 5 \sin \theta - 2$ for $0 \leqslant \theta \leqslant \pi$ radians.

$$2 \sin^2 \theta = 5 \sin \theta - 2$$

Rewrite the equation:

$$2 \sin^2 \theta - 5 \sin \theta + 2 = 0$$

Factorise the quadratic:

$$(2 \sin \theta - 1)(\sin \theta - 2) = 0$$

There are two possible solutions

either $\quad 2 \sin \theta - 1 = 0, \quad$ so $\quad \sin \theta = \dfrac{1}{2}$

or $\quad \sin \theta - 2 = 0, \quad$ so $\quad \sin \theta = 2$

$\sin \theta = 2$ has no solutions. You can see this by considering the graph of $y = \sin \theta$.

You can now solve these simple trigonometric equations in the usual way by

○ finding the associated acute angles and then

○ using the properties of the sine function and its graph to evaluate the other solutions in the given interval.

The associated acute angle is $\theta = \dfrac{\pi}{6}$

This gives a further solution in the given interval of $\theta = \pi - \dfrac{\pi}{6}$

hence the solutions are $\theta = \dfrac{\pi}{6}$ and $\theta = \dfrac{5\pi}{6}$

C2

EXAMPLE 6

Solve the equation $\quad 2 \tan 2x - 1 = \dfrac{1}{\tan 2x}$

for $-180° \leqslant x \leqslant 180°$.

$$2 \tan 2x - 1 = \dfrac{1}{\tan 2x}$$

Multiply through by $\tan 2x$ to eliminate the fraction:

$$2 \tan^2 2x - \tan 2x = \dfrac{\tan 2x}{\tan 2x}$$

$$2 \tan^2 2x - \tan 2x = 1$$

You may need to use the formula if the quadratic does not factorise.

Rearrange: $\quad 2 \tan^2 2x - \tan 2x - 1 = 0$

Factorise: $\quad (\tan 2x - 1)(2 \tan 2x + 1) = 0$

so either $\tan 2x = 1$ or $\tan 2x = -\dfrac{1}{2}$

$2x = 45°, 225°, -135°, -315° \quad$ or $\quad -26.57°, -206.6°, 153.4°, 333.4°$

Use your calculator to find the associated acute angle and then use the properties and graph of the tangent function to find the further solutions in the given interval.

First let $\theta = 2x$ and solve for θ.

Then find the corresponding values for x.

The solutions are $x = -158°, -103°, -67.5°, -13.3°, 22.5°,$ $76.7°, 113°$ and $167°$ to 3 s.f.

To find the values of x between $-180°$ and $180°$ you must consider values of $2x$ between $-360°$ and $360°$.

Exercise 12.10

1 Solve these equations giving all solutions between $0°$ and $360°$.
   Give your answers to three significant figures where appropriate.

a $\sin x = 0.5$ b $\cos x = 0.5$

c $\tan x = 1$ d $\sin A = -0.7$

e $\cos A = -0.2$ f $\tan A = -3$

g $\sin \theta = 0.75$ h $\cos \theta = -0.75$

i $\tan \theta = 0.05$ j $\tan \theta = -\dfrac{4}{9}$

k $\sin x = 0.6$ l $\cos x = 2$

2 Solve these equations giving all solutions between $0°$ and $180°$.
   Write your answers to three significant figures where appropriate.

a $\sin 2x = 0.5$ b $\sin 3x = 1$

c $\cos 2x = 0.5$ d $\cos \left(\dfrac{x}{2}\right) = 0.5$

e $\tan 2x = 1$ f $\cos 2\theta = -0.6$

g $\tan 2\theta = -0.5$ h $\tan \left(\dfrac{\theta}{2}\right) = \sqrt{3}$

i $\sin 4x = \dfrac{\sqrt{2}}{2}$ j $\tan \left(\dfrac{\theta}{3}\right) = 0.3$

3 Solve these equations giving solutions between $0°$ and $180°$.
   Write your answers correct to three significant figures where appropriate.

a $2 \sin x - 1 = 0$ b $2 \sin 2x + 1 = 0$

c $2 \sin x = \cos x$ d $2 \cos 2x - 0.5 = 0$

e $3 \sin 2x - \cos 2x = 0$ f $4 \tan 2x = 5$

g $\dfrac{1}{2} \sin \left(\dfrac{x}{2}\right) - \dfrac{1}{4} = 0$ h $\cos \left(\dfrac{3x}{2}\right) + 0.5 = 0$

i $\sin x \,(1 + \sin 2x) = 0$ j $\cos 2x = \cos 2x(0.5 + \sin x)$

4   Solve these equations giving your solutions between 0° and 360°.

    a $\sin (x + 30°) = 0.5$ **b** $\cos (x - 30°) = 0.5$

    c $\tan (x + 20°) = 1$ **d** $\sin (30° + x) = -0.5$

    e $\tan (45° - x) = -1$ **f** $\cos (x + 90°) = -\dfrac{\sqrt{3}}{2}$

    g $\tan (x - 75°) = \sqrt{3}$ **h** $\sin (30° - x) = -1$

5   Solve the following equations, where θ is in radians, giving your
answers for $-\pi \leqslant \theta \leqslant \pi$

    a $\sin \left(\theta - \dfrac{\pi}{2}\right) = 1$ **b** $\sin 2\theta = 0.5$

    c $\cos \left(\theta + \dfrac{\pi}{3}\right) = \dfrac{\sqrt{3}}{2}$ **d** $\tan 2\theta = 1$

    e $\cos 2\theta = \dfrac{\sqrt{2}}{2}$ **f** $\tan \left(\theta + \dfrac{\pi}{3}\right) = \sqrt{3}$

    g $\sin \left(\theta + \dfrac{\pi}{2}\right) = 0$ **h** $\sin \left(\theta - \dfrac{\pi}{6}\right) = -\dfrac{1}{2}$

    i $\cos (\theta + 0.2) = -\dfrac{\sqrt{3}}{2}$ **j** $\tan \left(\dfrac{\theta}{2}\right) = -\dfrac{1}{\sqrt{3}}$

6   Solve the following equations giving your answers for $0° \leqslant x \leqslant 360°$
and correct to 3 s.f. where appropriate.

    a $\sin^2 x = 1$ **b** $4 \cos^2 x = 1$

    c $3 \tan^2 x = 1$ **d** $2 \sin^2 x - \sin x = 0$

    e $\sin x \cos x - \cos x = 0$ **f** $2 \sin^2 x = 3 \sin x \cos x$

    g $4 \cos x = 5 \sin x$ **h** $3 \cos^2 x - \sin x \cos x = 0$

    i $2 \tan x + 5 \tan^2 x = 0$ **j** $5 \sin x + 3 \cos x = 0$

7   Solve these equations in the interval $-180° \leqslant x \leqslant 180°$
giving your answers correct to 3 s.f. where appropriate.

    a $\sin^2 x + 2 \sin x + 1 = 0$ **b** $2 \cos^2 x + \cos x - 1 = 0$ **c** $\tan^2 x - \tan x - 2 = 0$

    d $3 \cos^2 x - 2 \sin x - 2 = 0$ **e** $6 \sin^2 x + 7 \cos x = 8$ **f** $\sin^2 x + \sin x = 1$

    g $2 \cos^2 x = \cos x + 2$ **h** $2 \sin^2 x + 3 \cos x - 1 = 0$ **i** $\tan x - \dfrac{2}{\tan x} + 2 = 0$

8   Write the solutions to these equations in radians for $0 \leqslant \theta \leqslant \pi$ and correct to 3 s.f. when appropriate.

   a $\sin^2 2\theta = 0.25$

   b $2 \sin^2 2\theta - 3 \sin 2\theta + 1 = 0$

   c $4 \cos^2 2\theta = 3$

   d $\tan^2 2\theta + 4 \tan 2\theta + 3 = 0$

   e $2 \cos^2 3\theta - 3 \sin 3\theta + 1 = 0$

9   If $a \cos \theta = k(b \sin \theta + c \cos \theta)$, where a, b, c and k are constants

   a   show that $\tan \theta = \dfrac{a - kc}{bk}$

   b   Hence, or otherwise, find the values of θ, for $0 \leqslant \theta \leqslant 2\pi$, which satisfy the equation

   $$a \cos \theta = k(b \sin \theta + c \cos \theta)$$

   when $a = 2$, $b = 3$, $c = -1$ and $k = 2$.

10 **a**   Given that $\tan 2\theta$ may be written as

   $$\tan 2\theta = \frac{2 \tan \theta}{1 - \tan^2 \theta}$$

   by using a right-angled triangle, or otherwise, obtain expressions for $\sin 2\theta$ and $\cos 2\theta$ in terms of $\tan \theta$.

   b   Hence, by using these results, or otherwise, show that the equation

   $$\sin 2\theta + \cos 2\theta = 2$$

   has no real solutions.

C2

INVESTIGATION

11 The following appeared in an exam script.

   To solve $\sin x = \sin x \tan x$
   $$1 = \tan x$$
   $$\text{so } x = 45°$$

   Explain why the candidate has missed out some solutions and find these missing solutions.

Give answers correct to three significant figures where appropriate.

1 a Find the vertical height of an equilateral triangle where the sides are of length 7.5 cm.

 b The diagonals of a rhombus are of lengths 12 cm and 10 cm. Find the size of the angles at the vertices of the rhombus.

2 In a triangle, ABC, $AB = 11$ cm, $BC = 14$ cm and $AC = 12$ cm. Use the cosine rule to find the size of angle ACB. Hence find the area of the triangle.

3 In the triangle ABC, $AB = 9$ cm, $BC = 5$ cm and angle $BAC = \dfrac{8\pi}{45}$ radians.

 a Use the sine rule to find the value of $\sin x$, giving your answer to 3 d.p. where angle $ACB = x$ radians.

 Given that there are two possible values of x

 b find these values of x, giving your answers to 2 d.p.

4 A triangle, ABC, is constructed inside a circle, centre O, with points A, B and C on the circumference. The chord AB is of length 15 cm and subtends an angle of 108° at the centre of the circle.

 a What is the radius of the circle?

 The chord AB cuts off a minor segment of the circle.

 b Find the area of this segment.

5 The logo of a performing company is made up of part of a circle and a triangle as shown in the diagram. Angle ACB is 63° and the radius AO, where O is the centre of the circle, is of length 9 cm. Find the total perimeter of the logo.

6 In the diagram OAB is a sector of a circle radius 5 m. The chord AB is 6 m long.

 a Show that $\cos AOB = \dfrac{7}{25}$

 b Hence find the angle AOB in radians, giving your answer to three decimal places.

 c Calculate the area of the sector OAB.

 d Hence calculate the shaded area.

[(c) Edexcel Limited 2006]

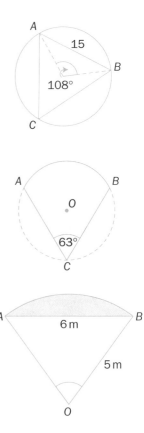

7 **a** Simplify $\sin(180° - \theta)$

 b Given that θ is an acute angle simplify the expression
  $2\cos(90° - \theta) - 3\sin(180° + \theta)$

8 Solve the equation $\sin x = \dfrac{\sqrt{2}}{2}$, writing down all the solutions in
 the interval $-360° \leqslant x \leqslant 360°$.

9 If $\sin x = \dfrac{1}{\sqrt{3}}$ and x is acute state the exact values of $\cos x$ and $\tan x$.

10 **a** Write the values of these ratios, in surd form where appropriate
  $\sin 300°$, $\cos 300°$ and $\tan 300°$.

 b For $-2\pi \leqslant x \leqslant 2\pi$ radians, find the values of x,
  in radians, when $\tan x = -\sqrt{3}$

11 Sketch the graph of $y = \cos x$, where x is measured in radians,
 taking values of x from 0 to 2π.

12 On separate diagrams sketch the graphs of the equations
 a $y = 3 + \sin x$ **b** $y = 3\sin x$
 taking values of x in the interval $0°$ to $180°$.

13 On separate diagrams sketch the graphs of the equations
 a $y = \cos\left(x + \dfrac{\pi}{2}\right)$ **b** $y = \tan 2x$
 where x is measured in radians and for the interval $0 \leqslant x \leqslant 2\pi$

14 **a** Use a graphical method, or otherwise, to show that
  $$\sin x = -\cos(90° + x)$$

 b Simplify the expression
  $$\sin 40° - 2\cos 130°$$

15 Solve, for $0 \leqslant x \leqslant 180°$, the equation
 a $\sin(x + 30°) = \dfrac{1}{2}$
 b $\cos 2x = -0.5$
 c $\tan^2 x = 0.25$, giving your answer to 1 d.p.

12 Exit →

Summary

Refer to

- The sine rule states that $\dfrac{a}{\sin A} = \dfrac{b}{\sin B} = \dfrac{c}{\sin C}$

  12.1

- The cosine rule states that

  $a^2 = b^2 + c^2 - 2bc \cos A,$

  or, alternatively $\cos A = \dfrac{b^2 + c^2 - a^2}{2bc}$

  12.2

- You can find the area of a triangle using

  $\text{area} = \dfrac{1}{2}ab \sin C$

  where the angle is included between the two given sides.

  12.3

- For a sector of radius r and subtended angle θ radians

  - arc length $s = r\theta$

  - $\text{area} = \dfrac{1}{2}r^2\theta$

  12.4

- The trigonometric ratios take different signs according to the quadrant the angle lies in.

  12.5

- Trigonometric curves are transformed by the inclusion of a constant or an angle

  12.8

- You can use trigonometric identities to solve trigonometric equations

  e.g. $\cos^2 x + \sin^2 x \equiv 1$ and $\tan x \equiv \dfrac{\sin x}{\cos x}$

  12.9

Links

Trigonometry occurs wherever angles and distances are involved and as such has a huge range of applications from surveying techniques to architecture.

Mountains have triangulation points, most commonly known as 'trig points'. These have been used to accurately plot the distance and position of one mountain top relative to another.

C2

1 **a** Show that $(x + 3)$ is a factor of $f(x) = x^3 + 4x^2 + x - 6$

b Hence, or otherwise, find the values of x which satisfy $f(x) = 0$

2 **a** When the function $f(x) = 2x^3 + 3x - a$ is divided by $(x - 2)$
the remainder is 12.
Find the value of a.

b Using this value of a show that a solution to $f(x) = 0$ lies in
the interval $x = 1$ to $x = 2$.

3 **a** A circle has centre at $(3, -2)$ and radius 3.
Write down the equation of the circle.

b Show that the y-axis is a tangent to the circle.

c The circle crosses the x-axis at the points A and B.
Find the value of x at these points,
giving your answer correct to two decimal places.

4 **a** Find the equation of the circle which passes through the
points $(1, 3)$ and $(5, 7)$, and has its centre on the line $y - x = 4$

b Determine whether the point $(3, 2)$ lies inside or outside the circle.

5 **a** Without using your calculator evaluate
  i $\log_3 27$
  ii $\log_5 625$

b Use logarithms to work out the values of x when
  i $10^x = 15$
  ii $10^x = 0.5$
  Giving your answers correct to two decimal places.

6 **a** Write as a single logarithm
  i $\log 5 + \log 4 - \log 2$
  ii $2 \log 4 + \log 4 - 3 \log 2$

b Write in terms of sums or differences of $\log a$, $\log b$ and $\log c$

  i $\log a^2 \sqrt{c}$

  ii $2 \log \dfrac{a\sqrt{b}}{c}$

C2

7 a Find the values of x which satisfy the equation $2^{2x} - 5(2^x) = 0$
Give your answers correct to three significant figures.

b Find the value of $\log_5 4$ to three significant figures.

c Solve the equation $\log_3 x + \log_x 3 = 9$

8 a The triangle ABC has sides $AB = 5$ cm, $BC = 8$ cm and
$AC = 7$ cm.
Calculate the size of the angle CAB giving your answer
correct to three significant figures.

b Find the area of the triangle ABC correct to three significant figures.

9 From an observation point, O, a ship, A, is on a bearing of $072°$ Draw a diagram.
and a boat, B, is on a bearing of $124°$.
The distance from the observation point to the boat is 7 km.
Ship A is due north of boat B.
Find the distance between the ship and the boat giving your
answer correct to one decimal place.

10 a Using a right-angled triangle prove that $(\sin x)^2 + (\cos x)^2 \equiv 1$
where x is an angle in the triangle.

b Using the relationship in part **a** find the values of $\sin x$
which satisfy the equation $5 - 6(\cos x)^2 + \sin x = 0$

c Given that x is an acute angle satisfying the equation find
the value of x, writing your answer correct to the nearest degree.

11 a An arc of a circle subtends an angle θ at the
centre of the circle. The length of the arc is 5 cm
and the radius of the circle is 8 cm.
Find the value of θ in degrees to the
nearest whole degree.

b Find the area of the sector containing the angle θ.

12 a Using an equilateral triangle prove that $\tan 60° = \sqrt{3}$

b If $\tan \theta = +\sqrt{3}$ and θ lies in the range $0°$ to $500°$ find all
the possible values of θ.

c If $\sin \theta = \dfrac{2t}{1+t^2}$ and $\cos \theta = \dfrac{1-t^2}{1+t^2}$ find an expression for
$\tan \theta$ in terms of t.

d Write the equation $3 \cos \theta + 4 \sin \theta = 2$ in terms of t and
hence find the values of t which satisfy the equation.
Give your answers correct to two decimal places.

C2

13

Sequences and series

This chapter will show you how to

○ find the general term and sum of a geometric series
○ use Pascal's triangle to expand a bracket raised to a power
○ apply the binomial theorem to expand brackets.

Before you start

You should know how to:

1 Use the sigma notation (Σ) to derive a series.

e.g. Write out the terms in

the series $\sum_{1}^{4} r(r + 1)$

$r = 1$, first term $1 \times 2 = 2$
$r = 2$, second term $2 \times 3 = 6$
$r = 3$, third term $3 \times 4 = 12$
$r = 4$, fourth term $4 \times 5 = 20$
Hence the series is

$2 + 6 + 12 + 20$

2 Solve problems using logarithms.

e.g. Find the least integer
value of n when $3^n > 400$.
Take logarithms to base 10:

$\log 3^n > \log 400$

Use the rules of logarithms:

$n \log 3 > \log 400$

$n > \dfrac{\log 400}{\log 3}$

$n > \dfrac{2.60206}{0.47712}$

$n > 5.4537$

The least integer value satisfying the
inequality is $n = 6$.

Check in:

1 Write out these series. [7]

a $\sum_{1}^{3} 4r$

b $\sum_{3}^{5} (r^2 + 1)$

c $\sum_{2}^{6} (r - 1)$

d $\sum_{1}^{5} r(2r + 3)$

e $\sum_{4}^{7} (3r - 1)(3r + 2)$

2 Find the least integer value [12]
of n which satisfies
each inequality.

a $2^n > 100$

b $1.5^n > 150$

c $1 + 4^n > 1000$

d $1 + 3^n > 2000$

e $2(3)^n > 5000$

A **geometric sequence** is defined by its first term, a, and a common ratio, r.

e.g. Consider the sequence $1, 3, 9, 27, \dots$

The first term is 1

The common ratio is $\dfrac{\text{2nd term}}{\text{1st term}} = \dfrac{\text{3rd term}}{\text{2nd term}} = \dfrac{\text{4th term}}{\text{3rd term}} = \dfrac{(n+1)\text{th term}}{n\text{th term}}$

Hence the common ratio $= 3$

Now look at each term: 1st term $= 1 \times (3)^0$ 2nd term $= 1 \times (3)^1$

                       3rd term $= 1 \times (3)^2$ 4th term $= 1 \times (3)^3$ and so on

○ **The general term of a geometric sequence with first term a and common ratio r is given by nth term $= ar^{n-1}$**

> Is the sequence which begins $1, 4, 9, 16, 25, \dots$ geometric? Explain your answer.

EXAMPLE 1

a Find the general term of the geometric sequence $3, 6, 12, 24, \dots$
b Hence find the 10th and 20th terms of the sequence.

- -

a First term $= 3$

Find the common ratio: $\dfrac{\text{2nd term}}{\text{1st term}} = \dfrac{6}{3} = 2$ Check: $\dfrac{\text{4th term}}{\text{3rd term}} = \dfrac{24}{12} = 2$

Hence nth term $= 3 \times 2^{n-1}$

b Use the general term to find the 10th and 20th terms.

Substitute $n = 10$:   10th term $= 3 \times 2^{10-2} = 768$

Substitute $n = 20$:   20th term $= 3 \times 2^{20-2} = 3 \times 2^{18}$

> You can leave your answers in index form.

Some geometric sequences have a negative common ratio. This gives an **alternating sequence** (a sequence whose terms alternate between positive and negative values).

> e.g If $r = -2$ in Example 1 then the resulting sequence is $3, -6, 12, -24, \dots$

You can find the term at which a sequence reaches a given value.

EXAMPLE 2

Find the first term in the geometric sequence $1, 3, 9, 27, \dots$ to exceed the value of $10\,000$.

- -

First term, $a = 1$, common ratio, $r = 3$

    general term $= 1 \times (3)^{n-1} = 3^{n-1}$

Set up an inequality: $3^{n-1} > 10\,000$

Take logarithms to base 10: $(n-1) \log_{10} 3 > \log_{10} 10\,000$

                      $(n-1)\, 0.47712 > 4$

                            $n - 1 > \dfrac{4}{0.47712}$

                            $n - 1 > 8.3836$

                               $n > 9.3836$

> You are looking for the first value of n for which nth term $> 10\,000$.

Hence $n = 10$ is the first term in the series to exceed the value of $10\,000$.   ▌n must be an integer.

You can check your solution by substituting values into the general term:

9th term $= 3^8 = 6561 < 10\,000$ and 10th term $= 3^9 = 19\,683 > 10\,000$

The terms of a geometric sequence can be algebraic.

The first three terms of a geometric sequence are $(x+1)$, $(x+2)$ and $(x+5)$.
Find the value of each term and the common ratio.

$r = \dfrac{\text{2nd term}}{\text{1st term}} = \dfrac{\text{3rd term}}{\text{2nd term}}$

The ratio between consecutive terms is constant in a geometric sequence.

Substitute the terms: $\dfrac{x+2}{x+1} = \dfrac{x+5}{x+2}$

Rearrange: $(x+2)(x+2) = (x+5)(x+1)$

Expand: $x^2 + 4x + 4 = x^2 + 6x + 5$

Rearrange and solve for x: $-2x = 1$, so $x = -\dfrac{1}{2}$

Substitute $x = -\dfrac{1}{2}$ to find the values of the terms:

1st term $= x+1 = \dfrac{1}{2}$ 2nd term $= x+2 = 1\dfrac{1}{2}$ 3rd term $= x+5 = 4\dfrac{1}{2}$

The common ratio is $r = 1\dfrac{1}{2} \div \dfrac{1}{2} = 3$

Check: $\dfrac{\text{3rd term}}{\text{2nd term}} = \dfrac{4\frac{1}{2}}{1\frac{1}{2}} = 3$

You can use geometric sequences to solve real-life problems.

If £100 is invested in a growth fund which increases by 8% each year find how many completed years have passed before the initial investment has doubled in value.

Some questions will involve a decreasing value.

At the end of year one   value $= 100 + (8\% \text{ of } 100)$
$= 100 + 100 \times 0.08$
$= 100(1 + 0.08)$
$= 100 \times (1.08)$

Take out common factor 100.

At the end of year two   value $= [100 \times (1.08)] \times (1.08)$
$= 100 \times (1.08)^2$

The sum increases by a factor of 1.08 each year.

At the end of year three   value $= [100 \times (1.08)^2] \times (1.08)$
$= 100 \times (1.08)^3$

Hence at end of the nth year value $= 100 \times (1.08)^n$

The terms form a geometric sequence

$100 \times [(1.08), (1.08)^2, (1.08)^3, \ldots, (1.08)^n, \ldots]$

You need the value of n such that $(1.08)^n \geqslant 2$

So that £100 is doubled.

Take logarithms to base 10: $n \log_{10} 1.08 \geqslant \log_{10} 2$

Rearrange: $n \geqslant \dfrac{\log_{10} 2}{\log_{10} 1.08}$

$n \geqslant 9.0065\ldots$

n must be an integer.

Therefore $n = 10$;
investment has more than doubled after 10 years.

Check solution by finding the 9th and 10th terms.

Exercise 13.1

1 Identify which of the following are geometric sequences.
   For those that are, give the common ratio.

   a $1, 2, 3, 4, \ldots$
   b $1, 2, 4, 8, \ldots$
   c $-1, -3, -5, -7, \ldots$

   d $9, 3, 1, \frac{1}{3}, \ldots$
   e $\frac{1}{4}, \frac{1}{2}, 1, 2, \ldots$
   f $4, -8, 16, -32, \ldots$

   g $25, 5, 2\frac{1}{2}, 1\frac{1}{4}, \ldots$
   h $\frac{1}{5}, \frac{1}{10}, \frac{1}{15}, \frac{1}{20}, \ldots$

2 Write down the first four terms of each geometric sequence.

   a first term 3; common ratio 2
   b first term 5; common ratio 3

   c first term $1\frac{1}{2}$; common ratio 2
   d first term 2; common ratio $1\frac{1}{2}$

   e first term -3; common ratio $\frac{1}{2}$
   f first term 5; common ratio -2

   g first term $\frac{1}{4}$; common ratio $-\frac{1}{2}$
   h first term 1; common ratio $\frac{1}{4}$

3 Find the general term of these geometric sequences.

   a $1, 2, 4, 8, \ldots$
   b $\frac{1}{2}, \frac{1}{4}, \frac{1}{8}, \frac{1}{16}, \ldots$
   c $4, 8, 16, 32, \ldots$

   d $\frac{3}{4}, \frac{3}{2}, 3, 6, \ldots$
   e $\frac{2}{5}, 1, 2\frac{1}{2}, 6\frac{1}{4}, \ldots$
   f $6, 30, 150, 750, \ldots$

   g $4, 24, 144, 864, \ldots$
   h $5, -2\frac{1}{2}, 1\frac{1}{4}, -\frac{5}{8}, \ldots$
   i $-3, -\frac{3}{4}, -\frac{3}{16}, -\frac{3}{64}, \ldots$

4 Find the sixth and tenth terms of each geometric sequence.

   a $4, 2, 1, \frac{1}{2}, \ldots$
   b $3, \frac{3}{2}, \frac{3}{4}, \frac{3}{8}, \ldots$
   c $6, 2, \frac{2}{3}, \frac{2}{9}, \ldots$
   d $1, -\frac{3}{4}, \frac{9}{16}, -\frac{27}{64}, \ldots$

5 The general terms of four geometric sequences are given.
   Find the third and seventh terms of each sequence.

   a $3(2)^{n-1}$
   b $5\left(-\frac{1}{2}\right)^{n-1}$
   c $\frac{1}{4}(3)^{n-1}$
   d $(0.1)(-2)^{n-1}$

6 Find the value of a if

   a the first three terms of a geometric sequence are 4, a and 36

   b the first three terms of a geometric sequence are a, $(a+2)$ and $(a+6)$

   c the first three terms of a geometric sequence are 9, a and 2.25.

7 **a** Find the value of x if the first three terms of a geometric sequence are
         $(x+1), (x+3), (x+8)$
         Hence find the common ratio.

   b Find the value of a if the first three terms of a geometric sequence are
         $6a^2, 3a, (a+1)$
         Hence find the common ratio.

8 **a** Find the first term of the geometric sequence
1, 2, 4, 8 … to exceed the value of 5000.

b Find the first term of the sequence
4, 6, 9, 13.5, … to exceed the value 15 000.

c Find the first term of the geometric sequence
$\frac{1}{2}, \frac{1}{4}, \frac{1}{8}, \frac{1}{16}, \dots$ to be less than 0.0001

9 **a** Mary puts £200 into a building society which pays
a fixed rate of compound interest of 5% per annum.
Show that the amount in the account at the end of each
year forms a geometric sequence.
Find how many years have elapsed before the initial investment
is doubled assuming that there are no further deposits or
withdrawals from the account during the time period.

b Chris bought a used Toyota car for £5500 and reckons
that it depreciates in value by 15% each year.
Show that the yearly value is represented by a geometric sequence.
Calculate how many whole years will elapse before
the car is worth half of its original value.

c A 'high-power' ball is dropped from a height on to a hard
surface and bounces up to two-thirds of the original height.
If it is originally dropped from a height of 10 metres
show that the heights to which it bounces form a
geometric sequence and hence find how many bounces the
ball makes before the height reached is 1 metre or less.

d **i** If the second term of a geometric sequence is 12 and
the fifth term is 40.5, find the first five terms.

ii If the sequence $a, ar, ar^2, ar^3, \dots$ is geometric
show that the sequence made up from the square
roots of the terms is also geometric.

C2

INVESTIGATION

10 Box *A* shows five different
sequences.

a Identify which are
geometric sequences.

b Find the next two terms
for each of the
geometric sequences,
choosing from
the terms in box *B*.

A

1,	8,	27
−1,	3,	−9
$\frac{1}{2}$,	1,	2
1,	5,	9
$\frac{1}{3}$,	$\frac{2}{3}$,	$\frac{4}{3}$

B

27	$\frac{8}{3}$
−81	$\frac{16}{3}$
2	−32
4	−1
16	−4
8	81

Sum of a geometric series

○ The sum of the terms of a geometric sequence is called a **geometric series**.

You learned about arithmetic sequences and series in C1.

A geometric sequence has the form $a, ar, ar^2, ar^3, \ldots, ar^{n-1}, ar^n, ar^{n+1}, \ldots$

A geometric series has the form $a + ar + ar^2 + ar^3 + \ldots + ar^{n-1} + ar^n + ar^{n+1} + \ldots$

You can find the sum to n terms, S_n, of a geometric series.

$$S_n = a + ar + ar^2 + ar^3 + \ldots + ar^{n-2} + ar^{n-1} \quad (1)$$

Multiply each term by the common ratio r:

$$rS_n = ar + ar^2 + ar^3 + ar^4 + \ldots + ar^{n-1} + ar^n \quad (2)$$

$(1) - (2)$: $S_n - rS_n = (a + ar + ar^2 + ar^3 + \ldots + ar^{n-2} + ar^{n-1})$
$$- (ar + ar^2 + ar^3 + ar^4 \ldots + ar^{n-1} + ar^n)$$

$\therefore S_n - rS_n = a - ar^n$

Factorise: $S_n(1 - r) = a(1 - r^n)$

$$S_n = \frac{a(1 - r^n)}{1 - r}$$

Subtracting (1) from (2) gives the alternative form

$$S_n = \frac{a(r^n - 1)}{r - 1}$$

Show this for yourself.

○ The sum to n terms, S_n, of a geometric series is

$$S_n = \frac{a(1 - r^n)}{1 - r} \quad \text{or} \quad S_n = \frac{a(r^n - 1)}{r - 1}$$

Learn this result and how to derive it.

EXAMPLE 1

Find the sum of the first eight terms of the geometric series $3 + 6 + 12 + 24 + \ldots$

First term $\qquad a = 3$
Common ratio $\qquad r = 2$
Number of terms to be summed $\qquad n = 8$

Use the formula for S_n:
$$S_n = \frac{a(r^n - 1)}{r - 1}$$

Use this form when $r > 1$ to avoid negative terms.

Substitute the values:
$$S_n = \frac{3(2^8 - 1)}{2 - 1}$$

Simplify:
$$S_n = \frac{3(256 - 1)}{1}$$

$$S_n = 3 \times 255$$

$$S_n = 765$$

Hence the sum of the first eight terms of the series is 765.

C2

You can find the term at which the sum of a series exceeds a given value.

The sum of the geometric series, $2 + 6 + 18 + 54 + \ldots$, exceeds 5000
Find the number of terms.

Use the formula $S_n = \dfrac{a(r^n - 1)}{r - 1}$ where $a = 2$ and $r = 3$:

$\qquad$ You need the value of n such that $S_n > 5000$.

Set up an inequality: $\qquad \dfrac{a(r^n - 1)}{r - 1} > 5000$

$\qquad\qquad\qquad \dfrac{2(3^n - 1)}{3 - 1} > 5000$

Simplify: $\qquad\qquad 3^n - 1 > 5000$

$\qquad\qquad\qquad 3^n > 5001$

Take logarithms to base 10: $\quad n \log_{10} 3 > \log_{10} 5001 \qquad$ Divide both sides by $\log_{10} 3$.

$\qquad\qquad\qquad n > 7.753$

Hence the number of terms required is 8. $\qquad$ n must be an integer.

You can solve real-life problems which involve the sum of a sequence.

Simon invests £500 in a savings scheme at a fixed rate of interest of 4.5% per annum. He invests a further £500 on each yearly anniversary of the first deposit. Assuming that no withdrawals are made, calculate the accumulated sum in the scheme at the end of the eighth year.

Start of first year $\qquad$ amount = £500

End of first year $\qquad$ amount = £500 × 1.045 $\qquad$ Original amount + interest

Start of second year $\qquad$ amount = £500 + (£500 × 1.045)

End of second year $\qquad$ amount = [£500 + (£500 × 1.045)] × 1.045
$\qquad\qquad\qquad\qquad\qquad = £500 \times 1.045 + £500 \times (1.045)^2$

Start of third year $\qquad$ amount = £500 + [£500 × 1.045 + £500 × $(1.045)^2$]

End of third year $\qquad$ amount = {£500 + [£500 × 1.045 + £500 × $(1.045)^2$]} × 1.045
$\qquad\qquad\qquad\qquad\qquad = £500 \times (1.045) + £500 \times (1.045)^2 + £500 \times (1.045)^3$

And so on until the end of the eighth year.

This leads to a geometric series (based on the amount at the *end* of each year)

$\qquad £500 \times (1.045) + £500 \times (1.045)^2 + £500 \times (1.045)^3 + \ldots + £500 \times (1.045)^8$

First term $\qquad a = £500 \times 1.045 = £522.50$

Common ratio $\quad r = 1.045 \qquad$ Number of terms $\quad n = 8$

Use the formula for the sum of the series $\quad S_n = \dfrac{a(r^n - 1)}{r - 1}$:

$$S_8 = \frac{£522.50[(1.045)^8 - 1]}{1.045 - 1} = £4901.06 \text{ to nearest penny}$$

Hence the total sum in the savings scheme after eight years is £4901.06.

Exercise 13.2

1 Find the sum of each geometric series.
Give your answers to a suitable degree of accuracy.

a $1 + 2 + 4 + 8 + \ldots$ to 9 terms

b $2 + -4 + 8 + -16 + \ldots$ to 8 terms

c $\frac{1}{2} + \frac{1}{4} + \frac{1}{8} + \frac{1}{16} + \ldots$ to 12 terms

d $3 + 4.5 + 6.75 + 10.125 + \ldots$ to 8 terms

e $0.1 + 0.2 + 0.4 + 0.8 + \ldots$ to 10 terms

f $7 + \frac{7}{3} + \frac{7}{9} + \frac{7}{27} + \ldots$ to 12 terms

2 Evaluate the sum of each geometric series.
Give your answers in index form.

a $\sum_{1}^{6} 3^r$

b $\sum_{1}^{8} (0.5)^r$

c $\sum_{1}^{5} 3(2)^r$

d $\sum_{1}^{8} 0.5(-2)^r$

e $\sum_{1}^{10} 2\left(\frac{1}{3}\right)^r$

f $\sum_{1}^{9} 1.5\left(-\frac{1}{2}\right)^r$

3 Find the number of terms needed for the sum of each geometric
series to exceed the given limit.

a geometric series $1 + 2 + 4 + 8 + \ldots$, limit 4000.

b geometric series $5 + 7.5 + 11.25 + 16.875 + \ldots$, limit 10 000.

4 a Find the least value of n such that $\sum_{1}^{n} 2(3)^r > 10^5$

b Find the least value of n such that $\sum_{1}^{n} 0.5(1.1)^r > 10$

5 a The first term of a geometric series is 6 and the fourth term is 0.75.
Write down the first five terms and find their sum.

b If the second term of a geometric series is 7.5 and the
fourth term is 16.875, find the first and third terms
of the series and the sum of the first four terms.

6 The sum of the geometric series, $6 + 12 + 24 + 48 + \ldots$, is 6138.
Find how many terms are needed to obtain this sum.

7 If the second term of a geometric series is 24 and the third term is
$3(x + 1)$ find, in terms of x, the first term.
The sum of the first three terms of the series is 84.
Find the possible values of x.

8 **a** The first term of a geometric series is x and the second term is y.
What is the fourth term of the series?
Deduce the nth term and hence write down the nineteenth term.

  b The sum of the first three terms of the geometric series,
$a + at^2 + at^4 + \ldots$, is equal to seven times the first term.
Show that the equation, $t^4 + t^2 - 6 = 0$, satisfies
this condition and find the possible values of t.

9 **a** William invests £100 in a Building Society at a compound
interest rate of 5% per annum. He invests a further
£100 on each anniversary of his first deposit.
Assuming that no withdrawals are made how much money will
have accumulated in the account at the end of the tenth year?

  b Harriet is saving up to buy a car. She deposits £250
each year, on her birthday, into a savings account
paying compound interest at 4% per annum.
If she continues to make this investment over a period of eight
years how much will be in the account at the end of the period?

  c Mark is taking a walking holiday in the Lake District
and aims to walk 10 km on the first day. He decides
to increase the distance he walks each day by 3%.
How far will he walk on the 14th day?
What total distance will he have walked during the 14-day holiday?

  d Lorraine is taking part in a trial to lose weight.
On the first day the total intake of food and
drink is limited to 3000 calories.
This is then reduced by 7.5% each day over a period of
14 days, which is the duration of the trial.
The guideline daily amount is 2000 calories.
Find the mean daily calorie intake during the 14-day trial
and state whether this falls above or below the
guideline daily amount and by how much it differs.

INVESTIGATION

10 A geometric sequence is such that its common ratio is $\frac{1}{2}$
and the sum of its first three terms is an integer.

  a Find the possible values of the first term.

  b Give three sequences that fit this criteria.

A geometric series can be either convergent or divergent.

- The sum of a divergent series has no limit.

e.g. Consider the sum of the series $\quad 1 + 3 + 9 + 27 + \ldots$

$$S_2 = 1 + 3 \qquad\qquad\qquad = 4$$
$$S_3 = 1 + 3 + 9 \qquad\qquad = 13$$
$$S_4 = 1 + 3 + 9 + 27 \qquad = 40$$
$$S_5 = 1 + 3 + 9 + 27 + 81 \quad = 121 \quad \text{and so on}$$

The terms are increasing in value. This is a divergent series and its sum tends towards infinity.

- The sum of a convergent series tends towards a specific value as the number of terms increases towards infinity. The limit of the sum of a convergent series is known as the sum to infinity.

e.g. Consider the sum of the series $1 + \dfrac{1}{3} + \dfrac{1}{9} + \dfrac{1}{27} + \ldots$

$$S_2 = 1 + \frac{1}{3} \qquad\qquad\qquad\qquad = 1.33\ldots$$
$$S_3 = 1 + \frac{1}{3} + \frac{1}{9} \qquad\qquad\qquad = 1.44\ldots$$
$$S_4 = 1 + \frac{1}{3} + \frac{1}{9} + \frac{1}{27} \qquad\qquad = 1.48148\ldots$$
$$S_2 = 1 + \frac{1}{3} + \frac{1}{9} + \frac{1}{27} + \frac{1}{81} \quad = 1.4938\ldots \text{ and so on}$$

The sum of this series tends towards the value 1.5. 1.5 is called the sum to infinity of the series. This is a convergent series.

- A geometric series converges if and only if $|r| < 1$ where r is the common ratio of the series.

$|r| < 1$ means the absolute value of r is less than 1. $-1 < r < 1$ is another way of writing it.

You can find the sum to infinity of a convergent geometric series.

Consider the sum to n terms of a convergent geometric series with first term a and common ratio r:

$$S_n = \frac{a(1 - r^n)}{1 - r}$$

For a convergent series, $|r| < 1$, so $r^n \to 0$ as $n \to \infty$

Therefore $S_\infty = \dfrac{a(1 - 0)}{1 - r} = \dfrac{a}{1 - r}$

Use this form when $|r| < 1$

Try some values on your calculator.

S_∞ stands for 'sum to infinity'.

- The sum to infinity of a convergent geometric series is
$$S_\infty = \frac{a}{1 - r} \quad \text{where } |r| < 1$$

S_∞ is a limit. It is never actually reached.

C2

EXAMPLE 1

Find the sum to infinity of the series $\quad 1, \frac{1}{3}, \frac{1}{9}, \frac{1}{27}, \ldots$

$\frac{1}{3} < 1$, so the series is convergent.

First term, $a = 1$ Common ratio, $r = \frac{1}{3}$

Number of terms $\quad n \to \infty$

$$S_\infty = \frac{1}{1 - \frac{1}{3}} = \frac{3}{2}$$

Using the formula $S_\infty = \frac{a}{1-r}$

You can represent a geometric series using sigma notation.

EXAMPLE 2

A series is given by $\quad \displaystyle\sum_1^n \left(\frac{1}{4}\right)^r$

Σ is the Greek letter sigma, meaning sum.

$\displaystyle\sum_1^n (r)$ is the sum of r from $r = 1$ to $r = n$

Find the sum when $\quad$ **a** $n = 5$ $\quad$ **b** $n \to \infty$

$$\sum_1^n \left(\frac{1}{4}\right)^r = \left(\frac{1}{4}\right) + \left(\frac{1}{4}\right)^2 + \left(\frac{1}{4}\right)^3 + \ldots + \left(\frac{1}{4}\right)^n$$

First term, $a = \frac{1}{4}$ $\quad$ Common ratio, $r = \frac{1}{4}$

a Number of terms $n = 5$

$$S_5 = \frac{\frac{1}{4}\left[1 - \left(\frac{1}{4}\right)^5\right]}{1 - \frac{1}{4}} = \frac{\left[1 - \left(\frac{1}{4}\right)^5\right]}{3} = 0.333 \quad \text{to 3 s.f.}$$

Using $S_n = \frac{a(1 - r^n)}{1 - r}$

b $S_\infty = \dfrac{\frac{1}{4}}{1 - \frac{1}{4}} = \dfrac{\frac{1}{4}}{\frac{3}{4}} = \dfrac{1}{3}$

Using $S_\infty = \frac{a}{1-r}$

Compare the answers to parts **a** and **b**.

C2

Exercise 13.3

1 Find the sum to infinity of each geometric series.

a $\quad 2 + 1 + \frac{1}{2} + \frac{1}{4} + \ldots$

b $\quad 7 + 3.5 + 1.75 + 0.875 + \ldots$

c $\quad 12 - 2 + \frac{1}{3} - \frac{1}{18} + \ldots$

d $\quad 5.4 + 1.8 + 0.6 + 0.2 + \ldots$

e $\quad -8 - 2 - 0.5 - 0.125 - \ldots$

f $\quad 0.5 + 0.1 + 0.02 + 0.004 + \ldots$

g $\quad \displaystyle\sum_1^\infty \left(\frac{4}{5}\right)^r$

h $\quad \displaystyle\sum_1^\infty 2\left(\frac{3}{4}\right)^r$

i $\quad a + a^2 + a^3 + a^4 + \ldots,$ where $-1 < a < 1$ $\quad$ **j** $\displaystyle\sum_1^\infty 2\left(\frac{a}{3}\right)^r,$ where $-3 < a < 3$

2 **a** The third term of a geometric series is 4 and the fifth term is 1. Find the sum to infinity of the series.

$\quad$ **b** The first term of a geometric series is p and the common ratio is $2p$. If the sum to infinity is 4 find the value of p.

Pascal's triangle

Consider the following expressions   Look at the coefficients

$(x + y)^1 \quad = x + y$ 1   1

$(x + y)^2 \quad = (x + y)(x + y)$
$\qquad\qquad = x^2 + 2xy + y^2$ 1   2   1

$(x + y)^3 \quad = (x + y)(x^2 + 2xy + y^2)$
$\qquad\qquad = x^3 + 3x^2y + 3xy^2 + y^3$ 1   3   3   1

$(x + y)^4 \quad = (x + y)(x^3 + 3x^2y + 3xy^2 + y^3)$
$\qquad\qquad = x^4 + 4x^3y + 6x^2y^2 + 4xy^3 + y^4$ 1   4   6   4   1

You can display the coefficients together in a triangular pattern

$3 = 1 + 2$

$4 = 3 + 1$

The rows begin and end with the number 1.
The coefficients are generated by adding the terms either side on the row above.

You can continue this pattern to give Pascal's triangle.

○ The first eight rows of Pascal's triangle are

```
                    1
                 1     1
              1     2     1
           1     3     3     1
        1     4     6     4     1
     1     5    10    10     5     1
  1     6    15    20    15     6     1
1     7    21    35    35    21     7     1
```

$(x + y)^0 = 1$

You can use Pascal's triangle to expand $(1 + x)^2$, $(1 + x)^3$, $(1 + x)^4$, etc

---

EXAMPLE 1

Expand $(1 + x)^6$

From Pascal's triangle you know the coefficients are
    1, 6, 15, 20, 15, 6, 1   For $(1 + x)^6$ use row 7.

Expand using these coefficients:
    $(1 + x)^6 = 1 + 6x + 15x^2 + 20x^3 + 15x^4 + 6x^5 + x^6$ $1^6 = 1$

C2

You can use Pascal's triangle to expand brackets containing other terms.

EXAMPLE 2

Find the expansion of $(1 + 3x)^4$

Use the coefficients 1, 4, 6, 4, 1:

$$(1 + 3x)^4 = 1^4 + 4(3x) + 6(3x)^2 + 4(3x)^3 + (3x)^4$$
$$= 1 + 12x + 54x^2 + 108x^3 + 81x^4$$

Use row 5.

Treat $3x$ as the variable.

EXAMPLE 3

Find the expansion of $(1 - 2x)^6$

Use the coefficients 1, 6, 15, 20, 15, 6, 1:

$$(1 - 2x)^6 = 1^6 + 6(-2x) + 15(-2x)^2 + 20(-2x)^3$$
$$+ 15(-2x)^4 + 6(-2x)^5 + (-2x)^6$$
$$= 1 - 12x + 60x^2 - 160x^3 + 240x^4 - 192x^5 + 64x^6$$

Treat $-2x$ as the variable.

Take care with the negative signs.

To expand expressions such as $(a + x)^n$, where $a \neq 1$, you can take the factor a out of the bracket first.

C2

EXAMPLE 4

Expand $(3 + x)^4$

Take out the factor 3:

$$(3 + x)^4 = \left(3\left(1 + \frac{x}{3}\right)\right)^4 = 3^4\left(1 + \frac{x}{3}\right)^4$$

The sum of the powers of each term are equal to 4. e.g. in $6(3)^2x^2$; $2 + 2 = 4$ As the powers of 3 decrease the powers of x increase.

Expand using the coefficients 1, 4, 6, 4, 1:

$$3^4\left(1 + \frac{x}{3}\right)^4 = 81\left(1 + 4\left(\frac{x}{3}\right) + 6\left(\frac{x}{3}\right)^2 + 4\left(\frac{x}{3}\right)^3 + \left(\frac{x}{3}\right)^4\right)$$

$$= 81 + 108x + 54x^2 + 12x^3 + x^4$$

Hence $\quad (3 + x)^4 = 81 + 108x + 54x^2 + 12x^3 + x^4$

You can use Pascal's triangle to expand expressions involving two or more brackets.

EXAMPLE 5

Multiply out completely $(1 + x)(2 - x)^3$

Use the coefficients, 1, 3, 3, 1, for the second bracket:

$$(1 + x)(2 - x)^3 = (1 + x)[(2)^3 + 3(2)^2(-x) + 3(2)(-x)^2 + (-x)^3]$$
$$= (1 + x)\,[8 - 12x + 6x^2 - x^3]$$

Expand: $\quad = 8 - 12x + 6x^2 - x^3 + 8x - 12x^2 + 6x^3 - x^4$

Simplify: $\quad = 8 - 4x - 6x^2 + 5x^3 - x^4$

You can use Pascal's triangle to find missing constants.

EXAMPLE 6

In the expansion of $(a + x)(1 + x)^3$ the coefficient of x is 13. Find the value of the constant a.

Expand the second bracket using Pascal's triangle:

$$(a + x)(1 + x)^3 = (a + x)(1 + 3x + 3x^2 + x^3)$$
$$= a + 3ax + 3ax^2 + ax^3 + x + 3x^2 + 3x^3 + x^4$$

Collect like terms: $\quad = a + (3a + 1)x + (3a + 3)x^2 + (a + 3)x^3 + x^4$

The coefficient of x is 13

so $3a + 1 = 13$

$$a = \frac{12}{3} = 4$$

Hence the value is a is 4.

Exercise 13.4

1 Use Pascal's triangle to expand these brackets.

  a $(1 + x)^5$ b $(1 - x)^4$ c $(1 + 2x)^3$

  d $(1 - 3x)^4$ e $\left(1 + \frac{x}{2}\right)^3$ f $(1 - 2x)^5$

  g $(1 + 4x)^3$ h $(1 + 2x)^7$

2 Use Pascal's triangle to expand these brackets.

  a $(2 + x)^4$ b $(3 - x)^4$ c $(2 + 3x)^3$

  d $(3 - 2x)^5$ e $(3x - 4)^3$ f $(2x - 1)^6$

  g $\left(\frac{x}{2} - 1\right)^4$ h $(x^2 + y^2)^3$

3 Expand each expression completely and simplify the result.

  a $(1 + x)(1 - x)^4$ b $(2 - x)(1 + x)^4$

  c $(1 - x)(1 + 2x)^3$ d $(x + 3)^2(x - 1)^3$

4 Expand these brackets and simplify the result.

  a $(1 + x + x^2)^3$ b $[1 + (x - 1)^2]^3$

  c $(x^2 + x - 2)^3$ d $(a + b + c)^3$

5 a Find the coefficient of x^3 in the expansion of $x^2(1-x)^3$

b Find the coefficient of x in the expansion of $(1+x)^3(1-x)^4$

c Find the term in x^3 in the expansion of $(1-x)^3(1+2x)^4$

d Find the term in x^3 in the expansion of $(1+x)(1-3x)^5$

6 a In the expansion of $(1+ax)(1-x)^5$ the term in x^3 has a coefficient of 20.
Find the value of the constant a.

b In the expansion of $(a+bx)(1+x)^4$ the coefficient of x is 7 and the coefficient of x^2 is 8.
Find the value of a and the value of b.
Hence determine the coefficient of x^3.

7 Find the term independent of x in the expansion of $\left(x+\dfrac{1}{2x}\right)^4$

A term independent of x is a term without an x.

8 a In the expansion of $(a+b)^5$ the ratio of the second term to the third term is $3:4$.
Use this information to find the ratio of $a:b$.

b For the expansion of $(1+a)^3(1+b)^4$ find the value of the constant k in the term ka^2b^2.

c In the expansion of $(1+a)^2(1-x)^5$ the coefficient of x^2 is equal to 40.
Find the two possible values of a which satisfy this condition.

INVESTIGATION

9 Consider expanding an expression of the form
$$\left(x+\frac{1}{x}\right)^n$$

a Give the expansion when
  i $n=3$
  ii $n=4$.

b Hence give conditions on n such that the expansion gives a term independent of x.

The binomial theorem

Factorials

- The factorial of a number is the product of all the positive integers up to and including that number.
- Factorial n is denoted $n!$
- $n! = n \times (n-1) \times (n-2) \times \ldots \times 3 \times 2 \times 1$

- By definition $0! = 1$

e.g. Factorial $5 = 5 \times 4 \times 3 \times 2 \times 1$

e.g. $10! = 10 \times 9 \times 8 \times 7 \times 6$
$\times 5 \times 4 \times 3 \times 2 \times 1$

You can simplify fractions containing factorials by cancelling common factors.

EXAMPLE 1

a Evaluate $\dfrac{7!}{4!}$ **b** Simplify $\dfrac{(n-1)!}{(n-3)!}$

a $\dfrac{7!}{4!} = \dfrac{7 \times 6 \times 5 \times 4 \times 3 \times 2 \times 1}{4 \times 3 \times 2 \times 1} = 7 \times 6 \times 5 = 210$

b $\dfrac{(n-1)!}{(n-3)!} = \dfrac{(n-1)(n-2)(n-3)!}{(n-3)!}$

$= (n-1)(n-2) = n^2 - 3n + 2$

$(n-1)!$
$= (n-1)(n-2)(n-3)(n-4)$
$\times \ldots \times 3 \times 2 \times 1$
$= (n-1)(n-2)(n-3)!$

Permutations

- A permutation is an arrangement of n items.

EXAMPLE 2

How many different ways can you arrange the letters A, B and C?

Investigate with four or more letters.

The number of possible outcomes is

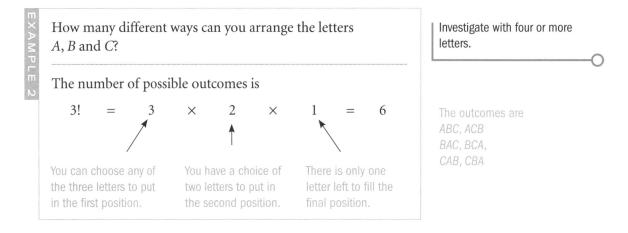

$3! \quad = \quad 3 \quad \times \quad 2 \quad \times \quad 1 \quad = \quad 6$

You can choose any of the three letters to put in the first position.   You have a choice of two letters to put in the second position.   There is only one letter left to fill the final position.

The outcomes are
ABC, ACB
BAC, BCA,
CAB, CBA

- The number of permutations of n items is $n!$

C2

If you only choose some of the *n* items there will be fewer permutations.

EXAMPLE 3

Four books are chosen from six different titles.
How many different permutations are there?

Any of the 6 books can be chosen first
→   6 choices

Any of the 5 remaining books can be chosen second, and each choice can be combined with any of the first choices.
→ 6×5 permutations

Any of the 4 remaining books can be chosen third.
→ $6 \times 5 \times 4$ permutations

Any of the 3 remaining books can be chosen for the last choice.
→ $6 \times 5 \times 4 \times 3$ permutations

In Example 3 the number of permutations $= 6 \times 5 \times 4 \times 3$
$$= \frac{6 \times 5 \times 4 \times 3 \times 2 \times 1}{2 \times 1}$$
$$= \frac{6!}{(6-4)!}$$

C2

○ The number of permutations of *r* items chosen from a total of *n* items is $\dfrac{n!}{(n-r)!}$

If the order of the items is not important then there are fewer **combinations**.

A combination is a permutation in which order does not matter.

EXAMPLE 4

How many ways can four books be chosen from six books if the order doesn't matter?

From Example 3 you know that the number of permutations of 4 books chosen from 6 is $\dfrac{6!}{(6-4)!}$

The number of permutations of each possible set of 4 books is 4!
However, the order of the books within each set is not important.

∴ number of combinations $= \dfrac{6!}{4!(6-4)!}$
$$= \frac{6 \times 5}{2!}$$
$$= 15$$

- The number of possible combinations of r items chosen from n items when order does not matter is

$$^nC_r = \frac{n!}{(n-r)!\,r!}$$

^nC_r can also be written $\binom{n}{r}$ and stands for 'n choose r'.

'n choose r' means that you choose r items from a total of n items.

EXAMPLE 5

Evaluate   **a** $\binom{5}{3}$ **b** $\binom{10}{7}$

a Use $\binom{n}{r} = \frac{n!}{(n-r)!\,r!}$:

$$\binom{5}{3} = \frac{5!}{(5-3)!\,3!} = \frac{5!}{2!\,3!} = \frac{5\times4\times3!}{2!\times3!} = \frac{5\times4}{2\times1} = 10$$

b Use $\binom{n}{r} = \frac{n!}{(n-r)!\,r!}$:

$$\binom{10}{7} = \frac{10!}{(10-7)!\,7!} = \frac{10!}{3!\,7!} = \frac{10\times9\times8\times7!}{3!\times7!}$$

$$= \frac{10\times9\times8}{3\times2\times1} = \frac{720}{6} = 120$$

You can use combinations to expand an expression of the form $(a+x)^n$

- The binomial expansion of $(a+x)^n$ is

$$(a+x)^n = \binom{n}{0}a^n + \binom{n}{1}xa^{n-1} + \binom{n}{2}x^2a^{n-2} + \binom{n}{3}x^3a^{n-3} + \ldots + \binom{n}{n}x^n$$

This is the binomial expansion of $(a+x)^n$.

EXAMPLE 6

Find the first four terms in the expansion of $(1+2x)^7$

Use the binomial theorem

$$(1+x)^n = 1 + nx + \frac{n(n-1)(x)^2}{2!} + \frac{n(n-1)(n-2)(x)^3}{3!} + \ldots:$$

$$(1+2x)^7 = 1 + (7)(2x) + \frac{(7)(6)(2x)^2}{(2)(1)} + \frac{(7)(6)(5)(2x)^3}{(3)(2)(1)} + \ldots$$

$n = 7$
Replace x with $2x$.

Simplify:

$$(1+2x)^7 = 1 + 14x + 84x^2 + 280x^3 + \ldots$$

EXAMPLE 7

Find the first four terms in the expansion of $(1 - 3x)^5$

Use the binomial theorem

$$(1 + x)^n = 1 + nx + \frac{n(n - 1)(x)^2}{2!} + \frac{n(n - 1)(n - 2)(x)^3}{3!} + \ldots :$$

$n = 5$
Replace x with $-3x$

$$(1 - 3x)^5 = 1 + (5)(-3x) + \frac{(5)(4)}{(2)(1)}(-3x)^2 + \frac{(5)(4)(3)}{(3)(2)(1)}(-3x)^3 + \ldots$$

Simplify:

$$(1 - 3x)^5 = 1 - 15x + (10)(9x^2) - (10)(27x^3) + \ldots$$

$$= 1 - 15x + 90x^2 - 270x^3 + \ldots$$

Examples 6 and 7 involved expressions of the form $(a + bx)^n$ where a, b and n are constants.

○ The binomial expansion of $(a + bx)^n$ is

$$(a + bx)^n = \binom{n}{0}a^n + \binom{n}{1}bxa^{n-1} + \binom{n}{2}(bx)^2a^{n-2} + \binom{n}{3}(bx)^3a^{n-3} + \ldots + \binom{n}{n}(bx)^n$$

EXAMPLE 8

Find the first three terms in the expansion of $(2 + 3x)^5$

Use the binomial theorem

$$(a + bx)^n = \binom{n}{0}a^n + \binom{n}{1}bxa^{n-1} + \binom{n}{2}(bx)^2a^{n-2} + \binom{n}{3}(bx)^3a^{n-3} + \ldots + \binom{n}{n}(bx)^n :$$

$a = 2$
$b = 3$
$n = 5$

$$(2 + 3x)^5 = 2^5 + \binom{5}{1}(2)^4(3x) + \binom{5}{2}(2)^3(3x)^2 + \ldots$$

$$= 32 + 240x + 720x^2 + \ldots$$

When x is very small, higher powers of x will become increasingly smaller and so can be neglected after a point.

e.g. $0.05^5 = 0.000\,000\,3$

C2

EXAMPLE 9

If x is small such that terms in x^3 and higher can be neglected, find the approximate expansion of $(1 - x)(1 - 2x)^5$

Use the binomial theorem to expand the second bracket:

$$(1 - x)(1 - 2x)^5 = (1 - x)\left[1 + (5)(-2x) + \frac{(5)(4)}{(2)(1)}(-2x)^2 + \ldots\right]$$

$n = 5$, $b = -2$, $a = 1$

$$= (1 - x)[1 - 10x + 40x^2 + \ldots]$$

An approximation means that you only give an appropriate number of terms.

Expand:

$$(1 - x)(1 - 2x)^5 = 1 - 10x + 40x^2 + \ldots - x + 10x^2 + \ldots$$

$$= 1 - 11x + 50x^2 + \ldots$$

Hence the first three terms are $1 - 11x + 50x^2$

Hence $(1 - x)(1 - 2x)^5 \approx 1 - 11x + 50x^2$

Expansions are written with the powers of x in ascending order.

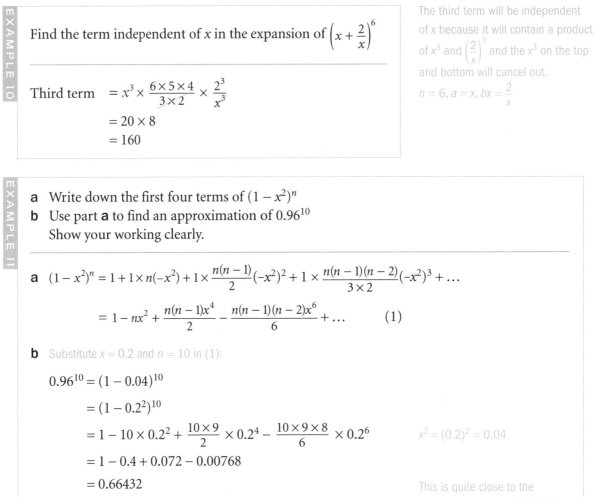

C2

EXAMPLE 10

Find the term independent of x in the expansion of $\left(x + \dfrac{2}{x}\right)^6$

The third term will be independent of x because it will contain a product of x^3 and $\left(\dfrac{2}{x}\right)^3$ and the x^3 on the top and bottom will cancel out.

$n = 6$, $a = x$, $bx = \dfrac{2}{x}$

Third term $= x^3 \times \dfrac{6 \times 5 \times 4}{3 \times 2} \times \dfrac{2^3}{x^3}$

$\qquad = 20 \times 8$

$\qquad = 160$

EXAMPLE 11

a Write down the first four terms of $(1 - x^2)^n$

b Use part **a** to find an approximation of 0.96^{10}

Show your working clearly.

a $(1 - x^2)^n = 1 + 1 \times n(-x^2) + 1 \times \dfrac{n(n-1)}{2}(-x^2)^2 + 1 \times \dfrac{n(n-1)(n-2)}{3 \times 2}(-x^2)^3 + \ldots$

$\qquad = 1 - nx^2 + \dfrac{n(n-1)x^4}{2} - \dfrac{n(n-1)(n-2)x^6}{6} + \ldots \qquad (1)$

b Substitute $x = 0.2$ and $n = 10$ in (1):

$0.96^{10} = (1 - 0.04)^{10}$

$\qquad = (1 - 0.2^2)^{10}$

$\qquad = 1 - 10 \times 0.2^2 + \dfrac{10 \times 9}{2} \times 0.2^4 - \dfrac{10 \times 9 \times 8}{6} \times 0.2^6 \qquad x^2 = (0.2)^2 = 0.04$

$\qquad = 1 - 0.4 + 0.072 - 0.00768$

$\qquad = 0.66432$

This is quite close to the calculator answer of 0.66483

Hence $0.96^{10} \approx 0.66432$

Exercise 13.5

1 Find the value of the following factorial expressions.

    a $5!$ **b** $7!$ **c** $\dfrac{9!}{6!}$ **d** $\dfrac{3!}{5!}$

    e $3! \times 4!$ **f** $2! \times 4! \times 6!$ **g** $\dfrac{4!\,5!}{3!}$ **h** $2! + 3! + 4!$

2 Find the value of each expression.

    a $\dbinom{4}{2}$ **b** $\dbinom{5}{2}$ **c** $\dbinom{6}{3}$ **d** $\dbinom{6}{5}$

    e $\dbinom{7}{4}$ **f** $\dbinom{8}{6}$ **g** $\dbinom{9}{4}$ **h** $\dbinom{9}{2}$

3 Use the binomial theorem to find the first four terms in each expansion.

Write the terms in ascending order of powers of x.

    a $(1 + x)^9$ **b** $(1 + 2x)^8$ **c** $(1 - x)^{10}$

    d $(1 + 3x)^6$ **e** $(1 - 3x)^7$ **f** $\left(1 + \dfrac{x}{2}\right)^8$

4 Use the binomial theorem to obtain the first three terms in each expansion.

a $(2+x)^7$ **b** $(3-x)^8$ **c** $\left(2+\dfrac{x}{2}\right)^{10}$

d $\left(\dfrac{1}{2}-x\right)^8$ **e** $(2+3x)^6$ **f** $(x-4)^7$

5 a In the expansion of $(1+ax)(2-3x)^5$ the coefficient of x^2 is 240. What is the value of the constant a?

b If $(1+2x)^5 + (1-2x)^5 \approx a + bx + cx^2$, find the values of the constants a, b and c.

c What is the coefficient of x^3 in the expansion of $(1-2x)(1+2x)^7$?

d In the expansion of $(1+x)(1-x)^n$ the first three terms in ascending order of powers of x are $1, -3x$ and $2x^2$. Find the value of n.

e Find the term independent of x in the expansion of $\left(x+\dfrac{1}{x}\right)^8$

6 a If x is so small that terms in x^3 and higher powers may be neglected show that
$$(1+x)(1-2x)^4 \approx 1 - 7x + 16x^2$$

b If x is small such that terms in x^2 and greater powers of x can be disregarded, show that
$$(2+3x)(1-2x)^6 \approx 2 - 21x$$

7 a Write down the sixth term in the expansion of $(x+2y)^{10}$ in ascending powers of x.

b Find the first four terms in the expansion of $(1+x+x^2)^7$ in ascending powers of x.

Write as $[(1+x)+x^2]^7$.

c Given that $(1-x)^n = 1 + ax + bx^2 + cx^3 + \dots$, where a, b and c are constants, find the possible values of n such that $2b = c + a$

d Write down the first four terms in the expansion of $(1-x)^n$. Use the expansion to four terms to determine the value of $(0.9)^{10}$ showing your working clearly. Estimate the percentage error caused by taking only the first four terms in the expansion.

Let $x = 0.1$

1 The second term of a geometric series is 4, the third term is x and the fourth term is 36. Find

   a   the common ratio

   b   the first term of the series

   c   the value of x.

2 The second and fourth terms of a geometric series are 7.2 and 5.832 respectively.
The common ratio of the series is positive.
For this series, find

   a   the common ratio

   b   the first term

   c   the sum of the first 50 terms, giving your answer to three decimal places

   d   the difference between the sum to infinity and the sum of the first 50 terms, giving your answer to three decimal places.   [(c) Edexcel Limited 2005]

3 The first term of a geometric series is 2. The sum to infinity of the series is 4.

   a   Show that the common ratio, r, is $\frac{1}{2}$.

   b   Find, to two decimal places, the difference between the sixth and seventh terms.

   c   Calculate the sum of the first ten terms correct to three decimal places.

4 A geometric series is $a + ar + ar^2 + \ldots$

   a   Prove that the sum of the first n terms of this series is given by

$$S_n = \frac{a(1 - r^n)}{1 - r}$$

   b   Find $\displaystyle\sum_{k=1}^{10} 25(2^k)$

   c   Find the sum to infinity of the geometric series with general term $25(0.2^k)$.

5 A geometric series has first term a and common ratio r. The second term of the series is 4 and the sum to infinity of the series is 25.

   a Show that $25r^2 - 25r + 4 = 0$

   b Find the two possible values of r.

   c Find the corresponding two possible values of a.

Given that r takes the larger of its two possible values,

   d show that the sum, S_n, of the first n terms of the series is given by
$$S_n = 25(1 - r^n)$$

   e find the smallest value of n for which S_n exceeds 24.   [(c) Edexcel Limited 2006]

6 In the binomial expansion of $(1 + ax)^8$ the ratio of the coefficients of the fourth term to the third term is 4. Find the value of the constant a. Hence write down the first four terms in the expansion.

7 Find the first three terms, in ascending powers of x, of the binomial expansion of $(3 - x)^6$, giving each term in its simplest form.

8 **a** Find the first three terms, in ascending powers of x, of the binomial expansion of $(1 + ax)^8$, where a is a constant.

   The first three terms are 1, $-16x$ and bx^2, where b is a constant.
   b Find the value of a and the value of b.

9 If x is small such that x^3 and higher powers may be ignored and
$$(1 + 2x)(1 - x)^5 \approx a + bx + cx^2$$
find the values of the constants a, b and c.

10 **a** Find the first three terms, in ascending powers of x, of the binomial expansion of $\left(1 - \frac{x}{2}\right)^7$. Give each term in its simplest form.

   b If x is small, so that x^3 and higher powers can be ignored, show that
$$(1 - x)\left(1 - \frac{x}{2}\right)^7 \approx 1 - \frac{9}{2}x + \frac{35}{4}x^2$$

11 The first three terms in the expansion of $(a + 3x)^n$ are
$$16b, \ 144bx \text{ and } 540bx^2$$
Find the values of the constants a, b and n.

Exit

C2

Summary

Refer to

- The general term of the geometric series $a + ar + ar^2 + ar^3 + , \ldots$ where a is the first term and r is the common ratio is ar^{n-1}

  13.1

- The sum S_n to n terms of a geometric series is given by

  $$S_n = \frac{a(1 - r^n)}{1 - r}$$

  13.2

- The sum to infinity of a geometric series is given by $S_\infty = \dfrac{a}{1 - r}$, where $|r| < 1$ in order for the series to be convergent.

  13.3

- Pascal's triangle can be used to obtain the coefficients of the terms in the expansion of $(a + bx)^n$

  13.4

- The combinatorial notation $\binom{n}{r}$ or ^nC_r stands for the number of combinations of r items chosen from n and is equal to

  $$\frac{n!}{r!(n - r)!}$$

  where $n! = n(n - 1)(n - 2)\ldots(3)(2)(1)$

  13.5

- The binomial theorem gives the expansion of $(a + x)^n$ as

  $$(a + x)^n = \binom{n}{0}a^n + \binom{n}{1}a^{n-1}x + \binom{n}{2}a^{n-2}x^2 + \ldots + \binom{n}{n}x^n$$

  and the general term is $\binom{n}{r}a^{n-r}x^r$

  13.5

Links

You will have met compound interest at GCSE. If you invest £100 at 5% interest per year, then at the end of years 1, 2 and 3 you will have £105, £110.25 and £115.76 respectively. This is a geometric sequence. Accountants and fund managers can use mathematical methods to work out when an investment will double in value or to find a suitable interest rate for the investment to increase in a given time period.

Mortgage advisors use geometric sequences when working out the amount of interest to be paid back. If you borrow £100 000 to buy a house and pay back £12 000 per year, then after 1 year you only need to pay interest on the *balance* of £88 000 plus the interest rate rather than the initial amount. This allows them to develop an appropriate interest rate so that the whole balance is paid back after say 25 or 30 years.

14 Differentiation

This chapter will show you how to
- recognise increasing and decreasing functions
- identify maximum and minimum turning points and points of inflexion
- solve problems and sketch graphs using differentiation.

Before you start

You should know how to:

1 Differentiate equations.

e.g. Differentiate the equation $y = 4x^3 - 2x^2 + 1$ with respect to x.

$$\frac{dy}{dx} = 4(3x^2) - 2(2x)$$

$$= 12x^2 - 4x$$

2 Sketch curves.

e.g. Sketch the graph of the equation $y = x^3 + 1$

Use the shape of the graph of $y = x^3$ and translate it by 1 unit in the positive y-direction:

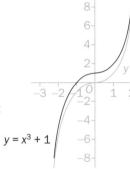

3 Solve inequalities.

e.g. Find the values of x for which $x(x - 3) > 0$

Solve $x(x - 3) = 0$:

$x = 0$ or $x = 3$

Study the sign of $x(x - 3)$:

for $x < 0$, $x(x - 3) = (-)(-) = (+)$

for $0 > x > 3$, $x(x - 3) = (+)(-) = (-)$

for $x > 3$, $x(x - 3) = (+)(+) = (+)$

The solution is $x < 0$ or $x > 3$.

Check in:

1 Differentiate y wrt x.

'wrt' means 'with respect to'.

a $y = 6x^2 - 2x + 3$

b $y = (x + 1)(x - 4)$

c $y = x^2(1 - x^2)$

d $y = x - \dfrac{4}{x}$

e $y = (2x - 3)^2$

2 Sketch the curves

a $y = \dfrac{1}{x}$

b $y = 2 + \dfrac{1}{x}$

c $y = x^3 - 8$

d $y = \dfrac{x^3}{4}$

e $y = \dfrac{1}{x^2}$

3 Find the values of x which satisfy each inequality.

a $x(x - 4) < 0$

b $x^2 - 9 > 0$

c $(x + 1)(x - 3) > 0$

d $2x - x^2 < 0$

e $2x^2 + 3x - 2 < 0$

C2

14.1 Increasing and decreasing functions

- A function $f(x)$ is described as an increasing function if $f(x_2) > f(x_1)$ when $x_2 > x_1$ for all values of x.

A function $f(x)$ is increasing in the interval $a \leqslant x \leqslant b$ if $f(x_2) > f(x_1)$ when $x_2 > x_1$ for all $a \leqslant x \leqslant b$

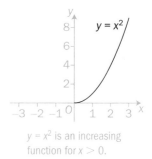

$y = x^2$ is an increasing function for $x > 0$.

It follows that

$f(x)$ is an increasing function if and only if $f'(x) > 0$ for all values of x in the given interval.

f(x) is an increasing function if and only if its gradient is positive for all values of x in the given interval.

- A function $f(x)$ is described as a decreasing function if $f(x_2) < f(x_1)$ when $x_2 > x_1$ for all values of x

A function $f(x)$ is decreasing in the interval $a \leqslant x \leqslant b$ if $f(x_2) < f(x_1)$ when $x_2 > x_1$ for all $a \leqslant x \leqslant b$

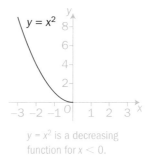

$y = x^2$ is a decreasing function for $x < 0$.

It follows that

$f(x)$ is a decreasing function if $f'(x) < 0$ for all values of x in the given interval.

f(x) is a decreasing function if and only if its gradient is negative for all values of x in the given interval.

Is the function $f(x) = 3x^2 - 2x$ increasing or decreasing when
a $x = -2$ **b** $x = 4$?

Sketching the graph will give you an idea of when the function is increasing or decreasing.

Differentiate f(x) wrt x: $f'(x) = 6x - 2$

a Evaluate f'(x) when x = −2:
$f'(-2) = 6(-2) - 2 = -14$
Hence $f'(-2) < 0$

$\therefore$ $f(x)$ is decreasing when $x = -2$.

b Evaluate f'(x) when x = 4:
$f'(4) = 6(4) - 2 = +22$
Hence $f'(4) > 0$

$\therefore$ $f(x)$ is an increasing function when $x = 4$.

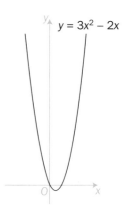

Consider the curve given by the equation

$$f(x) = x(x+1)(x-2)$$

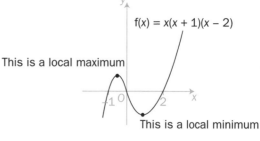

The curve crosses the x-axis
at the points where $f(x) = 0$
i.e. at $x = 0$, $x = -1$ and $x = 2$.

The curve crosses the y-axis at
the points where $x = 0$ i.e. at $(0, 0)$.

There are two points on the graph
where the curve changes direction.
These are called stationary points or turning points.

○ A maximum point is where the gradient of the curve
changes from positive to negative.
At a maximum point the gradient, $f'(x) = 0$

The function changes from
increasing to decreasing.

○ A minimum point is where the gradient of the curve
changes from negative to positive.
At a minimum point the gradient, $f'(x) = 0$

The function changes from
decreasing to increasing.

Now consider the curve given by the equation

$$f(x) = (x-1)^3$$

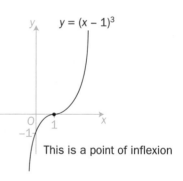

The curve crosses the x-axis
where $f(x) = 0$, i.e. at $x = 1$.

The curve crosses the y-axis
where $x = 0$, i.e. at $(0, -1)$.

○ At a point of inflexion the gradient, $f'(x) = 0$
However, the gradient has the same sign on both sides
of the point.

If the function is increasing before
a point of inflexion then it is also
increasing after that point.
If the function is decreasing before
a point of inflexion then it is also
decreasing after that point.

These results are summarised in the following table:

Type of point	f'(x)	behaviour
maximum	0	increasing to decreasing
inflexion	0	no change in direction
minimum	0	decreasing to increasing

o A stationary point can either be a maximum point, a minimum point or a point of inflexion.
At a stationary point the gradient is zero.

o To find the coordinates of a stationary point you solve the equation $f'(x) = 0$

You can identify the type of stationary point by considering the sign of the gradient before and after that point.

You can investigate the stationary points of a function and the intervals in which a function is increasing or decreasing and hence sketch its curve.

Investigate the values of x for which the function, $f(x) = x^2(x-4)$, is an increasing function or a decreasing function.

$$f(x) = x^2(x-4)$$

Expand: $\qquad\qquad f(x) = x^3 - 4x^2$

Differentiate wrt x: $\quad f'(x) = 3x^2 - 8x$

Factorise: $\qquad\qquad f'(x) = x(3x-8)$

Stationary points are located where $f'(x) = 0$.

Solve the equation $f'(x) = 0$ to find the x-values of the stationary points:

$$x(3x-8) = 0$$

when $x = 0$ or $3x - 8 = 0$

Hence the stationary points are at $x = 0$ and $x = \dfrac{8}{3}$

At a maximum point the gradient changes from being positive to negative.
At a minimum point the gradient changes from being negative to positive.

To decide the nature of the stationary points, investigate the three intervals

$$x < 0 \qquad 0 < x < \frac{8}{3} \qquad \text{and} \qquad x > \frac{8}{3}$$

using the equation in the form $f'(x) = x(3x-8)$:

See Chapter 4 for a reminder about inequalities.

when $x < 0$ $\qquad f'(x) = (-)(-) = (+)$ so $f'(x) > 0$
$\qquad\qquad\qquad$ so $f(x)$ is increasing when $x < 0$

when $0 < x < \dfrac{8}{3}$ $\quad f'(x) = (+)(-) = (-)$ so $f'(x) < 0$

$\qquad\qquad\qquad$ so $f(x)$ is decreasing in the range $0 < x < \dfrac{8}{3}$

$\qquad\qquad\qquad$ so there is a maximum point at $x = 0$

when $x > \dfrac{8}{3}$ $\qquad f'(x) = (+)(+) = (+)$ so $f'(x) > 0$

$\qquad\qquad\qquad$ so $f(x)$ is increasing when $x > \dfrac{8}{3}$

$\qquad\qquad\qquad$ so there is a minimum point at $x = \dfrac{8}{3}$

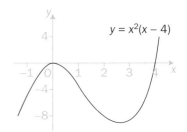

Hence $f(x)$ is an increasing function when $x < 0$ and $x > \dfrac{8}{3}$

and a decreasing function when $0 < x < \dfrac{8}{3}$

EXAMPLE 3

Find the turning points on the curve $y = x^4 - 2x^3 + 2$ and identify their type.

$y = x^4 - 2x^3 + 2$

Differentiate y wrt x: $\dfrac{dy}{dx} = 4x^3 - 6x^2$

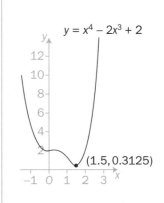

Evaluate the points where $\dfrac{dy}{dx} = 0$:

$$4x^3 - 6x^2 = 0$$

Factorise: $2x^2(2x - 3) = 0$

Either $x = 0$ or $x = \dfrac{3}{2}$

Investigate the three intervals $x < 0$, $0 < x < \dfrac{3}{2}$ and $x > \dfrac{3}{2}$ using the equation in the form $f'(x) = 2x^2(2x - 3)$:

for $x < 0$ $\quad f'(x) = (+)(-) = (-)$ so $f'(x) < 0$

for $0 < x < \dfrac{3}{2}$ $\quad f'(x) = (+)(-) = (-)$ so $f'(x) < 0$

for $x > \dfrac{3}{2}$ $\quad f'(x) = (+)(+) = (+)$ so $f'(x) > 0$

Hence there is a point of inflexion when $x = 0$

and there is a minimum point when $x = \dfrac{3}{2}$

Use the equation for $\dfrac{dy}{dx}$ in its fully factorised form.

$f'(x)$ has same sign either side of $x = 0$.

$f'(x)$ changes from negative to positive at $x = \dfrac{3}{2}$.

Find the coordinates of the turning points by substituting $x = 0$ and $x = \dfrac{3}{2}$ into the original equation $y = x^4 - 2x^3 + 2$:

At $x = 0$, $y = (0)^4 - 2(0)^3 + 2 = 2$
At $x = 1.5$, $y = (1.5)^4 - 2(1.5)^3 + 2 = 0.3125$

Hence there is a point of inflexion at $(0, 2)$ and a minimum point at $(1.5, 0.3125)$.

Exercise 14.1

1 Find the gradient of each function at the point where $x = 2$. Hence decide if each function is increasing, decreasing or stationary at this point.

a $y = 3x^2 - 1$

b $y = (x + 1)(x - 3)$

c $y = (2x - 1)^2$

d $y = 1 - x - x^2$

e $y = \dfrac{1}{x}$

f $y = \sqrt{x}$

g $y = 3x$

h $y = 0.53$

i $f(x) = 4x^2 - 12x$

j $f(x) = 1 - 4x^2$

k $f(x) = x^2 - 6x + 1$

l $f(x) = (3x - 1)(x - 4)$

m $f(x) = 3 - \dfrac{1}{x}$

n $f(x) = 7 + \sqrt{(2x)}$

o $f(x) = (x - 1)^3$

p $f(x) = 5x^2 - 2x^3$

2 Find the values of x for which each function is increasing or decreasing.

a $f(x) = x^2 - 6x$

b $f(x) = (x + 3)(2x - 5)$

c $f(x) = x^2(x - 6)$

d $f(x) = 5x - 15x^2$

e $f(x) = 2x^2(1 - x)$

f $f(x) = 4x^3 - 6x^2 - 72x + 96$

g $f(x) = 7 - 2x$

h $f(x) = \frac{1}{3}x^3 - 4x$

i $f(x) = (2 - x)(7 - 2x)$

j $f(x) = 6x^2 - 4x + 7$

k $f(x) = x^3 - 12x^2 + 45x - 9$

l $f(x) = 4x^2(2 - x)$

3 The function $f(x) = 4x + \dfrac{1}{x}$ is defined for $x > 0$

a Find the value of $f(0.5)$

b Find $f'(x)$ and hence determine the values of x for which $f(x)$ is increasing.

4 Find the values of x for which the function

$$f(x) = \frac{x}{4} + \frac{1}{x}, \quad \text{where } x > 0, \text{ is a decreasing function.}$$

5 For each of the following equations find the value(s) of x for which the graph of the function is a stationary point.

a $y = x^2 + 2x$

b $y = 2x^3 - 6x$

c $y = x(x + 4)$

d $y = (x - 3)(x - 5)$

e $y = 8x - \frac{1}{4}x^4$

f $y = 5x^3 - 3$

g $y = (2 - x)^2$

h $y = 8x^2 - 4x^3$

6 Find the coordinates of the stationary points on each curve, stating whether they are maximum or minimum points or points of inflexion.

a $y = 2x^2 - 4x$

b $y = 4x - 3x^2$

c $y = 2x^3$

d $y = (x + 1)(x + 3)$

e $y = (3 - x)^2$

f $y = (3 - x)(4 + x)$

g $y = x^2(1 - x)$

h $y = x^2 - 16$

7 Find the stationary points on these curves and state their type.

   a $y = \dfrac{x^3}{3} - 9x$ b $y = x^2 + \dfrac{54}{x}$

   c $y = 2x^3 + 3x^2 - 36x$ d $y = 12x - 3x^2 - 2x^3$

   e $y = -4x^3 + 21x^2 - 18x$ f $y = x^4 - \dfrac{9}{2}x^2 + 3$

8 Find the minimum value of s if $s = (1 - 3t)^2$
Show how you know this is the minimum value.

9 Find the coordinates of the stationary points on the curve with
the equation $y = (x - 2)(x + 1)^2$
Identify the type of each point.

INVESTIGATIONS

10 You want to draw a graph of $y = x + \dfrac{1}{x}$

   a Differentiate the expression to find the
      coordinates of the turning points.

   b Consider very large positive values of x, and very
      large negative values of x to find out how the
      curve behaves as it approaches infinity.

   c Hence sketch the graph.

   d What are the equations of the asymptotes?

11

The picture shows a wire suspending a bridge from two
points. Assume that the origin is taken as the left fixed
point. The bridge is four metres in length.

   a Explain why the curve $y = x(x - 4)$ may be
      a suitable model for the suspension wire.

   b Use this model to find the coordinates of the
      middle point of the bridge (where the wire is at its
      lowest point).

You can use the second derivative to determine the nature of a stationary point.

See Chapter 8 for revision of differentiation.

Consider the graph of the function, f(x), and the gradient function, f′(x).

Suppose the graph of f(x) has two turning points; a maximum point at A and a minimum point at B.

The gradient changes from positive to negative at A.
The gradient changes from negative to positive at B.

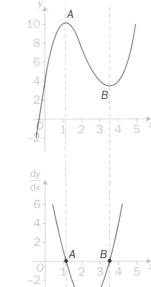

Compare the graph of f(x) to the graph of f′(x).

On the graph of f′(x):

at A the gradient, or rate of change of f′(x), is negative, f″(x) < 0

at B the gradient, or rate of change of f′(x), is positive, f″(x) > 0

f″(x) is the derivative of f′(x).

- A function, f(x), has a stationary point when f′(x) = 0
- A stationary point is a maximum point if f″(x) < 0
- A stationary point is a minimum point if f″(x) > 0
- If f″(x) = 0,   the stationary point can be a maximum, a minimum, or a point of inflexion.

You can determine the nature of the point by looking at the sign change of the gradient.

- If f′(x) = 0 and f″(x) = 0 but f‴(x) ≠ 0 then the point is a point of inflexion.

f‴(x) is the derivative of f″(x).

C2

EXAMPLE 1

A curve has equation $y = x^2 - 3x + 7$. Find the value of x at the stationary point and determine its nature.

$$y = x^2 - 3x + 7$$

Differentiate y wrt x: $\quad \dfrac{dy}{dx} = 2x - 3$

Solve $\quad = 0$: $\quad 2x - 3 = 0$, so $x = \dfrac{3}{2}$

$\quad$ is the derivative of $\quad$ wrt x.

Differentiate again wrt x: $\quad \dfrac{d^2y}{dx^2} = 2$

Hence $\quad \dfrac{d^2y}{dx^2} > 0$

Hence the curve has a minimum point at $x = \dfrac{3}{2}$

EXAMPLE 2

Find the coordinates of the stationary points on the curve $y = 24x - 2x^3$ and identify their nature. Hence sketch the curve.

$$y = 24x - 2x^3$$

Differentiate y wrt x: $\quad \dfrac{dy}{dx} = 24 - 6x^2$

Solve $\dfrac{dy}{dx} = 0$: $\quad 24 - 6x^2 = 0$

$$6x^2 = 24$$
$$x^2 = 4,$$

so $\quad x = -2 \quad$ or $\quad x = 2$

Differentiate again wrt x:

$$\dfrac{d^2y}{dx^2} = -12x$$

Substitute $x = -2$ and $x = 2$:

When $x = -2 \quad \dfrac{d^2y}{dx^2} = -12(-2) = 24 > 0$

Hence there is a minimum point at $x = -2$.

When $x = 2 \quad \dfrac{d^2y}{dx^2} = -12(2) = -24 < 0$

Hence there is a maximum point at $x = 2$.

Find the coordinates of the stationary points by substituting $x = -2$ and $x = 2$ into the original equation $y = 24x - 2x^3$:

When $x = -2$, $y = 24(-2) - 2(-2)^3 = -32$
When $x = 2$, $y = 24(2) - 2(2)^3 = 32$
Hence there is a minimum point at $(-2, -32)$
and a maximum point at $(2, 32)$.

Remember to include both values of x.

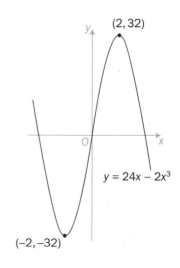

C2

Identifying the stationary points and their nature helps you to sketch a curve.

Other features which help in the sketching of a curve include
○ finding where the curve intersects the x- and y-axes
○ determining if the curve has asymptotes and where they are
○ recognising if the curve is a transformation of a familiar curve.

EXAMPLE 3

Sketch the curve given by the equation
$y = 2x^2 - x - 15$

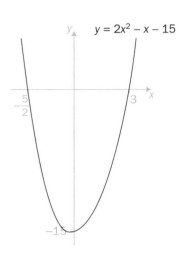

$y = 2x^2 - x - 15$

The curve intersects the x-axis when $y = 0$
when $\qquad 2x^2 - x - 15 = 0$
Factorise: $\quad (2x + 5)(x - 3) = 0$
Either $\qquad 2x + 5 = 0 \quad$ or $\quad x - 3 = 0$

Hence the points of intersection on the x-axis are
at $\left(-\dfrac{5}{2}, 0\right)$ and $(3, 0)$.

The curve intersects the y-axis when $x = 0$
When $x = 0$, $y = -15$
Hence the curve intersects the y-axis at $(0, -15)$.

Find the turning points of the curve by differentiating:

$$y = 2x^2 - x - 15$$

$$\frac{dy}{dx} = 4x - 1$$

Let $\dfrac{dy}{dx} = 0$:

$$\text{when} \quad 4x - 1 = 0$$

$$x = \frac{1}{4}$$

Substitute this value into the original equation:

$$y = 2(0.25)^2 - (0.25) - 15 = -15.125$$

Evaluate the second derivative wrt x:

$$\frac{d^2y}{dx^2} = 4 \quad \text{which is positive}$$

When $x = \dfrac{1}{4}$, $\dfrac{d^2y}{dx^2} > 0$

Hence $(0.25, -15.125)$ is a minimum point.

C2

EXAMPLE 4

Sketch the curve given by the equation
$y = x(5 - x)^2$

The curve intersects the x-axis when $y = 0$
When $\quad x(5 - x)^2 = 0, \quad x = 0 \quad$ or $\quad x = 5$
$\therefore$ Curve crosses x-axis at $(0, 0)$ and $(5, 0)$.

The curve intersects the y-axis when $x = 0$
When $\quad x = 0, y = 0$
$\therefore$ Curve passes through the origin.

Multiply out the brackets: $\quad y = x(5 - x)^2$
$$\begin{aligned} &= x(5 - x)(5 - x) \\ &= x(25 - 10x + x^2) \\ &= 25x - 10x^2 + x^3 \end{aligned}$$

Investigate the turning points on the curve:

Differente y wrt x: $\qquad \dfrac{dy}{dx} = 25 - 20x + 3x^2$

Let $\dfrac{dy}{dx} = 0$:

$$\text{When } 25 - 20x + 3x^2 = 0$$

Factorise: $\qquad (5 - x)(5 - 3x) = 0$
Either $\quad 5 - x = 0 \quad$ or $\quad 5 - 3x = 0$
$\qquad$ so $x = 5 \quad$ or $\quad \dfrac{5}{3}$

You may have to solve using the formula.

You need to investigate the nature of the turning points.

Differente again wrt x: $\qquad \dfrac{d^2y}{dx^2} = -20 + 6x$

When $x = 5$, $\quad \dfrac{d^2y}{dx^2} = -20 + 6(5) = 10 \quad$ so $\dfrac{d^2y}{dx^2} > 0$

There is a minimum turning point at $x = 5$.

When $x = \dfrac{5}{3}$, $\quad \dfrac{d^2y}{dx^2} = -20 + 6\left(\dfrac{5}{3}\right) = -10,$ $\quad$ so $\dfrac{d^2y}{dx^2} < 0$

There is a maximum turning point at $x = \dfrac{5}{3}$.

For $x = 5$, $y = x(5 - x)^2 = 0$

For $x = \dfrac{5}{3}$, $y = x(5 - x)^2 = \dfrac{5}{3}\left(5 - \dfrac{5}{3}\right)^2 = \dfrac{500}{27} = 18\dfrac{14}{27}$

There is a minimum point at $(5, 0)$
and a maximum point at $\left(\dfrac{5}{3}, \dfrac{500}{27}\right)$.

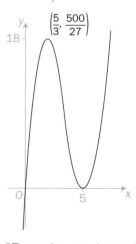

The y-values are also needed.

Exercise 14.2

1 Find the values of $\dfrac{dy}{dx}$ and $\dfrac{d^2y}{dx^2}$ when $x = 2$ for each curve.

a $y = 3x^3$

b $y = x^2 + 2x$

c $y = \dfrac{1}{x}$

d $y = \sqrt{x}$

e $y = (x + 3)^2$

f $y = 2 - \dfrac{1}{x}$

g $y = x^2(x + 2)(x - 3)$

h $y = x^2 - \dfrac{1}{x}$

2 For each function find the value of x for which $f'(x) = 0$ and use $f''(x)$ to determine whether this is a maximum or minimum point for the curve.

a $f(x) = x^2 + 2x$

b $f(x) = 4 - x^2$

c $f(x) = x(4 - x)$

d $f(x) = (x + 2)(3x - 2)$

e $f(x) = (2x - 3)(3x - 2)$

f $f(x) = 5x - 5x^2$

g $f(x) = \dfrac{x}{4}(1 - x)$

h $f(x) = 3(2x - 5)(2x - 1)$

3 Determine the stationary points, if any, for each equation. Identify the type of stationary point and sketch the curve.

a $y = 2x^3 - 24x$

b $y = x(27 - x^2)$

c $y = x^2 - 5x$

d $y = \dfrac{1}{x} + 9x + 2$

e $y = x^2(1 - x)$

f $y = \dfrac{2}{3}x^3 + \dfrac{x^2}{2} - 6x$

g $y = 2x^3 + 3x^2 - 120x$

h $y = (x - 1)^3 + 3x^2$

4 a Sketch the curve given by the equation $y = (4 - x)(x - 2)$, giving the coordinates of its turning points.

b Show that the curve with equation $y = (2x - 1)(x + 4)$ has a minimum turning point and find its coordinates. Hence sketch the curve.

c Sketch the graph of the equation $y = 6 - x - x^2$ giving the coordinates of the turning point and stating its nature.

d Sketch the curve with equation $y = (4 - x)(3 + x) - 10$ stating the nature and coordinates of the turning point.

5 Write the coordinates of the turning points correct to two decimal places, where appropriate.

a Sketch the curve given by the equation, $y = x(2 - x)^2$. Find the coordinates of the turning points.

b Sketch the graph of the equation given by $y = x^2(x + 3)$ and find the coordinates of the turning points.

c Sketch the curve given by the equation $y = x^3 - 9x$ and find the coordinates of the turning points.

d Sketch the graph of the equation $y = x(2x^2 - 3x - 12)$, distinguishing between the maximum and minimum turning points.
State the coordinates of the turning points.

e Find the coordinates of the turning points on the curve

$$y = (x - 1)(x + 2)(x - 3)$$

and also the coordinates of the points where the curve intersects the axes.
Hence sketch the curve.

INVESTIGATIONS

6 a Find the turning point of the graph given by

   i $y = x^2 + 6x + 9$
   ii $y = -x^2 - 6x - 9$

b By considering transformations, explain why the turning points are in the same position.

7 a Plot the graph of $y = x^3 - 6x^2 + 9x + 1$

b Plot graphs of the first and second derivatives on the same diagram.

c Use your graphs to explain why the cubic function has stationary points and what type they are.

You could use graphing software to investigate these curves.

Practical applications

You can use the analysis of stationary points to solve real-life problems.

EXAMPLE 1

The motion of a body in a straight line is given by the equation

$$s = 70t - 10t^2$$

where s is the displacement from the original position after t seconds.

Find the maximum value of s and the time taken to travel this displacement.

$$s = 70t - 10t^2$$

Differentiate s wrt t: $\quad \dfrac{ds}{dt} = 70 - 20t$

Determine the maximum value by considering $\dfrac{ds}{dt} = 0$:

$$\text{when } 70 - 20t = 0$$

$$t = \frac{7}{2}$$

Substitute the value $t = 3.5$ into $s = 70t - 10t^2$:

$$s = 70(3.5) - 10(3.5)^2$$
$$= 245 - 122.5 = 122.5 \text{ m}$$

Hence the maximum displacement is 122.5 m in 3.5 seconds.

You can check that this is a maximum value by showing that $\dfrac{d^2s}{dt^2} < 0$ when $s = 122.5$.

EXAMPLE 2

The surface area, A, of a container is given by the equation

$$A = 50x - 4x^2$$

where x cm is the length of the container.
Find the value of x which makes the surface area a maximum and hence find this maximum area.

$$A = 50x - 4x^2$$

Differentiate A wrt x: $\quad \dfrac{dA}{dx} = 50 - 8x$

Determine the maximum value by considering $\dfrac{dA}{dx} = 0$:

$$\text{when } 50 - 8x = 0$$

$$x = \frac{25}{4} = 6.25$$

Substitute the value $x = 6.25$ into $A = 50x - 4x^2$:

$$A = 50(6.25) - 4(6.25)^2 = 156.25$$

Hence the maximum surface area is 156.25 cm^2 when $x = 6.25$ cm.

EXAMPLE 3

A closed box in the shape of a cuboid has a rectangular base with dimensions x cm by $2x$ cm.

The total surface area of the box is 300 cm².
Show that the volume, V, of the box is given by

$$V = 100x - \frac{4x^3}{3}$$

Find the dimensions of the box which make the volume a maximum and hence find the maximum volume of the box.

Let the height of the box be y cm.

Total surface area of the box, $\quad A = 2(2x^2 + xy + 2xy)$

Simplify: $\qquad\qquad\qquad\qquad A = 4x^2 + 6xy$

Use the fact that $A = 300$ cm²: $\qquad 300 = 4x^2 + 6xy \qquad\qquad$ (1)

Write a formula for volume: $\qquad\qquad V = l \times b \times h \qquad\qquad$ (2)

$\qquad\qquad\qquad\qquad\qquad\qquad = 2x^2 y$

Make y the subject in equation (1):

$$y = \frac{300 - 4x^2}{6x}$$

Substitute this value of y into equation (2):

$$V = 2x^2 \left(\frac{300 - 4x^2}{6x} \right)$$

Simplify: $\qquad\qquad\qquad\qquad = 100x - \frac{4x^3}{3} \quad$ as required

To find the maximum volume, differentiate V wrt x and equate to 0:

$$\frac{dV}{dx} = 100 - 4x^2$$

Find the values of x which give $\frac{dV}{dx} = 0$:

$$\text{when} \quad 4x^2 = 100$$

$$x^2 = 25$$

$$x = -5 \text{ or } +5$$

x cannot be negative.

Substitute $x = +5$ to find the dimensions:

The dimensions are $x = 5$, $2x = 10$, $y = \dfrac{300 - 4x^2}{6x} = 6.66\ldots$

that is, 5 cm by 10 cm by 6.667 cm

and the maximum volume of the box $= 5 \times 10 \times 6.667$

$$= 333 \text{ cm}^3 \text{ (to 3 s.f.)}$$

x is the width of the box.

Check that this is a maximum value by looking at the second derivative.

$\dfrac{d^2y}{dx^2} = -8x$, negative when x is positive.

C2

Exercise 14.3

1 a A stone is projected into the air and its distance, s, above the ground is given by the equation $s = 50t - 5t^2$ where t is the time from the starting point.
Find the time taken to reach the maximum height and the maximum height of the stone above the ground.

   b A particle is moving such that its acceleration, a, is given by the equation $a = 4t(t - 1)$ m s^{-2}
Find the time, t seconds, when the acceleration is a minimum. Hence find this minimum acceleration.

2 a The area, A, of a triangle is given by the formula

$$A = 40x - 2x^2$$

Find the length, x cm, which makes the area a maximum and find this maximum area.

   b A cardboard box in the shape of a cuboid has sides of 5 cm, $(4 - x)$ cm and $(3 + x)$ cm.

Find an equation in terms of x for the volume of the box. Determine the value of x which makes the volume a maximum and hence find this maximum.

3 A positive number, x, and its reciprocal, $\frac{1}{x}$, are added together.
Find the value of x which makes the sum a minimum.

4 a A rectangular plot of land has a wall along one side. The remaining three sides have a total length 150 metres. If the plot measures x metres by y metres find an expression, in terms of x only, for the area of the plot.

   b Use this expression to find the value of x which makes the area a maximum and find this maximum.

5 A tray is made from a rectangular sheet of plastic. From each corner of the sheet a square of side x is cut and the sides are then folded to form the tray. The sheet measures 1 metre by 1.5 metres. Find the value of x which maximises the volume of the tray and find this maximum volume.

6 The volume of a closed cylindrical container is 400 cm^3 and the radius of the base is r cm.

Show that the total surface area, A, of the cylinder is given by the formula $A = 2\pi r^2 + \dfrac{800}{r}$

Find the value of r when A is a maximum and hence find the maximum surface area of the cylinder.

C2

7 **a** An open cylindrical container has base radius r,
surface area A and volume V.
Show that the volume of the container is given by
$$V = \frac{r}{2}(A - \pi r^2)$$

b When the volume of the container is a maximum
show that the surface area of the container is given
by $A = 3\pi r^2$

c Hence, or otherwise find the maximum volume of the
container in terms of π, if the surface area of the
container is 125π.

8 **a** An open container has a square base and a fixed
volume, V. If the sides of the base are of length x cm
and the total surface area of the container is A show that
$$A = x^2 + \frac{4V}{x}$$

b If the container is to have a minimum surface area show
that the value of x is given by $x = \sqrt[3]{2V}$

c If the volume of the container is 256 cm^3, find the
dimensions and total surface area of the container.

9 A symmetrical cone is inside a sphere of radius r cm, with
the vertex of the cone and the rim of the circular base in
contact with the surface of the sphere. The centre of the
base of the cone is x cm below the centre of the sphere.

Show that the volume, V, of the cone is $V = \frac{\pi}{3}(r - x)(r + x)^2$

For the volume of the cylinder to be a maximum show

that the value of x is $\frac{r}{3}$.

Hence, or otherwise, find the maximum volume of the
cone in terms of π and r.

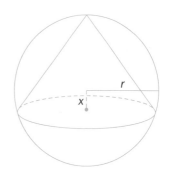

C2

INVESTIGATION

10 A population of birds on an island, P, is a function
of the number of predators, x.
The population follows the equation
$$P = x^3 - 12x^2 - 60x + 850 \quad \text{where } x > 0$$

a Explain the need for the restriction $x > 0$.

b Find the minimum size of the population and
the number of predators when this occurs.

c Sketch the graph of this function and discuss the
shape of the curve and its behaviour as $x \to \infty$
How can you explain this?

1 For the function $f(x) = 3x^2 - 12x$

    a find $f'(x)$

    b determine whether the function is increasing or decreasing when $x = -1$

    c find the value of x when $f'(x) = 0$

2 If $f(x) = 4x^3 - \frac{3}{2}x^2$ find the values of x for which

    $f(x)$ is an increasing function.

3 Find the coordinates of the stationary point on the curve with equation $y = x^3 - 2x^2$

4 A projectile is fired vertically upwards from the ground and the distance, s metres, above the ground is given by $s = 196t - 4.9t^2$, where t seconds is the time measured from the time of projection. Find the time taken to reach the maximum height and the maximum height attained by the projectile.

5 For the curve given by the equation $y = 5x^3 - 10x^2$ find the coordinates of the stationary points and determine their nature.

6 The diameter of a circle is AB and the ends of the diameter are connected to a variable point, P, which moves on the circumference of the circle.
The area of the triangle APB is to be a maximum.
Find the maximum area of the triangle if the sum of the lengths AP and PB is 20 cm.

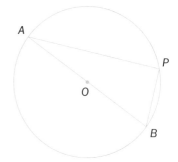

7 A diesel lorry is driven from Birmingham to Bury at a steady speed of v kilometres per hour. The total cost of the journey, £C, is given by $\quad C = \dfrac{1400}{v} + \dfrac{2v}{7}$

    a Find the value of v for which C is a minimum.

    b Find $\dfrac{d^2C}{dv^2}$ and hence verify that C is a minimum for this value of v.

    c Calculate the minimum total cost of the journey.

[(c) Edexcel Limited 2007]

8 The curve, C, has equation $\quad y = (x-1)(x-4)^2$

   a Find $\dfrac{dy}{dx}$

   b Using the result from part **a**, find the coordinates of the turning points of C.

   c Find $\dfrac{d^2y}{d^2x}$

   d Hence, or otherwise, determine the nature of the turning points of C.

9 The diagram shows the plan of a stage in the shape of a rectangle joined to a semicircle. The length of the rectangular part is $2x$ metres and the width is y metres. The perimeter of the stage is 80 metres.

   a Show that the area, A m^2, of the stage is given by

$$A = 80x - \left(2 + \frac{\pi}{2}\right)x^2$$

   b Use calculus to find the value of x at which A has a stationary value.

   c Prove that the value you found in part **b** gives a maximum value of A.

   d Calculate, to the nearest m^2, the maximum area of the stage.   [(c) Edexcel Limited 2005]

10 The curve of $f(x) = ax^2 + bx + c$ passes through the point $(2, 24)$ and the gradient of the curve at this point is 22
   The value of $f''(x)$ is 6
   Find the coordinates of the points where the curve crosses the x- and y-axes and of the minimum stationary point.

11 **a** Solve the equation $\quad x^2 + x - 15 = 0 \quad$ giving your answers correct to two decimal places.

   b Find the coordinates of the stationary point of the curve $y = x^2 + x - 15 \quad$ and state its nature.

   c Use the information from parts **a** and **b** to sketch the curve.

   d Find the points of intersection of the curve $y = x^2 + x - 15$ and the line $y = 2x + 5$

   e Find the gradient of the tangents to the curve at the points found in part **d**.

   f These tangents intersect with each other at point A; find the coordinates of A.

C2

Exit

14

Summary

Refer to

- A function is increasing when $\dfrac{dy}{dx} > 0$

  and decreasing when $\dfrac{dy}{dx} < 0$

  14.1

- At a stationary point on a curve the gradient is zero so

  $$\dfrac{dy}{dx} = 0$$

  A stationary point can be a maximum or minimum point
  or a point of inflexion.

  14.1

- At a stationary point:

  if $\dfrac{d^2y}{dx^2} < 0$ the stationary point is a maximum

  if $\dfrac{d^2y}{dx^2} > 0$ the stationary point is a minimum

  if $\dfrac{d^2y}{dx^2} = 0$ the stationary point could be a maximum or minimum

             or a point of inflexion.

  14.2

- You can apply analysis of maximum and minimum points to
  real-life problems.

  14.3

Links

The techniques used in this chapter can also be applied
in the manufacturing industry.

e.g   A company may want to produce a box with
the maximum possible volume whilst using the
minimum amount of packaging so that the costs
are kept low.

Differentiation can also be used to study the paths
of projectiles. This is useful in sports such as golf
and javelin throwing.

15

Integration

This chapter will show you how to
- process and evaluate definite integrals
- use integration to determine the area under a curve
- apply the trapezium rule to find areas and solve problems.

Before you start

You should know how to:

1 Evaluate an expression exactly.

e.g. Find y when $x = 3$

if $y = \dfrac{x^3}{3} + \dfrac{x^2}{2} - 1$

Substitute 3 for x:

$y = 9 + \dfrac{9}{2} - 1$

$y = 12\dfrac{1}{2}$

2 Find the area of a trapezium.

e.g. Find the exact area of the trapezium where the parallel sides are 3 cm and 5 cm and the distance between them is 4 cm.

Use area = $\ (a + b)$:

let $a = 3$ cm, $b = 5$ cm, $h = 4$ cm

area $= \dfrac{4}{2}(3 + 5)$

area $= 16$ cm²

3 Integrate an expression.

e.g. $\displaystyle\int (x^2 + 3)\,dx$

Use the general result $\displaystyle\int ax^n\,dx = \dfrac{ax^{n+1}}{n+1} + c$:

$I = \dfrac{x^3}{3} + 3x$

Add in the constant of integration:

$I = \dfrac{x^3}{3} + 3x + c$

Check in:

1 Find y when

a $y = x(x - 1)$ if $x = \dfrac{1}{3}$

b $y = \dfrac{x^2}{2} + x - \dfrac{1}{3c}$ if $x = 3$

c $y = (x + 2)(3 - x)$ if $x = \dfrac{1}{2}$

d $y = 3x^3 - \dfrac{x^2}{2}$ if $x = \dfrac{1}{2}$

2 Find the exact area of the trapezium given the length of the parallel sides and the distance between them.

a $a = 5$ cm, $b = 8$ cm, $h = 6$ cm

b $a = 3.5$ cm, $b = 7.5$ cm, $h = 3$ cm

c $a = 9$ cm, $b = 8$ cm, $h = 5$ cm

d $a = 1\dfrac{1}{3}$ cm, $b = 2\dfrac{1}{4}$ cm, $h = 6$ cm

3 Integrate

a $\displaystyle\int (x - 2)\,dx$

b $\displaystyle\int x(x - 2)^2\,dx$

c $\displaystyle\int (x - 2)^2\,dx$

d $\displaystyle\int x(x - 2)^2\,dx$

C2

307

In Chapter 8 you met integrals such as

$$\int (2x + 3)\, dx = x^2 + 3x + c$$

$$\int x^n\, dx = \frac{x^{n+1}}{n+1} + c \quad \text{for } n \neq -1$$

where c is the constant of integration.

Integrals of this form have no specified limits and are called indefinite integrals.

A definite integral includes limits and looks like this:

$$\int_a^b f(x)\, dx \quad \text{where } a \text{ and } b \text{ are given values of } x.$$

This is the integral of $f(x)$ between the limits $x = a$ and $x = b$.

You use the limits, a and b, to evaluate the integral exactly.

EXAMPLE 1

Evaluate $\displaystyle\int_1^2 (2x + 3)\, dx$

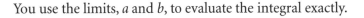

Integrate the function wrt x: $\displaystyle\int_1^2 (2x + 3)\, dx = [x^2 + 3x]_1^2$

Separate into two brackets, one for each limit value $x = 2$ and $x = 1$:

$$= (2^2 + 3 \times 2) - (1^2 + 3 \times 1)$$

Simplify the brackets: $= (4 + 6) - (1 + 3) = 6$

Hence $\displaystyle\int_1^2 (2x + 3)\, dx = 6$

The limits of the integral are $x = 1$ and $x = 2$.

Put the result of the integration in square brackets. The upper and lower limits go outside the brackets as shown.

Use round brackets to show the terms inside the brackets have been evaluated at the given limits.

▌Take care with the signs.

EXAMPLE 2

Evaluate $\displaystyle\int_2^4 (x - 3)\, dx$

Integrate $(x - 3)$ with respect to x: $\displaystyle\int_3^4 (x - 3)\, dx = \left[\frac{1}{2}x^2 - 3x\right]_2^4$

Separate into two brackets, one for each limit value $x = 4$ and $x = 2$:

$$= \left(\frac{1}{2} \times 4^2 - 3 \times 4\right) - \left(\frac{1}{2} \times 2^2 - 3 \times 2\right)$$

Simplify the brackets: $= (8 - 12) - (2 - 6) = 0$

Hence $\displaystyle\int_2^4 (x - 3)\, dx = 0$

Follow the steps:

↓

integrate

↓

square brackets

↓

evaluate with round brackets

↓

simplify.

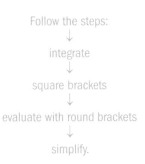

○ $\displaystyle\int_a^b f'(x)\, dx = f(b) - f(a)$ given that $f'(x)$ exists throughout the interval $a \leqslant x \leqslant b$.

Exercise 15.1

1 Evaluate each definite integral.

a $\displaystyle\int_0^1 x^2 \, dx$ b $\displaystyle\int_1^2 (4x + 3) \, dx$

c $\displaystyle\int_2^3 (6x - 1) \, dx$ d $\displaystyle\int_1^2 (3x^2 - 2x) \, dx$

e $\displaystyle\int_2^3 (x - 1)^2 \, dx$ f $\displaystyle\int_2^3 4x^3 \, dx$

2 Evaluate each integral.

a $\displaystyle\int_1^4 \sqrt{x} \, dx$ b $\displaystyle\int_1^2 (x + 1)(x - 3) \, dx$

c $\displaystyle\int_{-1}^1 (4 + x) \, dx$ d $\displaystyle\int_{-2}^0 3(x + 1) \, dx$

e $\displaystyle\int_{-2}^{-1} \left(\frac{2x - 3x^2}{x}\right) dx$ f $\displaystyle\int_{-1}^1 x(x - 2) \, dx$

g $\displaystyle\int_1^2 x^2(1 + \sqrt{x}) \, dx$ h $\displaystyle\int_{-1}^3 (2 - x)^2 \, dx$

i $\displaystyle\int_{0.5}^{1.5} (3x^2 - 2x) \, dx$

INVESTIGATIONS

3 Find the value of n such that
$$\int_0^1 nx^2 \, dx = 1$$

4 a Evaluate $\displaystyle\int_{-1}^1 (x^2 + 4) \, dx$

   b How could you obtain your answer using different limits?

C2

Area under a curve

You can use definite integration to find the area under a given curve.

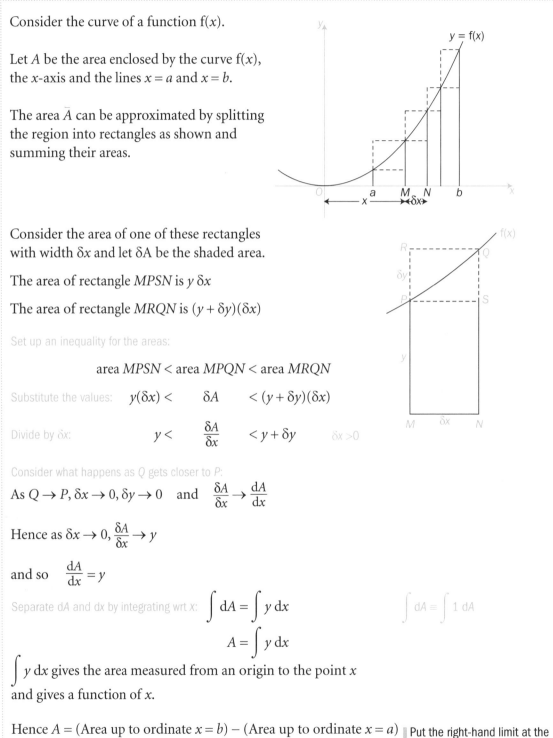

Consider the curve of a function $f(x)$.

Let A be the area enclosed by the curve $f(x)$, the x-axis and the lines $x = a$ and $x = b$.

The area A can be approximated by splitting the region into rectangles as shown and summing their areas.

Consider the area of one of these rectangles with width δx and let δA be the shaded area.

The area of rectangle $MPSN$ is $y \, \delta x$

The area of rectangle $MRQN$ is $(y + \delta y)(\delta x)$

Set up an inequality for the areas:

$$\text{area } MPSN < \text{area } MPQN < \text{area } MRQN$$

Substitute the values: $\quad y(\delta x) < \quad \delta A \quad < (y + \delta y)(\delta x)$

Divide by δx: $\qquad y < \quad \dfrac{\delta A}{\delta x} \quad < y + \delta y \qquad \delta x > 0$

Consider what happens as Q gets closer to P:

As $Q \to P$, $\delta x \to 0$, $\delta y \to 0$ and $\dfrac{\delta A}{\delta x} \to \dfrac{dA}{dx}$

Hence as $\delta x \to 0$, $\dfrac{\delta A}{\delta x} \to y$

and so $\quad \dfrac{dA}{dx} = y$

Separate dA and dx by integrating wrt x: $\displaystyle\int dA = \int y \, dx$ $\qquad \displaystyle\int dA = \int 1 \, dA$

$$A = \int y \, dx$$

$\displaystyle\int y \, dx$ gives the area measured from an origin to the point x and gives a function of x.

Hence $A = $ (Area up to ordinate $x = b$) − (Area up to ordinate $x = a$)

You write this as $A = \displaystyle\int_a^b y \, dx \quad$ or $\quad A = \displaystyle\int_a^b f(x) \, dx$

Put the right-hand limit at the top and the left-hand limit at the bottom.

C2

- The area enclosed between the curve $y = f(x)$, the x-axis and the lines $x = a$ and $x = b$ is given by

$$\text{Area} = \int_a^b y \, dx$$

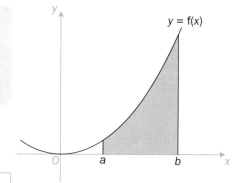

EXAMPLE 1

Find the area enclosed between the curve $y = x^2$, the x-axis and the lines $x = 1$ and $x = 3$.

Use the formula for area $\quad A = \int_a^b y \, dx$:

$$A = \int_1^3 x^2 \, dx$$

You may find a sketch useful.
You have to find the shaded area.

$a = 1$ and $b = 3$

Integrate wrt x: $\quad A = \left[\dfrac{x^3}{3} \right]_1^3$

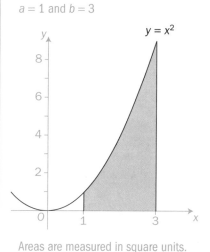

Evaluate using the limits: $\quad A = \left(\dfrac{27}{3} \right) - \left(\dfrac{1}{3} \right)$

$$= \frac{26}{3}$$

Hence the enclosed area is $\dfrac{26}{3}$ square units.

Areas are measured in square units.

Sometimes you will need to find where the curve intersects the x-axis before you can find the area under the curve.

C2

C2

Find the area enclosed by the x-axis and the curve given by the equation $y = (x - 1)(4 - x)$

Solve the equation $y = 0$ to find the x-axis crossings:

When $(x - 1)(4 - x) = 0$

$x = 1$ or $x = 4$

This gives the value of the limits,

$a = 1$ and $b = 4$

Use the formula for area $A = \displaystyle\int_a^b y\ dx$:

$$A = \int_1^4 (x - 1)(4 - x)\ dx$$

Expand and simplify the expression before you integrate.

$$= \int_1^4 (5x - x^2 - 4)\ dx$$

Integrate wrt x: $A = \left[\dfrac{5x^2}{2} - \dfrac{x^3}{3} - 4x \right]_1^4$

Evaluate by substituting the limit values:

$$A = \left(\frac{5 \times 16}{2} - \frac{64}{3} - 16 \right) - \left(\frac{5}{2} - \frac{1}{3} - 4 \right)$$

$$= \frac{8}{3} + \frac{11}{6} = \frac{9}{2}$$

Including round brackets at this step helps you to subtract correctly. Take care with the signs.

Therefore the area enclosed between the curve and the x-axis is $\dfrac{9}{2}$ square units.

Give your answer as a fraction.

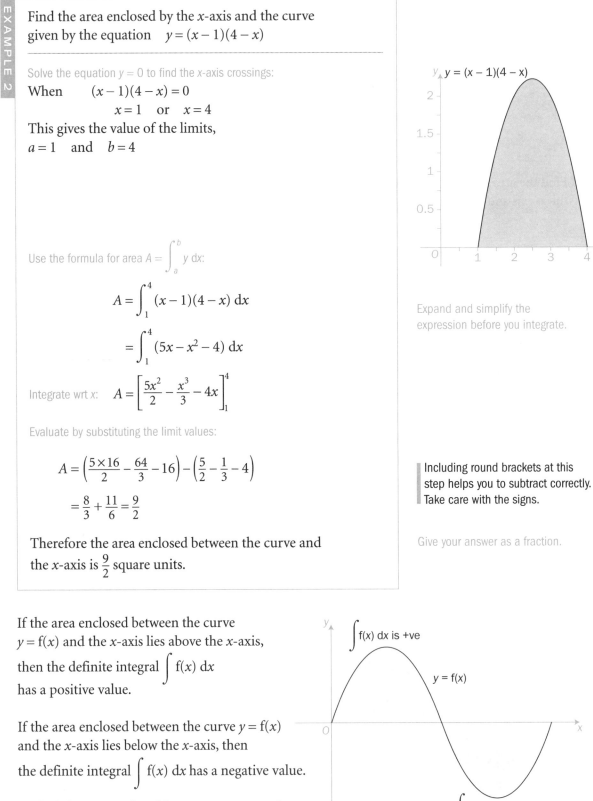

$y \quad y = (x - 1)(4 - x)$

If the area enclosed between the curve $y = f(x)$ and the x-axis lies above the x-axis, then the definite integral $\displaystyle\int f(x)\ dx$ has a positive value.

If the area enclosed between the curve $y = f(x)$ and the x-axis lies below the x-axis, then the definite integral $\displaystyle\int f(x)\ dx$ has a negative value.

To find the area enclosed between a curve and the x-axis when part of the curve is below the axis and part is above the axis you need to consider both sections separately.

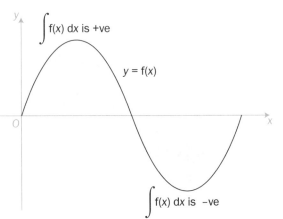

$\displaystyle\int f(x)\ dx$ is +ve

$y = f(x)$

$\displaystyle\int f(x)\ dx$ is −ve

EXAMPLE 3

Find the total area enclosed between the curve
$y = (x + 1)(x - 2)$, the x-axis and the lines $x = 0$ and $x = 3$.

Solve the equation $y = 0$ to find the x-axis crossings:

$$(x + 1)(x - 2) = 0$$

$$\Rightarrow \quad x = -1 \quad \text{or} \quad x = 2$$

Sketch the graph to see which parts of the graph are above the
x-axis and which parts are below for $0 \leqslant x \leqslant 3$:

The section between $x = 0$ and $x = 2$ is below the x-axis.
The section between $x = 2$ and $x = 3$ is above the x-axis.

Evaluate the definite integral for each section separately.
Let A_1 be the area under the graph between $x = 0$ and $x = 2$
and A_2 be the area under the graph between $x = 2$ and $x = 3$.

Use the formula $A = \int_a^b y \, dx$ for each section:

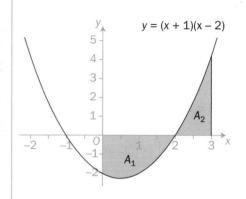

$$A_1 = \int_0^2 (x^2 - x - 2) \, dx$$

$$= \left[\frac{x^3}{3} - \frac{x^2}{2} - 2x \right]_0^2$$

$$= \left(\frac{8}{3} - 2 - 4 \right) - 0$$

$$= -\frac{10}{3}$$

The negative value for A_1 confirms that the area is below
the x-axis.
The actual area for the region A_1 is given by $|A_1| = \frac{10}{3}$

$|A_1|$ is the **absolute value** of A_1.
This is the positive value of A_1
regardless of the actual sign of A_1.

$$A_2 = \int_2^3 (x^2 - x - 2) \, dx$$

$$= \left[\frac{x^3}{3} - \frac{x^2}{2} - 2x \right]_2^3$$

$$= \left(9 - \frac{9}{2} - 6 \right) - \left(\frac{8}{3} - 2 - 4 \right)$$

$$= \left(-\frac{3}{2} \right) - \left(-\frac{10}{3} \right)$$

$$= \frac{11}{6}$$

Add the two areas to give the overall area:

The required area, $A = \frac{10}{3} + \frac{11}{6} = \frac{31}{6}$ square units

C2

To find the area enclosed between a curve and a
straight line you first need to find the points of intersection
of the curve and the line.

EXAMPLE 4

Find the area enclosed between the curve $y = x(4 - x)$
and the straight line $y = x$

The curve $y = x(4 - x)$ crosses the x-axis at $x = 0$ and $x = 4$.
The line $y = x$ passes through the origin, $(0, 0)$.

Set up an equation to find where the curve and line intersect:
$$x(4 - x) = x$$

Rearrange: $3x - x^2 = 0$
Factorise: $x(3 - x) = 0$

The points of intersection are at $(0, 0)$ and $(3, 3)$.

The required region, A_1, is found by subtracting the area of
the triangle, A_2, from the area bound by the curve and the
lines $x = 0$ and $x = 3$.

Use integration:
$$A = \int_a^b y \, dx$$

$$= \int_0^3 (4x - x^2) \, dx$$

$$= \left[2x^2 - \frac{x^3}{3} \right]_0^3$$

$$= (18 - 9) - 0$$
$$= 9$$

Use the formula for area of a right-angled triangle to find area A_2:

$$A_2 = \frac{1}{2} \text{ base} \times \text{height}$$

$$= \frac{1}{2} \times 3 \times 3$$

$$= \frac{9}{2}$$

Required area A_1 = area under the curve − area of the triangle
$$= A - A_2$$

Therefore the required area $A_1 = 9 - \frac{9}{2} = \frac{9}{2}$ square units

Sketch the graph.
You have to find the shaded area.

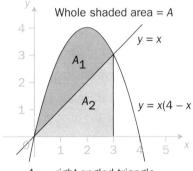

Whole shaded area = A

A_2 = right-angled triangle

Exercise 15.2

1 Find the area bounded by the x-axis, the given curve and the lines $x = 1$ and $x = 3$ in each case.

Sketch a diagram.

a $y = 4x^3$
b $y = 4 - x$

c $y = 3x^2 - 1$
d $y = x(x - 1)$

e $y = x^2(8x - 9)$
f $y = (1 - x)(1 + x)$

g $y = (2x + 1)(x - 4)$
h $y = \dfrac{x^2 + 3}{x^2}$

2 Find the area bounded by each curve and the x-axis.

a $y = x(2 - x)$
b $y = x(x - 3)$

c $y = x^2 - 1$
d $y = (x - 2)(x - 1)$

e $y = 3x(2x - 1)$
f $y = (x + 2)(x - 1)$

g $y = (x + 1)(x + 3)$
h $y = x^2 - 9$

3 Find the total area of the regions enclosed between each curve and the x-axis.
Sketch the given curve in each case.

a $y = x(x - 1)(x + 1)$
b $y = x(x - 3)(x + 3)$

c $y = x(x - 1)(x - 2)$
d $y = x(x + 1)(x - 2)$

e $y = x(x - 3)(x - 4)$

4 Find the area enclosed between each curve, the x-axis and the given lines.
Sketch the curve in each case.

a $y = (x + 2)(x - 1)$, lines $x = 0, x = 3$

b $y = x(x + 2)$, lines $x = -1, x = 1$

c $y = x^2(2 - x)$, lines $x = 0, x = 3$

d $y = x(x^2 - 4)$, lines $x = -2, x = 2$

e $y = x(x + 1)(x - 2)$, lines $x = -1, x = 2$

f $y = x(x + 1)^2$, lines $x = -1, x = 1$

g $y = x^3 - 4x$, lines $x = 0, x = 3$

h $y = (x + 1)(x - 1)(x - 2)$, lines $x = 0, x = 2$

C2

5   Find the areas of these regions.
    Sketch your own graphs for parts **c, d, e** and **f**.

    a   The area enclosed between the curve $y = x(3 - x)$
         and the line $y = x$

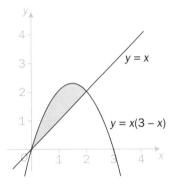

    b   The area enclosed between the curve $y = x^2 + 2$
         and the line $y = 6$

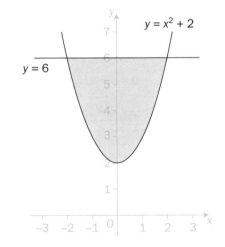

6   Find the area enclosed by

    a   the curve $y = 4 - x^2$ and the line $y = 3$

    b   the curve $y = x(2 - x)$ and the line $y = x$

    c   the curve $y = \dfrac{1}{x^2} + 4x$ and the line joining the points on

         the curve where $x = \dfrac{1}{2}$ and $x = 2$

    d   the curve $y = x^2 + \dfrac{1}{x^2}$ and the line joining the points

         on the curve where $x = 1$ and $x = 3$.

C2

INVESTIGATIONS

7

The cross-section of the tunnel above can be modelled by the graph

$$y = -x(x - 3)$$

assuming the origin is taken as the bottom left-hand corner of the tunnel.

a Use integration to find the area of the tunnel's cross-section.

b If the tunnel is 500 m long, find its volume in cubic metres.

8

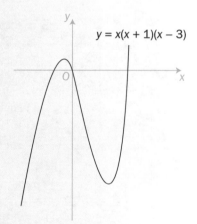

$$y = x(x + 1)(x - 3)$$

Lorna wishes to find the total area between the curve and the x-axis.

She attempts the integral $\displaystyle\int_{-1}^{3} x(x + 1)(x - 3)\ dx$

a Why will this not give her the answer she wants?

b What integrals should she work out to give the true area?

C2

15.3 The trapezium rule

In some cases you may want to find the area under a curve but not be able to integrate its equation.

You can use the trapezium rule to find an approximation to the area.

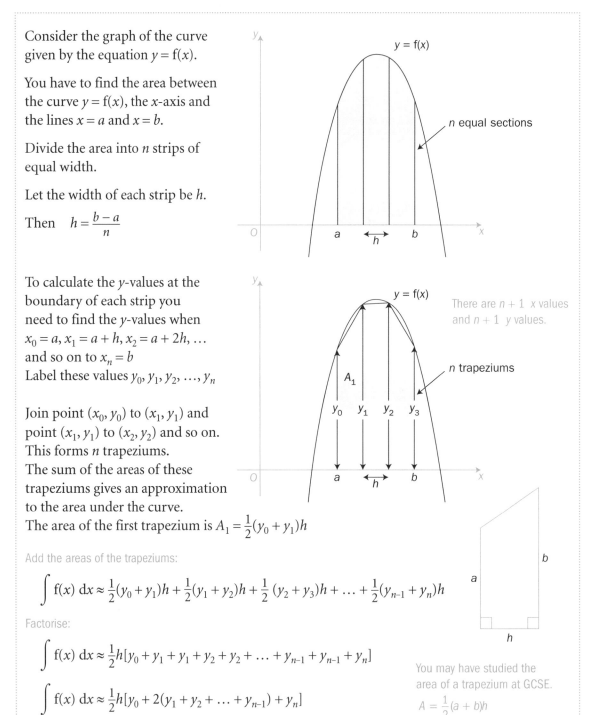

Consider the graph of the curve given by the equation $y = f(x)$.

You have to find the area between the curve $y = f(x)$, the x-axis and the lines $x = a$ and $x = b$.

Divide the area into n strips of equal width.

Let the width of each strip be h.

Then $h = \dfrac{b - a}{n}$

n equal sections

To calculate the y-values at the boundary of each strip you need to find the y-values when $x_0 = a, x_1 = a + h, x_2 = a + 2h, \ldots$ and so on to $x_n = b$
Label these values $y_0, y_1, y_2, \ldots, y_n$

There are $n + 1$ x values and $n + 1$ y values.

Join point (x_0, y_0) to (x_1, y_1) and point (x_1, y_1) to (x_2, y_2) and so on. This forms n trapeziums.
The sum of the areas of these trapeziums gives an approximation to the area under the curve.
The area of the first trapezium is $A_1 = \frac{1}{2}(y_0 + y_1)h$

n trapeziums

Add the areas of the trapeziums:

$$\int f(x)\,dx \approx \tfrac{1}{2}(y_0 + y_1)h + \tfrac{1}{2}(y_1 + y_2)h + \tfrac{1}{2}(y_2 + y_3)h + \ldots + \tfrac{1}{2}(y_{n-1} + y_n)h$$

Factorise:

$$\int f(x)\,dx \approx \tfrac{1}{2}h[y_0 + y_1 + y_1 + y_2 + y_2 + \ldots + y_{n-1} + y_{n-1} + y_n]$$

$$\int f(x)\,dx \approx \tfrac{1}{2}h[y_0 + 2(y_1 + y_2 + \ldots + y_{n-1}) + y_n]$$

You may have studied the area of a trapezium at GCSE.

$A = \frac{1}{2}(a + b)h$

C2

o The area under a curve $y = f(x)$ between $x = a$ and $x = b$
can be approximated using the trapezium rule

$$\int f(x)\, dx \approx \tfrac{1}{2}h[y_0 + 2(y_1 + y_2 + \dots + y_{n-1}) + y_n]$$

where $h = \dfrac{b - a}{n}$ and $y_i = f(x_i) = f(a + ih)$

Another way of writing this is

$\int f(x)\, dx \approx \dfrac{h}{2}$[first ordinate + last ordinate + 2 × other ordinates]

The trapezium rule gives
an approximation to the
area under a curve.
The more strips into which
the area is divided, the
better the approximation.

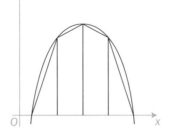
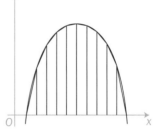

INVESTIGATION

How will the approximation
given by the trapezium rule
for a concave curve
differ from that given
for a convex curve?

concave curve   convex curve

C2

EXAMPLE 1

Use the trapezium rule to obtain an estimate for the value of $\displaystyle\int_2^6 \dfrac{x^2}{(x-1)}\, dx$
using eight strips.

$a = 2$ and $b = 6$, so $h = \dfrac{b-a}{n} = \dfrac{6-2}{8} = 0.5$

Record the values of x and y in a table:

x	2	2.5	3	3.5	4	4.5	5	5.5	6
$y = \dfrac{x^2}{(x-1)}$	4	4.167	4.5	4.9	5.333	5.786	6.25	6.722	7.2

Substitute into the trapezium rule formula $A \approx \tfrac{1}{2}h[y_0 + 2(y_1 + y_2 + \dots + y_{n-1}) + y_n]$:

$$A \approx \dfrac{0.5}{2}[4 + 2(4.167 + 4.5 + 4.9 + 5.333 + 5.786 + 6.25 + 6.722) + 7.2]$$

$$\approx \tfrac{1}{4}[4 + 75.316 + 7.2] = 21.6 \text{ square units} \quad \text{to 3 s.f.}$$

EXAMPLE 2

a Sketch the graph of the equation $y = x(6 - x)$

b Use the trapezium rule with six strips to find an estimate for the area between the curve and the x-axis.

c Use integration to find the area in **b**.

d Compare the results obtained by the two methods for this area.

---

a Find the x-axis crossings:

When $y = 0$, $x = 0$ or $x = 6$

Expand the bracket: $\quad y = 6x - x^2$

Differentiate wrt x: $\quad \dfrac{dy}{dx} = 6 - 2x$

At the turning points $\dfrac{dy}{dx} = 0$

Hence there is a turning point at $(3, 9)$

and this is a maximum turning point since $\quad \dfrac{d^2y}{dx^2} < 0$

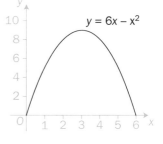

b $y = x(6 - x)$

Make a table of values:

x	0	1	2	3	4	5	6
y	0	5	8	9	8	5	0

Use the trapezium rule: $\quad A = \dfrac{1}{2}[0 + 2 \times (5 + 8 + 9 + 8 + 5)]$ $\qquad h = 1$

$$= \dfrac{1}{2}[70] = 35$$

c Use an integration method:

$$A = \int_0^6 (6x - x^2)\, dx = \left[3x^2 - \frac{x^3}{3} \right]_0^6$$

$$= \left(3 \times 36 - \frac{216}{3} \right) - (0)$$

$$= 108 - 72 = 36$$

d Integration gives an exact result of 36 while the trapezium rule gives 35.

The trapezium rule gives an underestimate since the curve is convex.

Exercise 15.3

1 Copy and complete the table and use the trapezium rule to estimate the area under the curve given by each equation.

Sketch a diagram of each curve.

a $y = \sqrt{(x + 1)}$, taking three strips

x	1	2	3	4
y	1.414		2	

b $y = \dfrac{10}{x}$, taking three strips

x	2	3	4	5
y	5			2

c $y = \sqrt{(x^2 - 2)}$, taking four strips

x	2	2.5	3	3.5	4
y	1.414				

d $y = \dfrac{x}{1 + x}$, taking five strips

x	1	2	3	4	5	6
y	0.5		0.75			

e $y = (1.5)^x$, taking six strips

x	2	2.5	3	3.5	4	4.5	5
y	2.25						

f $y = \dfrac{x^3 + 1}{x}$, taking eight strips

x	1	1.5	2	2.5	3	3.5	4	4.5	5
y	2		4.5						

2 Use the trapezium rule to estimate the value of each integral.

a $\displaystyle\int_1^5 \left(\dfrac{4}{x}\right) dx$, with four strips

b $\displaystyle\int_1^4 \dfrac{10}{(1 + x)} dx$, with six strips

c $\displaystyle\int_1^{11} \dfrac{x^2}{(x + 1)} dx$, with five strips

d $\displaystyle\int_1^3 \sqrt{(x^2 + 3)} \, dx$, with eight strips

e $\displaystyle\int_2^{14} x(x + 1)(x + 2) \, dx$, with six strips

f $\displaystyle\int_1^{3.5} \dfrac{x(x + 1)}{(x^2 + 1)} dx$, with five strips

3 Sketch the curve with equation $y = 2^x$
Find the area between the curve, the x-axis and the lines $x = 2$
and $x = 4$ using the trapezium rule with

  a four strips

  b eight strips.

4 Sketch the curve with equation $y = \dfrac{8}{x}$
Find the area between the curve, the x-axis and the lines $x = 1$
and $x = 3$ using the trapezium rule with

  a two strips

  b eight strips.

5 **a** Use the trapezium rule to find an estimate for the area under
the curve given by the equation $y = x\,(x - 2)$, the x-axis and
the lines $x = 2$ and $x = 5$, taking six strips.

  b Use integration to find an exact answer for the
area in part **a**.

6 The sketch shows the graph of the equation

$$y = 2\sqrt{2x}$$

Use the trapezium rule with eight strips to

estimate the value of $\displaystyle\int_{1}^{5} y \, dx$

With reference to the sketch graph state, with reason,
whether this is an overestimate or underestimate of
the shaded area under the curve.
Find the area using integration.
Give your answers correct to two decimal places.

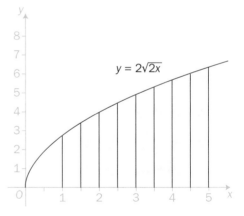

7 **a** Sketch the graph of the equation $y = \tan x$, where x is in
radian measure, taking values of x from 0 to $\dfrac{\pi}{2}$.

  b Find an estimate for the area between the curve $y = \tan x$,
the x-axis and the lines $x = \dfrac{\pi}{6}$ and $x = \dfrac{\pi}{3}$.

  c With reference to the sketch of the curve, deduce, giving a
reason, whether this is an underestimate or overestimate.
of the area under the curve.

INVESTIGATIONS

8 By considering trapezia under each graph, determine if the trapezium rule would give an overestimate or underestimate of the shaded area or the exact answer in each case.

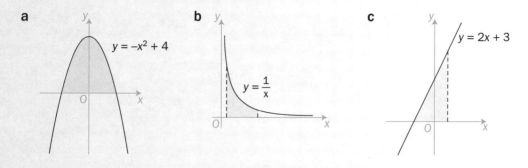

a $y = -x^2 + 4$

b $y = \dfrac{1}{x}$

c $y = 2x + 3$

9 This question concerns the area bounded by the x-axis and the lines $x = 0$ and $x = 1$ for the curve $y = 2^x$

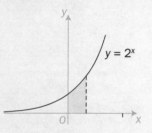

$y = 2^x$

The exact answer can be calculated as $\dfrac{1}{\ln 2}$ on your calculator.

Copy and complete the table to show how the accuracy of the answer depends on the number of strips.

The button is next to log on your calculator. The % error formula is

$$\dfrac{(\text{estimate} - \text{actual})}{\text{actual}} \times 100$$

No. of strips	Estimate	% error
1		
2		
4		

C2

1 Evaluate these integrals.

a $\displaystyle\int_0^4 (x+2)^2 \, dx$ **b** $\displaystyle\int_1^4 \frac{1}{(\sqrt{x})} \, dx$ **c** $\displaystyle\int_1^3 \frac{5}{x^2} \, dx$

d $\displaystyle\int_2^4 x(3x-2) \, dx$ **e** $\displaystyle\int_1^3 \left(x + \frac{1}{x^2}\right) dx$

2 The speed, v m s^{-1}, of a train at time t seconds is given by

$$v = \sqrt{(1.4^t - 1)}, \quad \text{where } 0 \leqslant t \leqslant 30$$

The following table shows the speed of the train at 5-second intervals.

t	0	5	10	15	20	25	30
v	0	2.09	5.28		28.91		

a Copy and complete the table, giving the values of v to two decimal places.
The distance, s metres, travelled by the train in 30 seconds

is given by $\displaystyle s = \int_0^{30} \sqrt{(1.4^t - 1)} \, dt$

b Use the trapezium rule, with all the values from your table, to estimate the value of s.

3 The figure shows the shaded region R which is bounded

by the curve $y = -2x^2 + 5x$ and the line $y = 2$

The points A and B are the points of intersection of the line and the curve.

Find

a the x-coordinates of the points A and B

b the exact area of R.

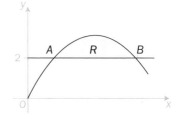

4 The figure shows part of the curve, C, with equation

$$y = 2x + \frac{8}{x^2} - 5, \quad x > 0$$

The points P and Q lie on C and have x-coordinates 1 and 4 respectively.
The region R, shaded in the figure, is bounded by C and the straight line joining P and Q.

a Find the exact area of R

b Use calculus to show that y is increasing for $x > 2$

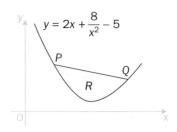

[(c) Edexcel Limited 2005]

5 A river, running between parallel banks, is 20 m wide.
The depth, y metres, of the river at a point x metres from one
bank is given by the formula

$$y = \frac{1}{10}x\sqrt{(20-x)}, 0 \leqslant x \leqslant 20$$

a Copy and complete the table below, giving values of y to three decimal places.

x	0	4	8	12	16	20
y	0		2.771			0

b Use the trapezium rule with all the values in the table to
estimate the cross-sectional area of the river.

Given that the cross-sectional area is constant and that the
river is flowing uniformly at 2 m s^{-1}

c estimate, in m^3, the volume of water flowing per minute,
giving your answer to three significant figures.   [(c) Edexcel Limited 2005]

6 The figure shows a sketch of part of the
curve, C, with equation
$y = x(x-1)(x-5)$
Use calculus to find the total area of the
finite region, shown shaded in the figure,
that is between $x = 0$ and $x = 2$ and is
bounded by C, the x-axis and the line $x = 2$

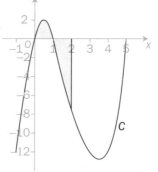

[(c) Edexcel Limited 2007]

7 A curve is given by the equation $y = x(x^2 - 1)$

a Sketch the curve for values of x from $x = -2$ to $x = 2$ giving the
coordinates of the points where the curve crosses the x-axis.

b Use calculus to find the total area enclosed between
the curve and the x-axis.

c Use the trapezium rule to find the area between $x = 0$ and $x = 1$ taking
four strips and hence deduce the total area enclosed between the curve
and the x-axis. Give your answer correct to three significant figures.

8 A curve is given by the equation $y = \sin x$ where x is measured in radians.
Sketch the graph of $y = \sin x$ taking values of x from

$x = 0$ to $x = \frac{\pi}{2}$ radians.

On the same sketch draw the line $y = 0.5$
Find, using the trapezium rule, the area between the curve, the

line $y = 0.5$ and the line $x = \frac{\pi}{2}$ radians. Take four strips and give

your answer correct to two decimal places.

Summary

◯ You can evaluate a definite integral using

$$\int_a^b f'(x)\,dx = f(b) - f(a)$$

given that $f'(x)$ exists throughout the interval $a \leqslant x \leqslant b$

◯ You can use integration to find the area enclosed between a curve $y = f(x)$, the x-axis and the lines $x = a$ and $x = b$.

◯ You can approximate the area between a curve and the x-axis using the trapezium rule

$$A = \int f(x)\,dx \approx \tfrac{1}{2}h[y_0 + 2(y_1 + y_2 + \ldots + y_{n-1}) + y_n]$$

where $h = \dfrac{b-a}{n}$ and $y_i = f(x_i) = f(a + ih)$

Refer to

15.1

15.2

15.3

C2

Links

Integration can be used in real life to calculate areas that cannot be measured.

By finding the area under a suitable polynomial and then rotating it around one of the axes, integration can also be used to evaluate volumes of three-dimensional shapes.

Using integration techniques combined with algebra makes it possible to find areas and volumes which would otherwise be impossible to measure.

1 **a** The first term in a geometric series is 5 and the common ratio is 2.
    Write down the first four terms in the series.

  b For this series find the sum to 10 terms.

  c Find the least number of terms in the series in order that
    the sum exceeds 20 000.

2 **a** Write down the first four terms in ascending powers of x
    in the expansion of $(1 + 2x)^{12}$

  b If terms in x^3 and higher powers may be neglected show that
    $$(1 - x)(1 + 2x)^{12} \approx a + bx + cx^2$$
    and find the values of the constants a, b and c.

3 **a** In the expansion in ascending powers of x of $(a - x)^6$ the third term is $240x^2$
    Find the value of the constant a.

  b Using this value of a determine the first three terms in the expansion.

4 **a** Find the value of x at which the gradient of the curve given by
    $y = (x + 5)(3 - 2x)$ is zero.

  b Find the coordinates of the turning point on the curve stating
    whether it is a maximum or minimum turning point.

5 A solid circular cylinder is cut from a solid sphere of radius r cm.
  If the height of the cylinder is h cm show that the volume, V cm^3,
  of the cylinder is given by the equation

  $$V = \pi h \left[r^2 - \frac{h^2}{4} \right]$$

  Find the value of h in terms of r for which the cylinder has a
  maximum volume.

6 **a** Find the coordinates of the turning points on the curve given
    by the equation $y = (2x - 5)(5 - x)$ stating whether they are
    maximum or minimum points.

  b Sketch the curve given by the equation
    $y = (2x - 5)(5 - x)$

  c Find the values of x for which the function
    $f(x) = (2x - 5)(5 - x)$ is
    i an increasing function
    ii a decreasing function

C2

7 Sketch the graph of the equation

$$y = x(x - 3)^2$$

stating the coordinates of the turning points and their nature.

8 **a** Evaluate $\displaystyle\int_1^3 (9x^2 - 4x)\,dx$

b If $\displaystyle\int_0^a (9x^2 - 4x)\,dx = 0$, find the possible values of a when $a > 0$.

9 Use the trapezium rule to evaluate the integral given by

$$\int_1^4 \log_{10} x\,dx$$

taking six strips.
Write your answer correct to two decimal places.

10 **a** Sketch the graph of $y = 1.5^x$ showing the coordinates of the point at which the graph meets the y-axis.

b Copy and complete the table, giving the values of 1.5^x to three decimal places.

x	0	0.2	0.4	0.6	0.8	1
1.5^x		1.084				1.5

c Use the trapezium rule, with all these values from your table, to find an approximation for the value of $\displaystyle\int_0^1 1.5^x\,dx$

11 **a** Sketch the graph of $y = 6\sqrt{x}$
taking values of x from $x = 0$ to $x = 3$

Work correct to two decimal places

b Use the trapezium rule with six strips to estimate the area between the curve, whose equation is $y = 6\sqrt{x}$, the x-axis and the line $x = 3$.
Is this an overestimate or an underestimate of the actual area?
Give a reason for this conclusion.

c Evaluate the integral $\displaystyle\int_0^3 6\sqrt{x}\,dx$ and use this result to compare with the area found by the trapezium rule.

d Express the difference between the two methods as a percentage of the exact area.

Answers

Before you start Answers

Chapter 1

1. **a** 1, 4, 9, 16, 25, 36, 49, 64, 81, 100, 121, 144, 169, 196, 225, 256, 289, 324, 361, 400
   b **i** 27   **ii** 64   **iii** 125
   c **i** 5   **ii** 6
   d 2, 4, 8, 16, 32, 64, 128, 256, 512, 1024

2. **a** 9   **b** 27   **c** 3.5   **d** 5
   e 5   **f** 4

3. **a** 280   **b** 520   **c** 180   **d** 560

Exercise 1.1

1. **a** 128   **b** 243   **c** 169   **d** 24
   e 57   **f** 0   **g** 64   **h** $\frac{64}{27}$
   i 0.064   **j** 0.04   **k** 9600   **l** −92

2. **a** 2^5 **b** 3^4 or 9^2 **c** 5^3 **d** $(0.1)^3$
   e $\left(\frac{5}{8}\right)^2$ **f** $(0.2)^2$ **g** $\left(\frac{1}{10}\right)^4$ **h** $\left(\frac{21}{20}\right)^2$
   i $\frac{2^7}{3^5}$

3. **a** $\frac{1}{4}$ **b** $\frac{1}{36}$ **c** 1   **d** 8
   e $\frac{27}{8}$ **f** 4   **g** 81   **h** 256

4. **a** p^4 **b** $60a^6$ **c** $4b^{-3}$ **d** $9y^4$
   e $16p^2$ **f** $5a^{-1}$ **g** $80b^8$ **h** 3^{-1}
   i $6p^3$ **j** $-108y^5$

5. **a** $\frac{25a^2}{b^4}$ **b** $16a^8b^4$ **c** $125t^6 - 125y^6$
   d $216y^3z^3$ **e** $\frac{1}{9a^2}$ **f** $\frac{r^6}{8}$ **g** $\frac{3y}{2z^2}$
   h $\frac{9}{64b}$ **i** $\frac{16}{y^4}$ **j** $81y^6t^6$

6. **a** $13a^2$ **b** not possible   **c** $36a^5$
   d $\frac{4}{9a}$ **e** not possible   **f** $\frac{9}{4a}$
   g $\frac{9}{4a^2}$ **h** $-5a$ **i** $36a^3 - 9a^2$
   j $-3\frac{5}{9}a$

7. Powers of 3: $\frac{1}{9}$ $\frac{1}{27}$ 81
   Powers of 4: 64 $\frac{1}{16}$

8. $\frac{4a^3}{(2a)^2}$, $\frac{3a^{-1}}{3a^{-2}}$, $\frac{\left(a^{-1}\right)}{(5a)^{-2}} \cdot \frac{1}{25}$

9. **a** £80 × $(1.05)^5$ **b** £80 × $(1.05)^n$
   c 4 years 7 months

Exercise 1.2

1. **a** 2   **b** 2   **c** 5   **d** 3
   e $\frac{2}{3}$ **f** $\frac{1}{5}$ **g** $\frac{9}{4}$ **h** 0.2

2. **a** $\frac{1}{3}$ **b** $\frac{2}{3}$ **c** 6   **d** 1
   e $\frac{6}{5}$ **f** $\frac{3}{5}$

3. **a** $\frac{4}{9}$ **b** $\frac{125}{64}$ **c** $\frac{9}{4}$ **d** $\frac{8}{27}$
   e 100   **f** $\frac{27}{8}$ **g** $\frac{8}{27}$ **h** $\frac{1}{49}$
   i $\frac{1}{32}$

4. **a** $\frac{1}{y}$ **b** $2a^3$ **c** $\frac{8a^6}{27}$ **d** $\frac{32}{b^5}$
   e $\frac{1}{y^{\frac{3}{2}}}$

5. **a** $4a^2$ **b** $\frac{10}{t}$ **c** $3p$ **d** $28t$
   e $3t$ **f** $\frac{a}{2}$

6. **a** $32t^5$ **b** $100t^6$

7. $x = -\frac{2}{3}$

Exercise 1.3

1. **a** $2\sqrt{2}$ **b** $4\sqrt{2}$ **c** $2\sqrt{6}$ **d** $5\sqrt{2}$
   e $4\sqrt{3}$ **f** $\frac{3\sqrt{2}}{5}$ **g** $\frac{7\sqrt{2}}{11}$ **h** $\frac{7\sqrt{5}}{10}$

2. **a** $6\sqrt{2}$ **b** -6 **c** $-4\sqrt{5}$ **d** 7
   e $\frac{-\sqrt{7}}{3}$ **f** -4 **g** $4 + 2\sqrt{3}$ **h** $\frac{3\sqrt{3}}{4}$
   i $3 + \sqrt{3}$ **j** 28

3. **a** $\frac{\sqrt{7}}{7}$ **b** $\frac{4\sqrt{13}}{13}$ **c** $\frac{7\sqrt{2}}{4}$ **d** $\frac{2\sqrt{21}}{7}$
   e $\frac{\sqrt{15}}{5}$ **f** $\frac{\sqrt{14}}{3}$ **g** $\frac{2\sqrt{6}}{9}$ **h** $\frac{8\sqrt{15}}{3}$

4. **a** $-1 + \sqrt{2}$ **b** $\frac{-3}{2} - \frac{3\sqrt{3}}{2}$ **c** $4 - 2\sqrt{2}$
   d $\frac{5}{2} + \frac{\sqrt{3}}{2}$ **e** $-1 + \sqrt{2}$ **f** $\frac{-3}{2} - \frac{\sqrt{3}}{2}$
   g $-3 - 2\sqrt{2}$ **h** $2 - \sqrt{3}$
   i $\frac{15 - 3\sqrt{6} + 5\sqrt{5} - \sqrt{30}}{4}$ **j** $4(\sqrt{3} + \sqrt{2})$

5. $p = -1, q = 2, r = 1$

6. $-3 + 3\sqrt{5}$ m

Review 1

1. **a** 64   **b** 1   **c** $\frac{25}{16}$
   d -27 **e** $\frac{1}{9}$ **f** $\frac{64}{729}$
   g 100   **h** 1

2. **a** 5^4 **b** $\left(\frac{5}{4}\right)^2$ **c** $(0.5)^3$
   d $\left(\frac{14}{13}\right)^2$

3. **a** $27p^3$ **b** $25y^6$ **c** $-18y^4$
   d $81a^8$ **e** $\frac{4}{9t^4}$ **f** $\frac{-125}{64t^3}$

4 a $\dfrac{3}{5}$ **b** $\dfrac{4}{3}$ **c** $\dfrac{1}{9}$ **d** $\dfrac{125}{8}$

   e 343   **f** 100 000   **g** $\dfrac{1}{128}$ **h** 0.01

5 a $3a^2$ **b** $\dfrac{1}{2}\sqrt{t}$ **c** $\dfrac{2}{3t}$ **d** $\dfrac{1}{y^2}$

   e $32t^5$ **f** $625p^8q^4$

6 a $10\sqrt{2}$ **b** $8\sqrt{2}$ **c** $\dfrac{10\sqrt{2}}{7}$

7 a $2\sqrt{2}$ **b** $\sqrt{2}$ **c** $\sqrt{5}$ **d** $\sqrt{14}$

8 a $15\sqrt{2}$ **b** 1   **c** $6+2\sqrt{5}$ **d** $\dfrac{23\sqrt{3}}{24}$

9 a $2-\sqrt{3}$ **b** $\dfrac{3(5+\sqrt{3})}{22}$ **c** $\dfrac{4+3\sqrt{2}}{2}$

   d $\dfrac{2(\sqrt{5}+\sqrt{2})}{3}$

10 a $7-4\sqrt{3}$ **b** $a=\dfrac{3}{4}, b=\dfrac{1}{4}$

    c $26-11\sqrt{7}$ **d** $11\sqrt{2}$

11 a $10+6\sqrt{3}$ cm   **b** $12+8\sqrt{3}$ cm^2

12 a $2\sqrt{3}$ **b** $3\sqrt{(\sqrt{3})}$ **c** $ab^2\sqrt{c^3}$

13 a $3\sqrt{5}$ **b** $9-4\sqrt{5}$

14 a $4\sqrt{5}$ **b** $14+6\sqrt{5}$

15 a 6   **b** $12-4\sqrt{3}$

16 a 9   **b** 27   **c** $\dfrac{1}{27}$

Before you start Answers

Chapter 2

1   **a, c** and **d**

2

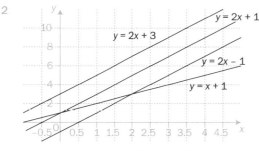

Lines **a**, **b** and **c** are parallel, **a** and **d** have the same y-intercept

3   **a** gradient 3; intercept 2
    b gradient 2; intercept 1
    c gradient –1; intercept 1
    d gradient $\dfrac{2}{3}$; intercept 1

Exercise 2.1

1   **a** $y=-x+6$ **b** $y=3x-6$
    c $y=-2x+1$ **d** $2y=x+5$
    e $3y=-2x+13$ **f** $y=-x+2$
2   **a** $3y=4x+6$ **b** $y=-x+1$
    c $y=-x-2$ **d** $7y=3x+26$
    e $8y=-5x+9$ **f** $5y=-3x-36$

3   **a** $-\dfrac{5}{3}$ **b** $3y=-2x$
    c $y=2x+3$ **d** $\dfrac{5}{2}, 2y=5x-19$
4   **a** $a=3$
    b $k=3$ and P and Q are the same point.
5   **a** $y=-2x+6$ **b** $2y+6x=1$
    c $a=\dfrac{1}{2}$ **d** $y=2x-3$
    e $\left(0,-\dfrac{1}{2}\right),\left(\dfrac{1}{3},0\right),\dfrac{3}{2}$ **f** $y=4x-5$
6 $y=x+1, y=x-1, y=-x+2, y=-x+4,$
    Area = 2

Exercise 2.2

1   **a** $x-y-3=0$ **b** $x-4=0$
    c $x-3y-3=0$ **d** $x-5y=0$
    e $y-7=0$ **f** $2x+3y-6=0$
    g $3x-4y=0$ **h** $3x+2y+1=0$
    i $3x-y+4=0$ **j** $2x+5y-19=0$
2   **a** $\left(\dfrac{1}{3},0\right),\left(0,\dfrac{1}{2}\right)$ **b** $2x+4y-3=0$
    c $a=8, b=-4; 2x-y=1$
    d i $P\left(\dfrac{8}{13},-\dfrac{1}{13}\right)$ **ii** lines are perpendicular
3   **a** $ae=bd$ **b** $ce=bf$ **c** $a=b$

Exercise 2.3

1   **a** parallel   **b** neither
    c perpendicular   **d** neither
    e perpendicular   **f** neither
    g parallel   **h** parallel
2   **a** $2y=3x+9$ **b** $y=\dfrac{x}{2}+2$
    c $y=-\dfrac{4}{3}x+4$ **d** $3y+4x=1$; perpendicular
    e $y=2x-8$ **f** $2y+4x=17$
    g $2y=-x+5$ **h** $2y=x-3$
3   **a** $m=-2$ **b** $a=\dfrac{3}{2}$
    c $m=-2, c=5;$ **d** $y=-\dfrac{1}{2}x+\dfrac{5}{2}$; gradient 2
       $y=-2x+5$
    e $x+y+2=0$ **f** $y-\dfrac{1}{3}x+3$
    g $y=-\dfrac{x}{2}+5;$ **h** $a=1$
       $m=-\dfrac{1}{2}, c=5$
4 $x-3y-2=0$

Review 2

1   **a** $y=-x+3$ **b** $y=-\dfrac{2x}{3}+2$
    c $y=-2x+\dfrac{1}{4}$
2   **a** $-2x+3y-5=0$ **b** $-x+2y+2=0$
    c $2x+3y-8=0$
3   **a** $a=-4, c=2$ **b** $c=4$
    c $2,\dfrac{5}{2}$ **d** $b=-2$
4   **a** yes   **b** $y=-2x-3$
    c $Q(0,3), P(6,0), y=2x+3$ **d** $a=3, b=-14$

C1

5   $B(3, 6), y = -x + 9$
6   $6y = 19x - 43$
7   **a** $y - 2x + 15 = 0$ **b** $(6, -3)$
    c 18.5 square units
8   **a** $p = 15, q = -3$,   **b** $7x - 5y - 46 = 0$,
    c $x = \dfrac{81}{7}$

9   **a** $P\left(\dfrac{12}{5}, \dfrac{21}{5}\right)$ **b** $A(0, 3)$ **c** $AP = \dfrac{6\sqrt{5}}{5}$

Before you start Answers

Chapter 3

1   **a** $3\sqrt{10}$ **b** $2\sqrt{15}$ **c** $5\sqrt{6}$
    d $2\sqrt{2}$ **e** $3\sqrt{6}$
2   **a** $y = 5; y = 0$ **b** $y = 2; y = 27$
    c $y = -4; y = -4$ **d** $y = 3; y = 243$
    e $y = 0; y = 40$ **f** $y = 24; y = -36$
3   **a** $x^2 + 7x + 10$ **b** $4x^2 - 8x + 3$
    c $1 - 4x + 3x^2$ **d** $1 - 4x^2$
    e $-25 + 20x - 4x^2$

Exercise 3.1

1   **a** 2, 3   **b** 0, -1   **c** 0, 3
    d -4, 5   **e** -7   **f** 2, 3
    g 4   **h** $-\dfrac{1}{2}, 5$ **i** $0, \dfrac{3}{2}$
    j $0, \dfrac{1}{3}$ **k** $\dfrac{3}{2}, \dfrac{5}{2}$ **l** $\dfrac{5}{3}$
    m $-\dfrac{1}{2}, \dfrac{1}{2}$ **n** $-\dfrac{2}{5}, -\dfrac{5}{2}$ **o** $\dfrac{3}{2}$
2   **a** 1, -2   **b** $-\dfrac{1}{4}, -3$ **c** $\dfrac{7}{2}, \dfrac{1}{3}$
    d $0.5, \dfrac{4}{3}$

3   **a** -1, -2

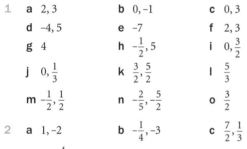

b -3, 2

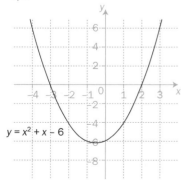

c 2, 5

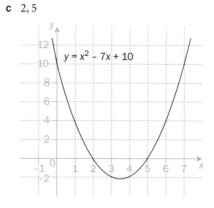

d -5, 6

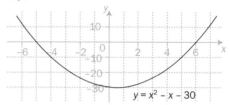

e 4, 7

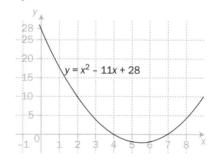

f -6, 4

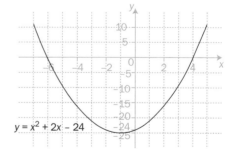

g -4, 9

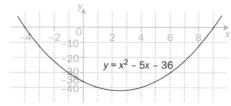

C1

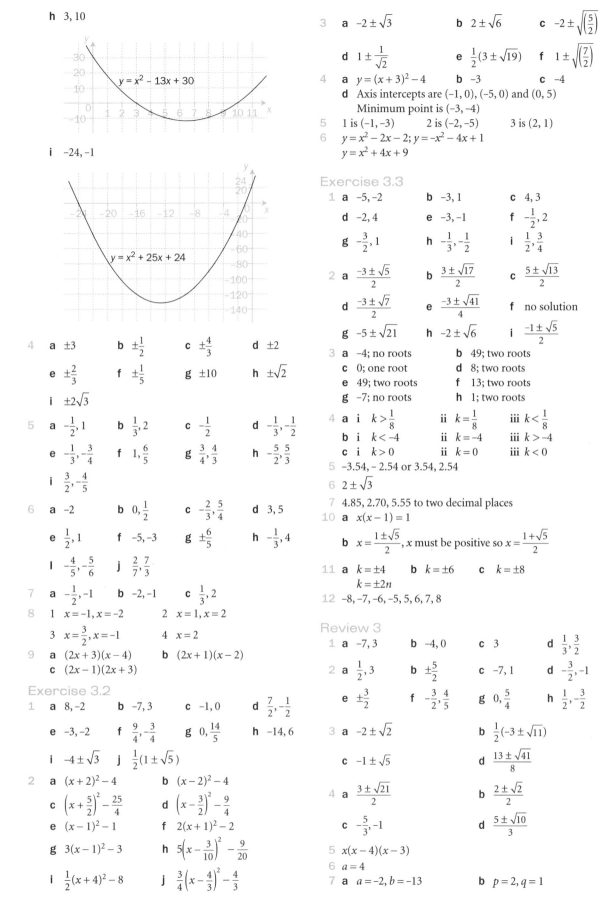

h 3, 10

$y = x^2 - 13x + 30$

i −24, −1

$y = x^2 + 25x + 24$

4 a ±3 **b** $\pm\frac{1}{2}$ **c** $\pm\frac{4}{3}$ **d** ±2

e $\pm\frac{2}{3}$ **f** $\pm\frac{1}{5}$ **g** ±10 **h** $\pm\sqrt{2}$

i $\pm 2\sqrt{3}$

5 a $-\frac{1}{2}, 1$ **b** $\frac{1}{3}, 2$ **c** $-\frac{1}{2}$ **d** $-\frac{1}{3}, -\frac{1}{2}$

e $-\frac{1}{3}, -\frac{3}{4}$ **f** $1, \frac{6}{5}$ **g** $\frac{3}{4}, \frac{4}{3}$ **h** $-\frac{5}{2}, \frac{5}{3}$

i $\frac{3}{2}, -\frac{4}{5}$

6 a −2 **b** $0, \frac{1}{2}$ **c** $-\frac{2}{3}, \frac{5}{4}$ **d** 3, 5

e $\frac{1}{2}, 1$ **f** −5, −3 **g** $\pm\frac{6}{5}$ **h** $-\frac{1}{3}, 4$

l $-\frac{4}{5}, -\frac{5}{6}$ **j** $\frac{2}{7}, \frac{7}{3}$

7 a $-\frac{1}{2}, -1$ **b** −2, −1 **c** $\frac{1}{3}, 2$

8 1 $x = -1, x = -2$ **2** $x = 1, x = 2$

3 $x = \frac{3}{2}, x = -1$ **4** $x = 2$

9 a $(2x + 3)(x - 4)$ **b** $(2x + 1)(x - 2)$

c $(2x - 1)(2x + 3)$

Exercise 3.2

1 a 8, −2 **b** −7, 3 **c** −1, 0 **d** $\frac{7}{2}, -\frac{1}{2}$

e −3, −2 **f** $\frac{9}{4}, -\frac{3}{4}$ **g** $0, \frac{14}{5}$ **h** −14, 6

i $-4 \pm \sqrt{3}$ **j** $\frac{1}{2}(1 \pm \sqrt{5})$

2 a $(x + 2)^2 - 4$ **b** $(x - 2)^2 - 4$

c $\left(x + \frac{5}{2}\right)^2 - \frac{25}{4}$ **d** $\left(x - \frac{3}{2}\right)^2 - \frac{9}{4}$

e $(x - 1)^2 - 1$ **f** $2(x + 1)^2 - 2$

g $3(x - 1)^2 - 3$ **h** $5\left(x - \frac{3}{10}\right)^2 - \frac{9}{20}$

i $\frac{1}{2}(x + 4)^2 - 8$ **j** $\frac{3}{4}\left(x - \frac{4}{3}\right)^2 - \frac{4}{3}$

3 a $-2 \pm \sqrt{3}$ **b** $2 \pm \sqrt{6}$ **c** $-2 \pm \sqrt{\left(\frac{5}{2}\right)}$

d $1 \pm \frac{1}{\sqrt{2}}$ **e** $\frac{1}{2}(3 \pm \sqrt{19})$ **f** $1 \pm \sqrt{\left(\frac{7}{2}\right)}$

4 a $y = (x + 3)^2 - 4$ **b** −3 **c** −4

d Axis intercepts are (−1, 0), (−5, 0) and (0, 5)
Minimum point is (−3, −4)

5 1 is (−1, −3) 2 is (−2, −5) 3 is (2, 1)

6 $y = x^2 - 2x - 2$; $y = -x^2 - 4x + 1$
$y = x^2 + 4x + 9$

Exercise 3.3

1 a −5, −2 **b** −3, 1 **c** 4, 3

d −2, 4 **e** −3, −1 **f** $-\frac{1}{2}, 2$

g $-\frac{3}{2}, 1$ **h** $-\frac{1}{3}, -\frac{1}{2}$ **i** $\frac{1}{2}, \frac{3}{4}$

2 a $\frac{-3 \pm \sqrt{5}}{2}$ **b** $\frac{3 \pm \sqrt{17}}{2}$ **c** $\frac{5 \pm \sqrt{13}}{2}$

d $\frac{-3 \pm \sqrt{7}}{2}$ **e** $\frac{-3 \pm \sqrt{41}}{4}$ **f** no solution

g $-5 \pm \sqrt{21}$ **h** $-2 \pm \sqrt{6}$ **i** $\frac{-1 \pm \sqrt{5}}{2}$

3 a −4; no roots **b** 49; two roots

c 0; one root **d** 8; two roots

e 49; two roots **f** 13; two roots

g −7; no roots **h** 1; two roots

4 a i $k > \frac{1}{8}$ **ii** $k = \frac{1}{8}$ **iii** $k < \frac{1}{8}$

b i $k < -4$ **ii** $k = -4$ **iii** $k > -4$

c i $k > 0$ **ii** $k = 0$ **iii** $k < 0$

5 −3.54, − 2.54 or 3.54, 2.54

6 $2 \pm \sqrt{3}$

7 4.85, 2.70, 5.55 to two decimal places

10 a $x(x - 1) = 1$

b $x = \frac{1 \pm \sqrt{5}}{2}$, x must be positive so $x = \frac{1 + \sqrt{5}}{2}$

11 a $k = \pm4$ **b** $k = \pm6$ **c** $k = \pm8$
$k = \pm2n$

12 −8, −7, −6, −5, 5, 6, 7, 8

Review 3

1 a −7, 3 **b** −4, 0 **c** 3 **d** $\frac{1}{3}, \frac{3}{2}$

2 a $\frac{1}{2}, 3$ **b** $\pm\frac{5}{2}$ **c** −7, 1 **d** $-\frac{3}{2}, -1$

e $\pm\frac{3}{2}$ **f** $-\frac{3}{2}, \frac{4}{5}$ **g** $0, \frac{5}{4}$ **h** $\frac{1}{2}, -\frac{3}{2}$

3 a $-2 \pm \sqrt{2}$ **b** $\frac{1}{2}(-3 \pm \sqrt{11})$

c $-1 \pm \sqrt{5}$ **d** $\frac{13 \pm \sqrt{41}}{8}$

4 a $\frac{3 \pm \sqrt{21}}{2}$ **b** $\frac{2 \pm \sqrt{2}}{2}$

c $-\frac{5}{3}, -1$ **d** $\frac{5 \pm \sqrt{10}}{3}$

5 $x(x - 4)(x - 3)$

6 $a = 4$

7 a $a = -2, b = -13$ **b** $p = 2, q = 1$

CI

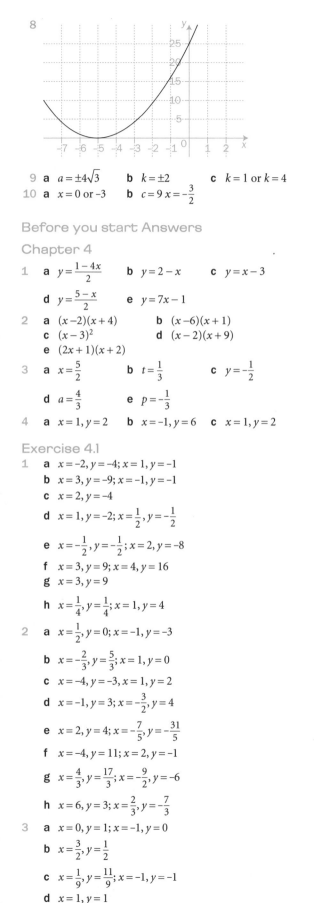

8

9 **a** $a = \pm 4\sqrt{3}$ **b** $k = \pm 2$ **c** $k = 1$ or $k = 4$

10 **a** $x = 0$ or -3 **b** $c = 9$ $x = -\dfrac{3}{2}$

Before you start Answers

Chapter 4

1 **a** $y = \dfrac{1 - 4x}{2}$ **b** $y = 2 - x$ **c** $y = x - 3$

   d $y = \dfrac{5 - x}{2}$ **e** $y = 7x - 1$

2 **a** $(x - 2)(x + 4)$ **b** $(x - 6)(x + 1)$
   c $(x - 3)^2$ **d** $(x - 2)(x + 9)$
   e $(2x + 1)(x + 2)$

3 **a** $x = \dfrac{5}{2}$ **b** $t = \dfrac{1}{3}$ **c** $y = -\dfrac{1}{2}$

   d $a = \dfrac{4}{3}$ **e** $p = -\dfrac{1}{3}$

4 **a** $x = 1, y = 2$ **b** $x = -1, y = 6$ **c** $x = 1, y = 2$

Exercise 4.1

1 **a** $x = -2, y = -4; x = 1, y = -1$
   b $x = 3, y = -9; x = -1, y = -1$
   c $x = 2, y = -4$
   d $x = 1, y = -2; x = \dfrac{1}{2}, y = -\dfrac{1}{2}$

   e $x = -\dfrac{1}{2}, y = -\dfrac{1}{2}; x = 2, y = -8$

   f $x = 3, y = 9; x = 4, y = 16$
   g $x = 3, y = 9$

   h $x = \dfrac{1}{4}, y = \dfrac{1}{4}; x = 1, y = 4$

2 **a** $x = \dfrac{1}{2}, y = 0; x = -1, y = -3$

   b $x = -\dfrac{2}{3}, y = \dfrac{5}{3}; x = 1, y = 0$

   c $x = -4, y = -3, x = 1, y = 2$

   d $x = -1, y = 3; x = -\dfrac{3}{2}, y = 4$

   e $x = 2, y = 4; x = -\dfrac{7}{5}, y = -\dfrac{31}{5}$

   f $x = -4, y = 11; x = 2, y = -1$

   g $x = \dfrac{4}{3}, y = \dfrac{17}{3}; x = -\dfrac{9}{2}, y = -6$

   h $x = 6, y = 3; x = \dfrac{2}{3}, y = -\dfrac{7}{3}$

3 **a** $x = 0, y = 1; x = -1, y = 0$

   b $x = \dfrac{3}{2}, y = \dfrac{1}{2}$

   c $x = \dfrac{1}{9}, y = \dfrac{11}{9}; x = -1, y = -1$

   d $x = 1, y = 1$

   e $x = 0, y = 1; x = \dfrac{4}{5}, y = -\dfrac{3}{5}$

   f $x = 6, y = -4; x = 2, y = 0$
   g $x = 8, y = 6; x = 4, y = 2$
   h $x = 6, y = 5; x = 2, y = 1$

4 **a** $x = 2, y = 3$
   b $x = 2, y = 3; x = -1, y = 0$

   c $x = -\dfrac{1}{2}, y = -\dfrac{3}{2}; x = 1, y = 0$

   d $x = 1, y = 1; x = -\dfrac{1}{3}, y = -\dfrac{5}{3}$

5 **a** $(\pm 3, 0), (0, \pm 3)$ **b** $(0, 3)$ and $(-3, 0)$
   c **i** 2 solutions   **ii** 2 solutions

6 **a** $a = \pm 2, b = \pm 3$ **b** $9x^2 + 4y^2 = 36$

   c $\left(\dfrac{6}{5}, \dfrac{12}{5}\right)$ or $\left(-\dfrac{6}{5}, -\dfrac{12}{5}\right)$

Exercise 4.2

1 **a** $x > -3$ **b** $x \leqslant \dfrac{3}{2}$ **c** $x \leqslant -\dfrac{3}{4}$

   d $x < -1$ **e** $x \leqslant 1$ **f** $x > -6$

   g $x > 12$ **h** $x \geqslant \dfrac{12}{5}$

2 **a** $t < -5$ **b** $y < -2$ **c** $y \geqslant \dfrac{3}{2}$

   d $a > 3$ **e** $p \leqslant -\dfrac{5}{4}$ **f** $x < -\dfrac{1}{2}$

3 **a** $x < -3, x > 2$ **b** $1 < x < 4$

   c $x > -1, x < -5$ **d** $-2 < x < \dfrac{1}{2}$

4 **a** $x < -2, x > 1$ **b** $t < -4, t > -3$
   c $-1 < p < 4$ **d** $q < -5, q > 2$

5 **a** $-\dfrac{1}{2} < x < 5$ **b** $-\dfrac{4}{3} < t < 2$

   c $p < -3, p > 3$ **d** $x < -\dfrac{5}{2}, x > \dfrac{5}{2}$

6 **a** $1 < x < 3$ **b** $1 < x < 3$
   c $x \leqslant -2$

Review 4

1 **a** $x = 3, y = 0; x = -5, y = -8$
   b $x = -1, y = -3; x = 7, y = 13$

   c $x = -\dfrac{3}{2}, y = \dfrac{11}{2}; x = 4, y = 11$

   d $x = 2, y = 9; x = -1, y = 6$

2 **a** $x = 2, y = 3$

     $x = -\dfrac{6}{5}, y = -\dfrac{17}{5}$

   b $x = -\dfrac{1}{2}, y = 0$

     $x = -\dfrac{1}{3}, y = \dfrac{1}{3}$

3 $P = (1, -1)$ $Q = (2, 0)$

4 $A = \left(-\dfrac{1}{2}, -2\dfrac{1}{2}\right)$

   $B = (4, 29)$

5 **a** $x > -\dfrac{3}{2}$ **b** $y < \dfrac{7}{5}$ **c** $t \geqslant -\dfrac{11}{2}$

6 **a** $y = x + 2$ **b** $y > 0, y \leqslant 2$
     $y = -2x + 5$ $y \leqslant -2x + 5, y \leqslant x + 2$

7 $x = 5, y = 2$ $x = -\dfrac{27}{5}, y = -\dfrac{16}{5}$

8 **a** $x < 4$ **b** $-1 < x < 5$ **c** $-1 < x < 4$

9 **a** $x = 0, y = -1, x = 8, y = 3$

10 **a** $x = \dfrac{3}{2}, y = 2; x = -7, y = 19$

  b $x > \dfrac{3}{2}, x < -7$

11 **a** $2x + 20 < 150$ **b** $x(x + 20) > 4800$

  c $60 < x < 65$

Revision 1

1 **a** $\dfrac{1}{5}$ **b** $3\sqrt{5}$

2 **a** $a^4 b^2 c$ **b** $10 + \sqrt{2}$

3 **a** $k = \dfrac{9}{4}$ **b** $a = \dfrac{3}{2}, b = -\dfrac{9}{4} + l$

  c $x = \dfrac{-3 \pm \sqrt{13 - 4m}}{2}$

4 **a**

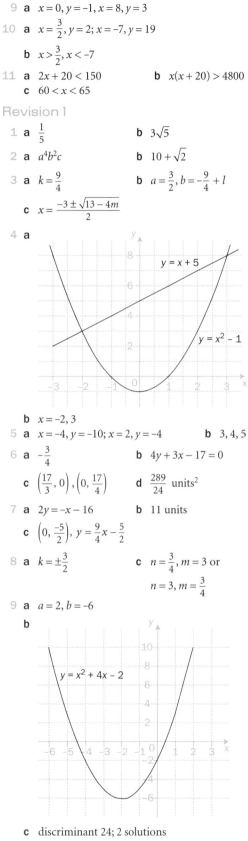

  b $x = -2, 3$

5 **a** $x = -4, y = -10; x = 2, y = -4$ **b** $3, 4, 5$

6 **a** $-\dfrac{3}{4}$ **b** $4y + 3x - 17 = 0$

  c $\left(\dfrac{17}{3}, 0\right), \left(0, \dfrac{17}{4}\right)$ **d** $\dfrac{289}{24}$ units^2

7 **a** $2y = -x - 16$ **b** 11 units

  c $\left(0, \dfrac{-5}{2}\right), y = \dfrac{9}{4}x - \dfrac{5}{2}$

8 **a** $k = \pm\dfrac{3}{2}$ **c** $n = \dfrac{3}{4}, m = 3$ or

         $n = 3, m = \dfrac{3}{4}$

9 **a** $a = 2, b = -6$

  b

  c discriminant 24; 2 solutions
  d $k > 4$

10 **a** $(x - 3)^2 + 9$

  b

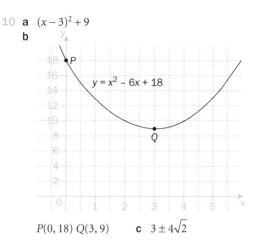

  $P(0, 18)\ Q(3, 9)$ **c** $3 \pm 4\sqrt{2}$

Before you start Answers

Chapter 5

1 **a** $y = x(x + 2)(x + 3)$
   b $y = 2x(x + 1)(x - 1)$
   c $y = x(x - 5)(x + 4)$
   d $y = 3x(x - 6)(x - 2)$
   e $y = 5x(x + 4)(x - 4)$
   f $y = x^2(4x - 5)$

2 **a**

   b

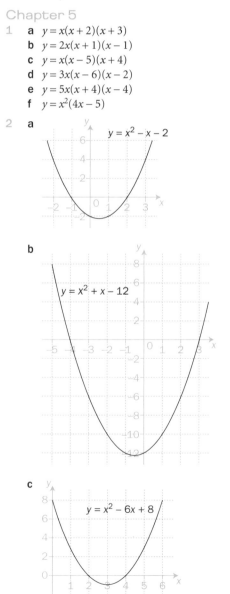

   c

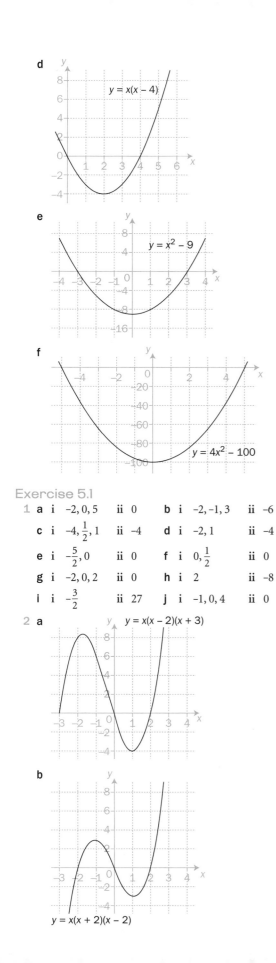

d

$y = x(x - 4)$

e

$y = x^2 - 9$

f

$y = 4x^2 - 100$

Exercise 5.1

1 **a** i $-2, 0, 5$ ii 0 **b** i $-2, -1, 3$ ii -6

   c i $-4, \frac{1}{2}, 1$ ii -4 **d** i $-2, 1$ ii -4

   e i $-\frac{5}{2}, 0$ ii 0 **f** i $0, \frac{1}{2}$ ii 0

   g i $-2, 0, 2$ ii 0 **h** i 2 ii -8

   i i $-\frac{3}{2}$ ii 27 **j** i $-1, 0, 4$ ii 0

2 **a**

$y = x(x - 2)(x + 3)$

b

$y = x(x + 2)(x - 2)$

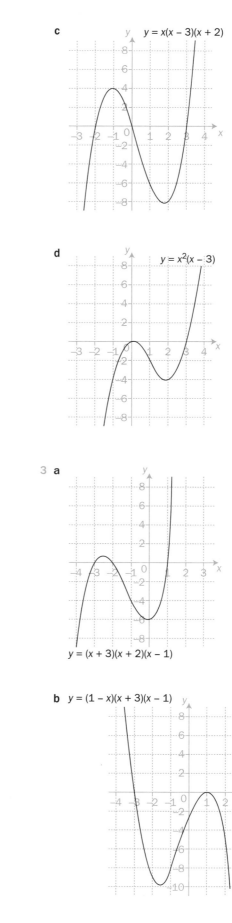

c $y = x(x - 3)(x + 2)$

d $y = x^2(x - 3)$

3 **a**

$y = (x + 3)(x + 2)(x - 1)$

b $y = (1 - x)(x + 3)(x - 1)$

335

c $y = (2x - 3)(x - 3)(x + 1)$

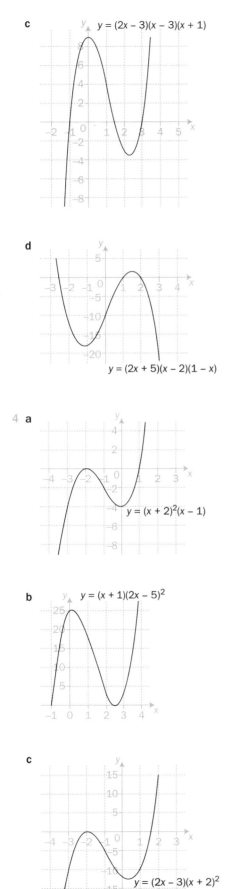

d $y = (2x + 5)(x - 2)(1 - x)$

4 a $y = (x + 2)^2(x - 1)$

b $y = (x + 1)(2x - 5)^2$

c $y = (2x - 3)(x + 2)^2$

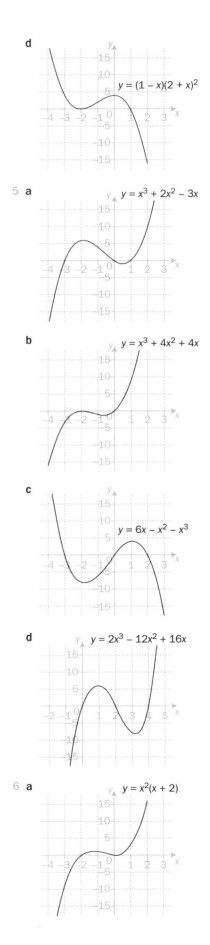

d $y = (1 - x)(2 + x)^2$

5 a $y = x^3 + 2x^2 - 3x$

b $y = x^3 + 4x^2 + 4x$

c $y = 6x - x^2 - x^3$

d $y = 2x^3 - 12x^2 + 16x$

6 a $y = x^2(x + 2)$

b

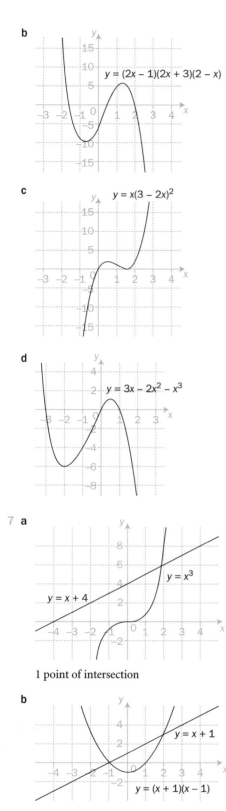

$y = (2x - 1)(2x + 3)(2 - x)$

c

$y = x(3 - 2x)^2$

d

$y = 3x - 2x^2 - x^3$

7 **a**

$y = x^3$

$y = x + 4$

1 point of intersection

b

$y = x + 1$

$y = (x + 1)(x - 1)$

2 points of intersection

c

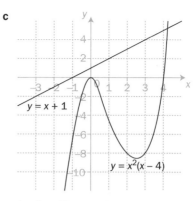

$y = x + 1$

$y = x^2(x - 4)$

1 point of intersection

d

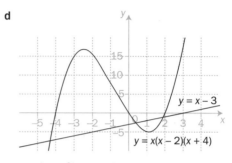

$y = x - 3$

$y = x(x - 2)(x + 4)$

3 points of intersection

8

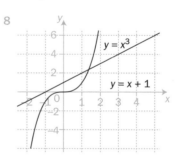

$y = x^3$

$y = x + 1$

1 solution

9 **a** $y = (x + 1)(x - 1)(x - 3)$
  b $y = (x + 2)(x - 4)^2$

10 **a** 0, 1 or 2   **b** 1, 2 or 3

Exercise 5.2

1 **a**

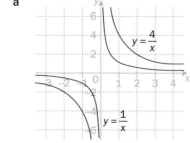

$y = \dfrac{4}{x}$

$y = \dfrac{1}{x}$

b

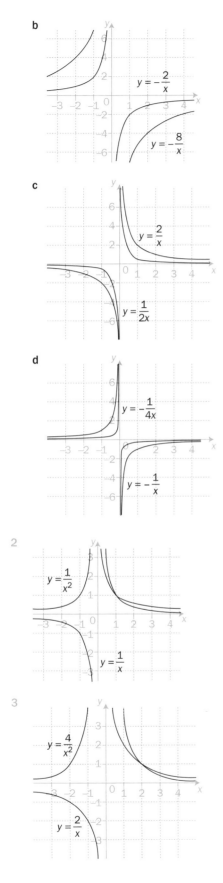

c

d

2

3

CI

4 **a** $x = -1$ **b** $(0, 0)$ **c** $y \to 1$

d

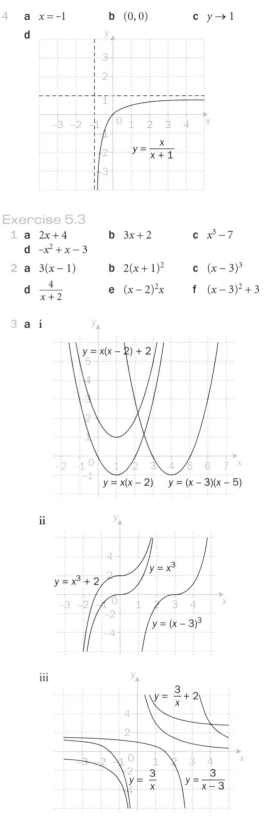

Exercise 5.3

1 **a** $2x + 4$ **b** $3x + 2$ **c** $x^3 - 7$
   d $-x^2 + x - 3$

2 **a** $3(x - 1)$ **b** $2(x + 1)^2$ **c** $(x - 3)^3$
   d $\dfrac{4}{x + 2}$ **e** $(x - 2)^2 x$ **f** $(x - 3)^2 + 3$

3 **a** **i**

ii

iii

b $y = f(x) + 2$ is $y = f(x)$ shifted 2 units up.
    $y = f(x - 3)$ is $y = f(x)$ shifted 3 units to the right.

4

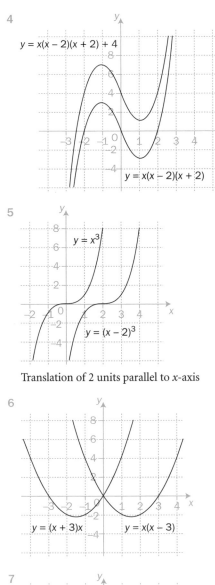

$y = x(x - 2)(x + 2) + 4$

$y = x(x - 2)(x + 2)$

5

Translation of 2 units parallel to x-axis

$y = x^3$

$y = (x - 2)^3$

6

$y = (x + 3)x$

$y = x(x - 3)$

7

$y = \dfrac{1}{x - 1}$

$y = \dfrac{1}{x}$

8

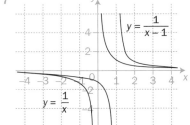

$y = x^2$

$y = (x + 2)^2$

Translation of −2 units parallel to x-axis

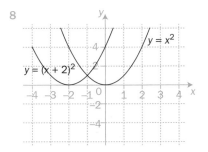

9

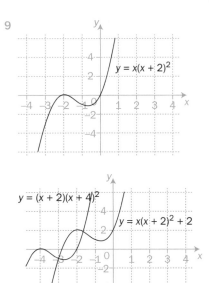

$y = x(x + 2)^2$

$y = (x + 2)(x + 4)^2$

$y = x(x + 2)^2 + 2$

Translation of 2 units parallel to y-axis
Translation of −2 units parallel to x-axis

10

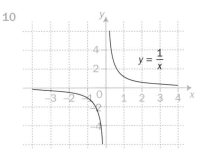

$y = \dfrac{1}{x}$

$y = 3$

$y = \dfrac{1}{x - 2} + 3$

$x = 2$

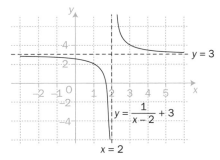

11 $y = (x - 1)^2 + 2$
$y = -(x - 1)^2 + 2$

Exercise 5.4

1 **a** $4x^2 + 1$

   b $2x^2 + 2$

   c $\dfrac{2}{9x^2}$

   d $2x - x^2$

   e $x^2 + 2x$

   f $18x^2$

   g $-\dfrac{1}{1 + x}$

   h $4x^2(1 - 2x)$

C1

2

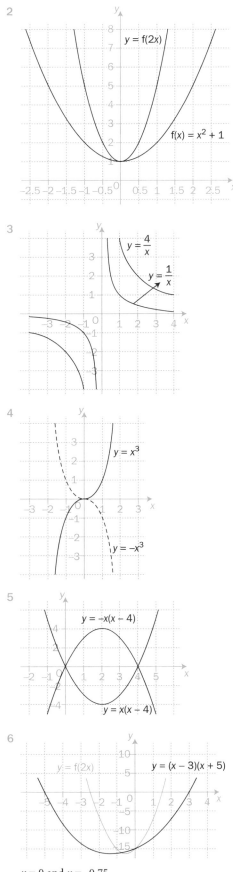

3

4

5

6

$x = 0$ and $x = -0.75$

CI

7

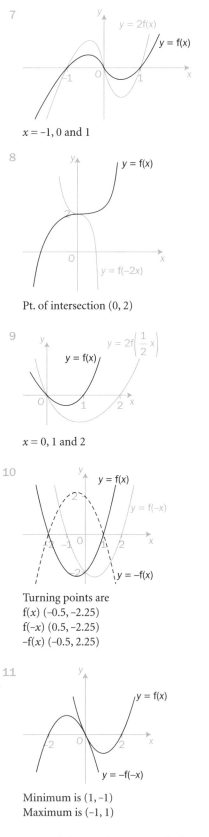

$x = -1, 0$ and 1

8

Pt. of intersection $(0, 2)$

9

$x = 0, 1$ and 2

10

Turning points are
$f(x)$ $(-0.5, -2.25)$
$f(-x)$ $(0.5, -2.25)$
$-f(x)$ $(-0.5, 2.25)$

11

Minimum is $(1, -1)$
Maximum is $(-1, 1)$

12 **a** parallel to y-axis and a translation
    b parallel to y-axis
    c parallel to either x- or y-axis

13 **a** ii   **b** i
    c iv   **d** iii

Exercise 5.5

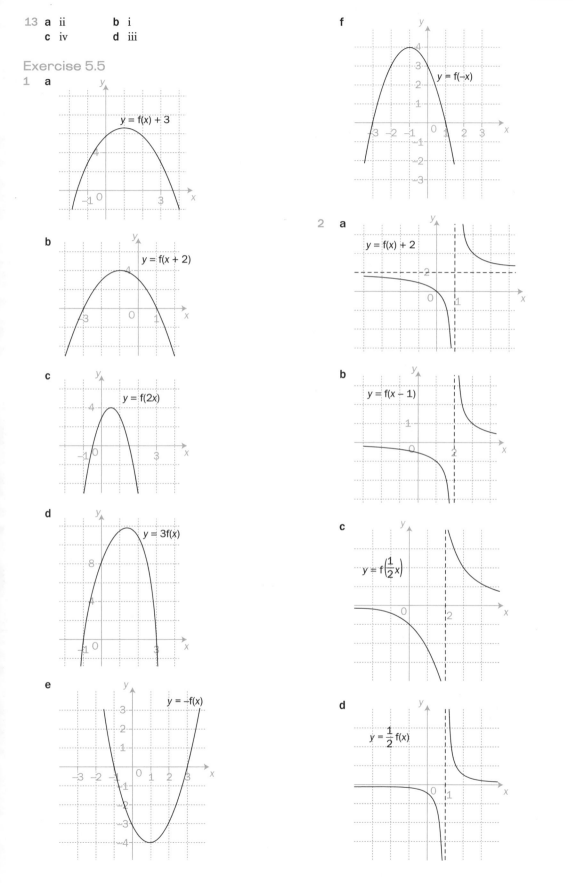

1 **a** $y = f(x) + 3$

b $y = f(x + 2)$

c $y = f(2x)$

d $y = 3f(x)$

e $y = -f(x)$

f $y = f(-x)$

2 **a** $y = f(x) + 2$

b $y = f(x - 1)$

c $y = f\left(\frac{1}{2}x\right)$

d $y = \frac{1}{2}f(x)$

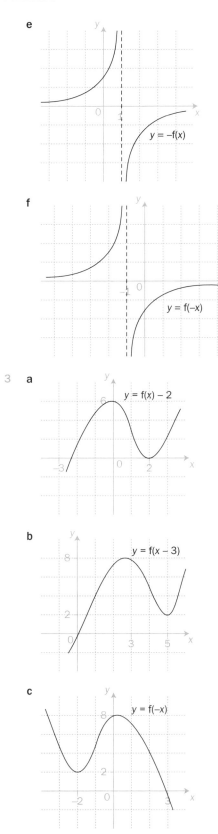

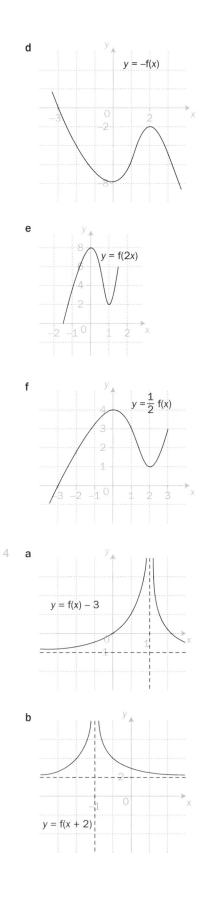

c

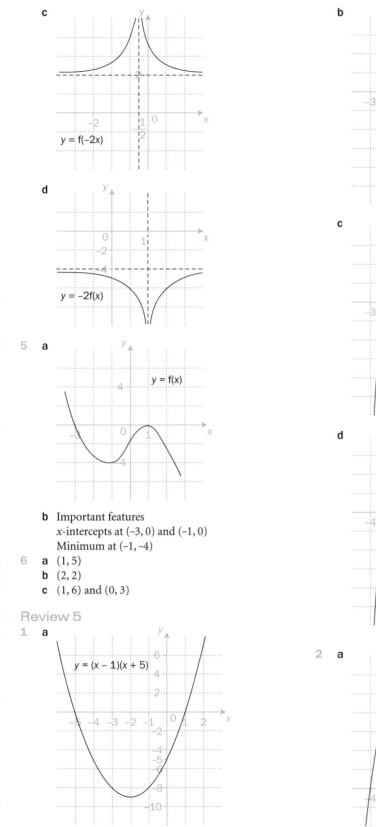

$y = f(-2x)$

d

$y = -2f(x)$

5 **a**

$y = f(x)$

b Important features
x-intercepts at $(-3, 0)$ and $(-1, 0)$
Minimum at $(-1, -4)$

6 **a** $(1, 5)$
b $(2, 2)$
c $(1, 6)$ and $(0, 3)$

Review 5

1 **a**

$y = (x - 1)(x + 5)$

b

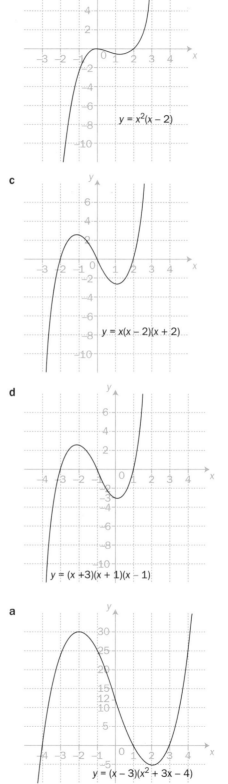

$y = x^2(x - 2)$

c

$y = x(x - 2)(x + 2)$

d

$y = (x + 3)(x + 1)(x - 1)$

2 **a**

$y = (x - 3)(x^2 + 3x - 4)$

b

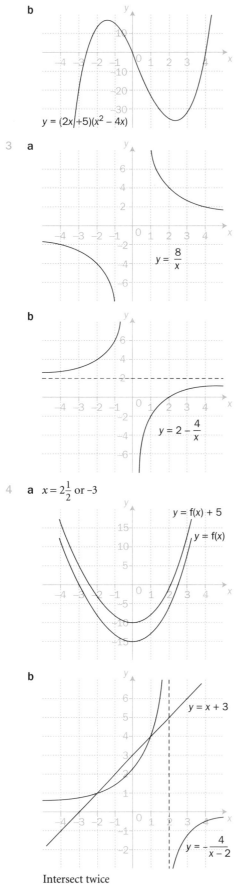

$y = (2x + 5)(x^2 - 4x)$

3 a

$y = \dfrac{8}{x}$

b

$y = 2 - \dfrac{4}{x}$

4 a $x = 2\frac{1}{2}$ or -3

$y = f(x) + 5$

$y = f(x)$

b

$y = x + 3$

$y = -\dfrac{4}{x - 2}$

Intersect twice

5 a $P(1, 1)\ Q(-1, -1)$

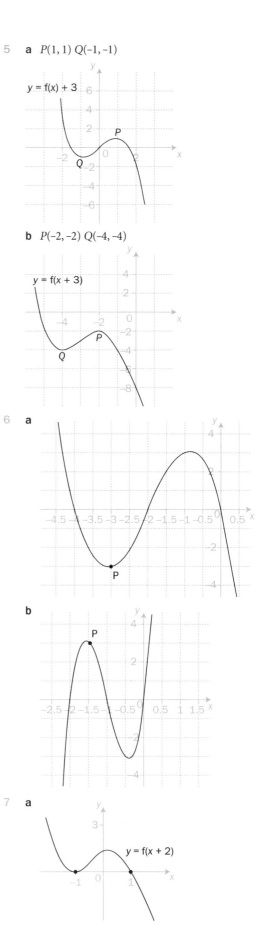

$y = f(x) + 3$

P

Q

b $P(-2, -2)\ Q(-4, -4)$

$y = f(x + 3)$

P

Q

6 a

P

b

P

7 a

$y = f(x + 2)$

C1

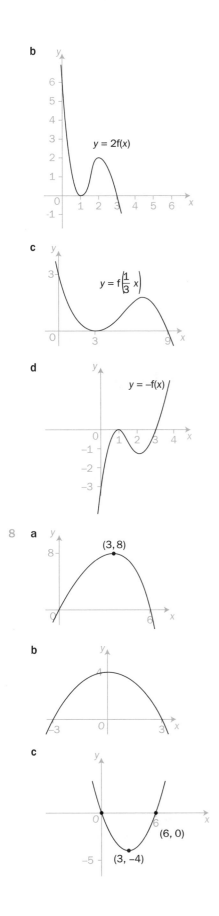

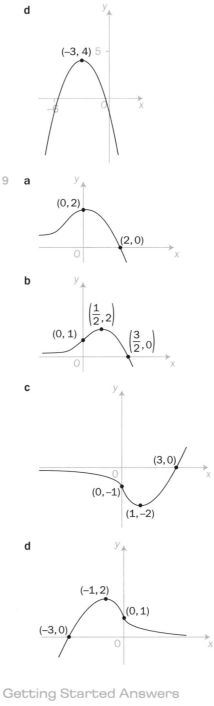

b

c

d

8 **a**

b

c

d

9 **a**

b

c

d

Getting Started Answers

Chapter 6

1   **a** $x = 2$ **b** $x = \frac{13}{2}$ **c** $x = \frac{12}{5}$

    d $x = \frac{5}{3}$ **e** $x = -2$

2   **a** $x = -4, x = 9$ **b** $x = 8, x = -12$
    c $x = -9, x = 10$ **d** $x = 13, x = -15$
    e $x = 18, x = -20$

C1

3   **a** $n + 3$ **b** $2n + 2$ **c** $3n + 1$
    d $6 - 2n$ **e** $8 - 4n$

Exercise 6.1

1   **a** $4, 7, 10, 13$ **b** $4, 9, 16, 25$ **c** $5, 0, -5, -10$
    d $\frac{1}{3}, \frac{1}{4}, \frac{1}{5}, \frac{1}{6}$ **e** $1, 1, 9, 25$ **f** $-1, 1, -1, 1$
    g $0, 3, 8, 15$ **h** $-2, 8, -24, 64$
    i $\frac{2}{3}, \frac{3}{4}, \frac{4}{5}, \frac{5}{6}$ **j** $2, 9, 64, 625$

2   **a**   5   **b**   10   **c**   15   **d**   12
    e   8   **f**   7   **g**   20   **h**   12
    i   7   **j**   any positive odd number

3   $a = 5$

4   $a = 3, b = -2$

5   $a = 2, b = -1$

6   **a** $a = 2, b = -3$ **b** $a = 1, b = -1, c = 1$

8   4

9   **a** $u_{2n+1} = 4n - 1$ which is odd
    b $3, 30, 75$

11   **a** $u_n = \dfrac{n+1}{n+2}$ **b** $u_n = (-1)^{n+1} \dfrac{n+1}{n+2}$

Exercise 6.2

1   **a** $u_{n+1} = u_n + 2$ **b** $u_{n+1} = u_n - 1$
    c $u_{n+1} = 2u_n$ **d** $u_{n+1} = 2u_n - 1$
    e $u_{n+1} = 4 - u_n$ **f** $u_{n+1} = u_n$
    g $u_{n+1} = -u_n$ **h** $u_{n+1} = 3u_n - 2$

2   **a** $4, 5, 6$ **b** $1, 1, 1$ **c** $0, 4, 0$ **d** $1, 0, 1$
    e $4, 16, 256$ **f** $1, \frac{1}{2}, \frac{1}{4}$

3   **a** $k = 3$ **b** $a = 4, b = -3$

4   **a** $3, 5, 8$ **b** $3, 4, 5$ **c** $2, 3, 4$ **d** $5, 7, 8$
    e $2, 6, 16$ **f** $6, 11, 19$ **g** $-3, -7, 4$

5   **a** $u_{n+2} = u_n + u_{n+1}$ **b** $u_{n+2} = 2u_{n+1} - u_n$
    c $u_{n+2} = u_n \times u_{n+1}$ **d** $u_{n+2} = u_n - u_{n+1}$

6   **b** $-2 + d$ **c**   4

Exercise 6.3

1   arithmetic series **b**, **c**

2   **a** $5, 8, 11$ **b** $3, -1, -5$ **c** $1\frac{1}{2}, 2, 2\frac{1}{2}$
    d $-6, -16, -26$

3   **a** $u_{n+1} = u_n + 2$ **b** $u_{n+1} = u_n + 3$
    c $u_{n+1} = u_n - 6$ **d** $u_{n+1} = u_n - 0.7$

4   **a** $29, 59, 3n - 1$ **b** $7, 14\frac{1}{2}, \frac{3}{4}n - \frac{1}{2}$
    c $\frac{28}{5}, \frac{58}{5}, \frac{3n-2}{5}$ **d** $-27, -47, -2n - 7$
    e $-4.1, -8.1, -0.4n - 0.1$
    f $57p, 117p, 6np - 3p$
    g $-\frac{7a}{4}, -\frac{17a}{4}, -\frac{1}{4}na + \frac{3}{4}a$
    h $10x + 9, 20x + 19, nx + n - 1$

5   **a**   11   **b**   21   **c**   31   **d**   16
    e   17   **f**   37   **g**   63   **h**   85

6   **a**   5   **b**   3   **c**   -2

7   **a**   -15   **b** $3, 19\frac{1}{2}$

8   **a**   34th   **b** $2, 7, 12, 17, 22$ **c** $y = \dfrac{x+z}{2}$
    d   -103   **e** $x = 1$ or 9

9   **a** $99, 100, 101$ **b** $100, 101, 102, 103$

Exercise 6.4

1   **a**   169   **b**   264   **c**   820   **d**   -315
    e   5050

2   **a** $13, 247$ **b** $20, 860$ **c**   672   **d**   -104
    e   2500

3   **a**   10   **b**   21   **c**   12

4   **a**   £750   **b**   £14 500   **c** $A = 155$

5   **a** $2a + 9d = 3, 2a + 15d = -3$
    b $a = 6 \;\; d = -1$

Exercise 6.5

1   **a** $4 + 8 + 12$ **b** $1 + 3 + 5 + 7 + 9$
    c $1 - 1 - 3 - 5$ **d** $32 + 35 + 38 + 41 + 44 + 47$
    e $-1 - 2 - 3 - 4 - 5 - 6 - 7$
    f $2 + 2\frac{1}{2} + 3$
    g $1 + 1\frac{1}{4} + 1\frac{1}{2} + 1\frac{3}{4} + 2 + 2\frac{1}{4}$
    h $4 + 4\frac{1}{3} + 4\frac{2}{3} + 5$

2   **a** $\sum_{1}^{7} 2r$ **b** $\sum_{1}^{8} (2r - 1)$ **c** $\sum_{1}^{10} (4r - 1)$
    d $\sum_{1}^{11} -(3r + 2)$ **e** $\sum_{1}^{15} \left(2r + \frac{1}{2}\right)$ **f** $\sum_{1}^{12} (5r + 10)$
    g $\sum_{1}^{21} (3 - 6r)$ **h** $\sum_{1}^{10} \dfrac{(3 - 4r)}{3}$ **i** $\sum_{1}^{q} p(5r - 2)$
    j $\sum_{1}^{n} [r(a + 2) - 1]$

3   **a**   275   **b**   120   **c**   610   **d**   -1030
    e   -420   **f** $\dfrac{1760}{3}$ **g**   -72.5   **h**   365
    i   792   **j**   110

5   **a** $\sum_{1}^{12} (20 - 6r)$

6   -172

7   30

9   650

10   **b**   5050

11   **b** $n = 1, u_1 = 11$
      $n = 13, u_{13} = -13$

Review 6

1   **a** $9, 25, 49, 81$ **b** $-3, 0, 5, 12$
    c $2, \frac{3}{2}, \frac{4}{3}, \frac{5}{4}$ **d** $12, 35, 70, 117$

2   **a**   12   **b**   15   **c**   9   **d**   8

3   **a** $a = 7, b = -2$ **b** $a = 2$
    c $a = 1, b = -2, c = 3$

4   **a**   **i** $u_{n+1} = u_n + 3$ **ii** $u_{n+1} = 1 - 2u_n$
    b   **i** $u_2 = -1, u_3 = -6, u_4 = -11$
      ii $u_2 = 1, u_3 = 0, u_4 = 1$

5   $u_2 = 2, u_3 = 6, u_4 = 42$ and $u_5 = 1806$

6   **a** $39, 55$ **b**   13   **c** $1\frac{1}{2}, 3$

7   **a**   490   **b**   40

8   **b**   £1900   **c**   £9600   **d**   26

9   **a** $1, 4, 7$ **b**   3

10 **b** £109 **d** 50 or 100

e $n = 100$ not sensible (would be making negative repayments)

11 **a** 77, 74 **b** –3 **c** 175

Before you start Answers

Chapter 7

1 **a** 3.03 **b** 4.141 **c** 40.4 **d** 60.06

2 **a** $x^2 - 2$ **b** $x - 3$ **c** $2x + 3$ **d** $-2x^2 + 1$

3 **a** $x^{\frac{3}{2}}$ **b** $x^{\frac{1}{2}}$ **c** $x^{-\frac{3}{2}}$ **d** x^{-3}

4 **a** $-12x^2 + 5x + 2$ **b** $3x^2 - 2$

   c $-12x^3 + 17x^2 - 6x$ **d** $4x^{\frac{5}{2}} - 5x^{\frac{3}{2}}$

Exercise 7.1

1 3.31, 3.0301, 3.003, 3, 3

2 6.1, 6.01, 6.001, 6 and 6

Exercise 7.2

1 **a** **i** $3(\delta x)$ **ii** 3 **iii** 3

   b **i** $-2x(\delta x) - (\delta x)^2$ **ii** $-2x - (\delta x)$ **iii** $-2x$

   c **i** $-3(\delta x)$ **ii** –3 **iii** –3

   d **i** $4x(\delta x) + 2(\delta x)^2$ **ii** $4x + 2(\delta x)$ **iii** $4x$

   e **i** $2x(\delta x) + (\delta x)^2 + (\delta x)$

       ii $2x + (\delta x) + 1$ **iii** $2x + 1$

   f **i** $2(\delta x) - 4x(\delta x) - 2(\delta x)^2$

       ii $2 - 4x - 2(\delta x)$ **iii** $2 - 4x$

2 **a** $2x$ **b** 4 **c** $2x + 2$

   d $-2x$ **e** $3x^2$ **f** $4x^3$

3 **a** $2x, 6$ **b** $9x^2, 0$ **c** $2x + 5, 7$

   d $3x^2 + 1, 13$

Exercise 7.3

1 **a** $8x$ **b** 7 **c** 0 **d** $9x^2$

   e x^3 **f** 0 **g** –2 **h** $\frac{2}{3}$

2 **a** $\frac{1}{\sqrt{x}}$ **b** $\frac{-3}{2\sqrt{x}}$ **c** $\frac{3\sqrt{x}}{2}$ **d** $\frac{-5}{2}x\sqrt{x}$

   e $\frac{1}{3\sqrt[3]{x^2}}$ **f** $\frac{-1}{x^2}$ **g** $\frac{2}{x^3}$ **h** $\frac{-1}{2x\sqrt{x}}$

   i $\frac{-1}{x\sqrt{x}}$ **j** $\frac{-2}{x^2\sqrt{x}}$ **k** $\frac{2}{3x\sqrt[3]{x}}$ **l** $\frac{2}{3\sqrt[3]{x}}$

3 **a** 10 **b** –8 **c** $\frac{1}{4}$ **d** 6

   e 3 **f** $-\frac{2}{3}$ **g** $\frac{1}{4}$ **h** 0

   i 9 **j** $\frac{4}{5}$

4 **i** $\leftrightarrow$ **e**

   ii $\leftrightarrow$ **f**

   iii $\leftrightarrow$ **d**

   iv $\leftrightarrow$ **b**

   v $\leftrightarrow$ **a**

   vi $\leftrightarrow$ **c**

Exercise 7.4

1 **a** $2x$ **b** 2 **c** $6x - 1$

   d $3 + 2x$ **e** $3x^2 - 4x$ **f** $2x - 1$

2 **a** $2x + 1$ **b** $2x - 3x^2$

   c $3x^2 + 6x + 1$ **d** $2x - 1$

3 **a** $\frac{1}{x^2}$ **b** $-\frac{2}{x^3} + 1$

   c $1 - \frac{1}{2\sqrt{x}}$ **d** $\frac{3}{2}\sqrt{x} + \frac{1}{2x\sqrt{x}}$

   e $x - 1 - \frac{1}{x^2}$ **f** $\frac{3}{2}\sqrt{x} - \frac{1}{\sqrt{x}}$

4 **a** $2x + 1$ **b** $2t - 3t^2$

   c $2r - 1$ **d** $32t - 16$

   e $3x^2 - 1$ **f** $6r - 4$

   g $\frac{5}{2}t\sqrt{t} + \frac{1}{2\sqrt{t}}$ **h** $-\frac{2}{x^3}$

   i $-18t^2 + 22t - 6$ **j** $4x^3 - 3x^2 - 1$

5 **a** $\frac{-1}{x^2}$ **b** $\frac{1}{2}$

   c $\frac{-1}{x^2} + \frac{1}{2x\sqrt{x}}$ **d** $\frac{2}{x^2} - \frac{8}{x^3}$

   e $\frac{-6}{x^4} + \frac{1}{x^2}$ **f** $\frac{1}{\sqrt{x}} + \frac{1}{x\sqrt{x}}$

   g $1 - \frac{9}{x^2}$ **h** $2x - 3$

   i $\frac{1}{4\sqrt{x}} + \frac{3\sqrt{x}}{4}$ **j** $\frac{-a}{cx^2} + \frac{b}{c}$

6 **a** $\frac{5}{2}t\sqrt{t} + \frac{1}{t^2}$ **b** $12r - 6r^2$

   c $\frac{-5}{x^2} + \frac{8}{x^3}$ **d** $28t - 35$

   e $1 + \frac{2}{\sqrt{x}}$ **f** $5r^4 + 3r^2 - 2r$

   g $\frac{5}{2}t\sqrt{t} - 1 + \frac{1}{2\sqrt{t}}$ **h** $\frac{-8a}{3x^3} + \frac{b}{3x^2}$

   i $3t^2$ **j** $\frac{4}{r^2} - \frac{2}{r^3}$

7 $\frac{2 + x}{x} \rightarrow -\frac{2}{x^2}$

   $\frac{x + 1}{x^{\frac{1}{2}}} \rightarrow \frac{1}{2}x^{-\frac{1}{2}} - \frac{1}{2}x^{-\frac{3}{2}}$

   $\frac{(x + 1)^2}{x} \rightarrow 1 - \frac{1}{x^2}$

   $\frac{2(x + 4)}{x^2} \rightarrow -\frac{2}{x^2} - \frac{16}{x^3}$

8 **a** $f'(x) = 1$ $g'(x) = 2x$

   b $h(x) = x^3 + 3x^2, h'(x) = 3x^2 + 6x$ **c** No

   d **i** $p'(x) = -\frac{1}{x^2} - \frac{6}{x^3}$

       ii No

Exercise 7.5

1 **a** 3, 3 **b** $-\frac{2}{x^2}, -2$ **c** $\frac{1}{\sqrt{x}}, 1$

   d $-\frac{2}{x^3} - \frac{3}{x^4}, -5$

2 97

3 **a** 1 **b** 10 **c** 3 **d** 0

4 The surface area increases

   $\frac{dA}{dr} = 8\pi r$

   a 40π **b** 16π

5   80 m/s
6   $x = 2$
7   ± 8
8   The rate of change of the volume is
    $4\pi r^2$ cm³/sec.

Exercise 7.6

1   **a** -20 **b** $y = -6x + 4$
    c $y = 2x - 3$ **d** 9
    e $y = x - 8$

2   **a** $7, -\dfrac{1}{7}$ **b** $y = 4x - \dfrac{15}{2}$

    c $4, -\dfrac{1}{4}$ **d** $2y = x + 3, 2y = -4x - 7$

3   **a** point $\left(-\dfrac{3}{4}, -\dfrac{9}{8}\right)$ **b** $(2, 0)$

4   **a** tangent $y = 3x + 1$, normal $3y = -x + 13$

    b $\left(-\dfrac{1}{3}, 0\right), (0, 1)$ **c** $(13, 0), \left(0, \dfrac{13}{3}\right)$

5   6 units²

Exercise 7.7

1   **a** $6x + 2, 6$ **b** $15x^2, 30x$ **c** $\dfrac{-1}{2\sqrt{x}}, \dfrac{1}{4x\sqrt{x}}$

    d $1 + \dfrac{2}{x^2}, \dfrac{-4}{x^3}$ **e** $12x + 5, 12$

    f $3x^2 + 2x, 6x + 2$

2   **a** $18, 6$ **b** $-\dfrac{4}{27}, \dfrac{4}{27}$ **c** $-\dfrac{1}{9}, \dfrac{2}{27}$

    d $\dfrac{2}{(\sqrt{3})}, \dfrac{1}{(3\sqrt{3})}$ **e** $-\dfrac{1}{(12\sqrt{3})}, \dfrac{\sqrt{3}}{72}$ **f** $-\dfrac{2}{27}, \dfrac{2}{81}$

3   **a** $8\pi, 2\pi$ **b** $\dfrac{9\pi}{4}, 6\pi$

4   **a** $x^3 \to 3x^2$ **b** $2x^2, 4x^3; 8x^3, 5x$
    $6x \to 6$
    $2x^4 \to 8x^3$
    $3x^2 \to 6x$
    c $2x^2 \to 4x$
    $4x^3 \to 12x^2$
    $2x^4 \to 8x^3$
    $\dfrac{5}{2}x^2 \to 5x$

Review 7

1   **a** $8, -\dfrac{1}{8}$ **b** $\left(\dfrac{1}{2}, 2\right), \left(-\dfrac{1}{2}, -2\right)$

    c $(0, 0), \left(\dfrac{4}{3}, -\dfrac{32}{27}\right)$ **d** $\dfrac{5}{2}$

2   $\sqrt{2}$

3   $2x + \dfrac{18}{x^4}$

4   $2y = x + 3$

5   **a** $P: x = -2; Q: x = 2$ **d** $R\left(\dfrac{5}{3}, -\dfrac{22}{27}\right)$

6   **a** $2 + \dfrac{3}{x^2}$ **b** $\dfrac{11}{4}$

    c $4y = 11x - 36$ **d** $\dfrac{36}{11}$

7   **b** $y = 16x - 30$ **c** $\left(-2, -\dfrac{61}{3}\right)$

8   **a** $3x^2 + 2$ **c** $y = \dfrac{x^4}{4} + x^2 - 7x + 10$

    d $5y + x - 22 = 0$

Before you start Answers

Chapter 8

1   **a** $\dfrac{7}{45}$ **b** $\dfrac{47}{12}$ **c** $\dfrac{36}{35}$ **d** $-\dfrac{41}{12}$

2   **a** $x^3 + 3x^2 - x$ **b** $2x^2 - 5x - 12$
    c $x^3 + 4x^2 - x - 4$ **d** $x^3 - 6x^2 + 3x + 10$
    e $x^3 - 9x^2 + 27x - 27$

3   **a** x^2 **b** $\dfrac{1}{2}x^{-\frac{1}{2}}$ **c** $x^{-\frac{3}{2}}$ **d** $x^{\frac{3}{2}}$

Exercise 8.1

All exercise must include the addition of 'c' the constant of integration.

1   **a** $\dfrac{x^5}{5}$ **b** $\dfrac{x^8}{8}$ **c** x^3

    d $\dfrac{x^{11}}{11}$ **e** x^5 **f** $\dfrac{x^6}{12}$

    g $\dfrac{-x^6}{3}$ **h** $\dfrac{-x^8}{32}$ **i** $2x^2$

2   **a** $\dfrac{-1}{2x^2}$ **b** $\dfrac{-1}{x^3}$ **c** $\dfrac{-1}{x}$

    d $\dfrac{-1}{x^2}$ **e** $\dfrac{1}{4x^4}$ **f** $\dfrac{5}{2x^2}$

    g $\dfrac{-1}{3x^2}$ **h** $\dfrac{1}{5x^4}$ **i** $3x$

3   **a** $\dfrac{x^5}{5}$ **b** $2x^4$ **c** $\dfrac{-1}{5x^5}$

    d $\dfrac{-9}{x}$ **e** $\dfrac{-4}{x^2}$ **f** $\dfrac{2x^4}{27}$

    g $\dfrac{-1}{3x^3}$ **h** $27x^3$

4   **a** $\dfrac{2}{3}x^{\frac{3}{2}}$ **b** $\dfrac{4}{5}x^{\frac{5}{4}}$ **c** $x^{\frac{1}{2}}$

    d $\dfrac{2}{5}x^{\frac{5}{2}}$ **e** $\dfrac{2}{3}x^{-\frac{3}{2}}$ **f** $-16x^{-\frac{1}{2}}$

5   **a** $b = 1$ **b** $y = x^2 + x + 3$

6   $x^{\frac{1}{2}} \to \dfrac{2}{3}x^{\frac{3}{2}}$

    $x^{-\frac{1}{2}} \to 2x^{\frac{1}{2}}$

    $x^{\frac{3}{2}} \to \dfrac{2}{5}x^{\frac{5}{2}}$

    $x^{-\frac{3}{2}} \to -2x^{-\frac{1}{2}}$

Exercise 8.2

1   **a** $2x^2 + c$ **b** $\dfrac{p^2}{2} + c$ **c** $\dfrac{s^6}{2} + c$

    d $\dfrac{-2}{w} + c$ **e** $\dfrac{3x^2}{8} + c$ **f** $\dfrac{5}{4y^2} + c$

    g $0.1a^2 + c$ **h** $\dfrac{16x^3}{3} + c$ **i** $-\dfrac{1}{z^3} + c$

C1

2 $\dfrac{dx}{da} = \dfrac{2}{3a^2}$

$\left(\dfrac{dx}{da} = \dfrac{2a^{-2}}{3}\right)$

$x = \int \dfrac{2}{3a^2}\,da$

$x = -\dfrac{2}{3a} + c$

3 a $\dfrac{2}{5}x^{\frac{5}{2}} + c$ b $2x^{\frac{3}{2}} + c$ c $\dfrac{8}{7}x^{\frac{7}{2}} + c$

d $\dfrac{3}{5}x^{\frac{5}{3}} + c$ e $\dfrac{3}{7}x^{\frac{7}{3}} + c$ f $\dfrac{5x^{\frac{6}{5}}}{6} + c$

4 a $2x^{\frac{1}{2}} + c$ b $\dfrac{-2}{3}x^{-\frac{3}{2}} + c$ c $-2x^{-\frac{1}{2}} + c$

d $8x^{\frac{1}{2}} + c$ e $x^{\frac{1}{4}} + c$ f $10x^{\frac{3}{5}} + c$

5 a $\dfrac{x^3}{3} - x^4 + c$ b $x^3 - \dfrac{2}{x} + c$ c $4x + \dfrac{1}{x} + c$

d $x^5 + x^4 + x$ c e $\dfrac{-1}{2x} + \dfrac{1}{6x^2} + c$ f $0.4x^2 + 0.8x + c$

g $\dfrac{x^4}{5} - \dfrac{x^3}{4} + \dfrac{x^2}{3} + c$ h $\dfrac{-1}{x} + \dfrac{1}{2x^2} + c$

i $\dfrac{ax^2}{2} + \dfrac{bx^3}{3} + \dfrac{cx^4}{4} + c$ j $\dfrac{px^3}{3q} + \dfrac{q}{px} + c$

6 a $2x^{\frac{3}{2}} - 2x + c$ b $\dfrac{t^3}{3} - \dfrac{1}{t} + c$

c $\dfrac{2v^{\frac{7}{2}}}{7} + \dfrac{2v^{-\frac{3}{2}}}{3} + c$ d $8r^{\frac{1}{2}} - 10r^{-\frac{1}{2}} + c$

e $\dfrac{2x^{\frac{3}{2}}}{3} + 2x^{\frac{1}{2}} + c$ f $\dfrac{2x^{\frac{5}{2}}}{5} + 6x^{-\frac{1}{2}} + c$

g $\dfrac{2t^{\frac{7}{2}}}{7} - \dfrac{4t^{\frac{9}{2}}}{9} + c$ h $\dfrac{r^{\frac{1}{2}}}{2} - 6r^{-\frac{1}{2}} + c$

7 a $\dfrac{x^3}{3} - \dfrac{x^2}{2} + c$ b $\dfrac{x^3}{3} + 2x^2 + 4x + c$

c $\dfrac{x^4}{2} - 6x + c$ d $2x^3 - \dfrac{11x^2}{2} + 3x + c$

e $\dfrac{5x^4}{4} + x^3 + c$ f $x^4 + 4x^3 + \dfrac{9x^2}{2} + c$

g $\dfrac{x^4}{4} - x^3 + \dfrac{3x^2}{2} - x + c$ h $\dfrac{x^6}{6} - x^4 + c$

8 a $x - \dfrac{1}{x} + c$ b $\dfrac{-2}{\sqrt{t}} + \dfrac{2}{t} + c$ c $\dfrac{x^{\frac{3}{2}}}{3} - \dfrac{x^{\frac{5}{2}}}{5} + c$

d $\dfrac{-3}{2t^2} + \dfrac{1}{t} + 3t + c$ e $2\sqrt{t}\left(1 - \dfrac{t^2}{5}\right) + c$

f $\dfrac{-2}{\sqrt{r}} + 2\sqrt{r} + c$

9 $\dfrac{x^2}{2} + \dfrac{1}{x} + \dfrac{2}{5}x^{\frac{5}{2}}$

10 $\dfrac{x^3}{2} + cx + k$

11 $-2x^{-\frac{1}{2}}$

12 a Yes   b Cubic

c $\dfrac{1}{x}$: not possible $\dfrac{1}{x^2} : \dfrac{-1}{x}$

13 3

Exercise 8.3

1 a $y = x^2 - x - 1$ b $y = x^3 + x^2$

c $y = \dfrac{x^2}{2} - 4x + 3$ d $y = \dfrac{2x^3}{3} - \dfrac{x^2}{2} + \dfrac{11}{6}$

e $y = 2x^2 + \dfrac{19}{9}$ f $y = \dfrac{2}{3}(x\sqrt{x} - 2)$

g $y = \dfrac{x^2}{2} - \dfrac{1}{x} - \dfrac{9}{2}$ h $y = 2\sqrt{x} - 2\sqrt{2}$

i $y = \dfrac{2x^{\frac{5}{2}}}{5} - \dfrac{7}{5}$ j $y = x^4 - x^3 - 11$

2 a $y = \dfrac{-2}{x} + 3$ b $y = \dfrac{2}{3}x\sqrt{x} + 2\sqrt{x} - \dfrac{34}{3}$

c $y = \dfrac{-1}{2x^2} + \dfrac{1}{x} - \dfrac{3}{8}$ d $y = \dfrac{x^3}{3} - x^2 + x - \dfrac{5}{3}$

e $y = \dfrac{x^3}{3} - 2x^2 + 4x + \dfrac{25}{3}$

f $y = \dfrac{2}{5}x^2\sqrt{x} - 2x + \dfrac{1}{5}$ g $y = \dfrac{-2}{\sqrt{x}} + 2\sqrt{2}$

h $y = x^3 + \dfrac{5x^2}{2} - 2x + \sqrt{3} - 6$

i $y = \dfrac{2x^{\frac{7}{2}}}{7} - \dfrac{x^3}{3} + \dfrac{1}{21}$

j $y = \dfrac{x^2}{2} - \dfrac{4}{3}x\sqrt{x} + x + \dfrac{13}{96}$

3 $y = \dfrac{x^2}{2} + \dfrac{3}{2}x - 2$

4 a $y = \dfrac{x^2}{2} - \dfrac{1}{x} + c$ b $y = -\dfrac{3}{2}$

5 $f(x) = x + 2x^{\frac{3}{2}} + 4x^{\frac{1}{2}} - 3$

6 a $f'(x) = 3x^2 - 2x + 6$ b $f(x) = x^3 - x^2 + 6x - 2$

Review 8

The constant of integration needs to be included where appropriate.

1 a $\dfrac{2x^3}{3}$ b $-x^5$ c $0.2x^4$ d $\dfrac{4x^3}{3}$

e $\dfrac{-4}{x}$ f $\dfrac{-2}{\sqrt{x}}$ g $\dfrac{4}{5}x^{\frac{5}{4}}$ h $\dfrac{-4}{x^2}$

i $\dfrac{3}{7}x^{\frac{7}{3}}$ j $4x^{\frac{1}{2}}$ k $x^{\frac{3}{4}}$ l $2x^{-\frac{1}{2}}$

2 a $t^3 + \dfrac{1}{t}$ b $r - r^2 + \dfrac{r^3}{3}$ c $\dfrac{-1}{x^2} + \dfrac{1}{x}$ d $2v^3 - \dfrac{v^2}{2}$

3 a $\dfrac{x^4}{4} - \dfrac{x^3}{3} - \dfrac{x^2}{2} + x$ b $t + \dfrac{1}{t}$

c $\dfrac{2}{7}r^{\frac{7}{2}} - \dfrac{3}{4}r^4$ d $2\sqrt{x} + \dfrac{5}{x}$

4 $\dfrac{2x^3}{3} + \dfrac{3}{x^2}$

5 $y = 3x + 2x^{\frac{7}{2}} + 2x^{\frac{1}{2}} + 1$

6 $2x\sqrt{x} + \dfrac{1}{x}$

7 $\dfrac{x^2}{2} + \dfrac{4}{x}$

8 a i $6x - 3$ ii 6 b $2x + \dfrac{4}{3}x\sqrt{x} + \dfrac{1}{2x} + c$

9 $2x^2 + 2x\sqrt{x}$

10 $y = \dfrac{x^3}{3} - \dfrac{1}{x} - \dfrac{70}{9}, y = \dfrac{-76}{9}$

11 $\dfrac{4}{3}x^3 + 6x^2 + 9x$

12 $y = \dfrac{-1}{x} - \dfrac{2}{3x^3} - \dfrac{7}{3}$

13 **a** $y = x^2 - 2x + 2$ **b** $y = x^2 - 2x - 5$

Revision 2

1 **a** $5, 9, 13, 17, 21$ **b** 21
2 **a** $-8, -5, -2, 1$ **b** $n = 48$ **c** 71st
3 $-8, 59$
4 £750, £5250
5 **a** $2x - 3$ **b** $-5, 5$
6 **a** $3\dfrac{3}{4}$ **b** $4y = 15x - 12$
7 **b** $9, -\dfrac{1}{9}$ **c** $y = 9x - 19, 9y = -x + 75$

8 $\dfrac{2x^{\frac{3}{2}}}{3} + 2\sqrt{x} + c$

9 **b** $a = 2, c = -3$

10 **a** $3\sqrt{x} + \dfrac{3}{2\sqrt{x}}$ **b** $\dfrac{4x^{\frac{5}{2}}}{5} + 2x^{\frac{3}{2}} + c$

11 **a** $2y = 8x - 9$ **b** $y = x - 2x^2 + \dfrac{4}{3}x^3$
 c $8y = -2x + 15$

12 **b** $y = -2x + 4$ **c** $\left(\dfrac{2}{3}, \dfrac{104}{27}\right)$

Before you start Answers

Chapter 9

1 **a** 52 **b** 68 **c** 74 **d** 45 remainder 2
 e 56 remainder 8 **f** 49 remainder 12
2 **a** $4a$ **b** $-4a$ **c** $-5a$ **d** $3a$
 e $-2a$
3 **a** -1 **b** 1 **c** 0 **d** -32
 e 24 **f** 0

Exercise 9.1

1 **a** $x + 1$ **b** $x - 1$ **c** $x - 3$ **d** $x + 2$
 e x **f** $2x - 1$ **g** $\dfrac{3x + 1}{x + 1}$ **h** $\dfrac{x + 2}{2x + 1}$
 i $\dfrac{x - 3}{x - 4}$
2 **a** $x^2 + 2x - 1$ **b** $x^2 + 3x - 1$ **c** $x^2 + x + 2$
 d $x^2 + 2x + 3$ **e** $x^2 + 3x - 1$ **f** $x^2 - 2x - 1$
 g $2x^2 - x - 1$ **h** $x^2 - 5x + 4$ **i** $6x^2 + x - 1$
 j $4x^2 - 5x + 3$
3 **a** $x^2 - 2x + 3$ **b** $x^2 - 3x + 4$ **c** $x^2 + 4x + 3$
 d $x^2 + 2x + 2$ **e** $x^2 + 2x - 4$
 f $x^3 + 3x^2 - x + 1$ **g** $2x^3 + 3x - 2$
 h $3x^3 + x^2 + 2$ **i** $x^2 + x - 1$
 j $x^3 - 2x^2 - 4x + 8$
4 **a** $x + 2, R = -3$ **b** $x, R = 4$
 c $2x - 1, R = 4$ **d** $x^2 + 5x + 4, R = 5$
 e $2x^2 - 6x + 19, R = -58$
 f $x^2 + x + 1, R = 0$ **g** $2x^2 - 2x + 2, R = -7$
 h $x^3 + x^2 + x + 1, R = 0$

5 **a** $x + 4$ **b** $x - 2$, remainder 6
 c $x + 1$, remainder $-2x - 4$
 d $2x + 3$, remainder $-x - 2$
6 **a** $1 + \dfrac{3}{x + 1}$ **b** 1 **c** $1 + \dfrac{1}{x + 5}$

Exercise 9.2

1 **a** -3 **b** 3 **c** 1 **d** -5
 e 12 **f** -2 **g** $-1\dfrac{1}{2}$ **h** 5
 i $-\dfrac{148}{9}$ **j** $\dfrac{151}{2}$ **k** $\dfrac{65}{81}$ **l** $\dfrac{225}{64}$
 m 0 **n** $\dfrac{15}{8}$

2 **a** $a = -\dfrac{1}{2}$ **b** $a = -4$ **c** $a = 6$ **d** $a = 2$
 e $a = -1$
3 **a** $a = -3, a = \dfrac{1}{2}$ **b** remainder 29
 c i $p = -20$ **ii** remainder 18
4 $k = 3$
5 $a = -\dfrac{13}{3}, b = \dfrac{16}{3}$
6 **a** $a = -1, b = -5$ **b** $(x + 2)(x^2 - 3x + 1)$
7 **a i** $p = 6, q = -6$ **ii** $(x + 4)(2x + 1)(3x - 2)$
 b $(x^2 - 9)(x + 2)(x - 3)$ or
 $(x - 3)^2 (x + 3)(x + 2)$
8 **a** $\dfrac{39}{8}$ **b** $-\dfrac{7}{8}$ **c** 3

Exercise 9.3

1 all 'yes' except part **f**
2 **a** $(x + 1)(x - 1)(x + 2)$
 b $(x - 1)(x + 2)(x + 3)$
 c $(x - 3)(x + 1)(x + 4)$
 d $(2x + 1)(x + 3)(x + 4)$
 e $x(3x - 1)(x - 4)$
 f $(x + 1)(x^2 - 3x + 3)$
 g $(x + 2)(x^2 - x + 4)$
 h $(x + 4)(3x + 4)(x - 1)$
3 **a** $(x + 1)(x - 2)(x - 3)$
 b $(x - 2)(x + 3)(x + 4)$
 c $(x - 2)(x + 4)(x + 5)$
 d $(x - 1)(x - 2)(x - 3)$
 e $(x - 3)(x - 4)(x + 5)$
 f $(x - 1)(2x + 3)(x + 2)$
4 **a** $x = -2, -\dfrac{1}{2}, -\dfrac{3}{2}$ **b** $x = -3, \dfrac{3}{2}$
 c $x = -2, -\dfrac{1}{3}, \dfrac{1}{4}$ **d** $x = -4, -\dfrac{3}{2}, -\dfrac{2}{3}$
5 **a** $a = \dfrac{3}{2}$ **b** $a = 2$ **c** $a = -7$
 d $a = -\dfrac{5}{2}, b = -\dfrac{1}{2}$
 e $a = -\dfrac{1}{2}, b = -\dfrac{7}{2}$ **f** $a = 2, b = -9, c = -2$
 g $(a + b)(a + 2b)(2a + b)$
6 $k = -6, (1, 0), (4, 0)$

Review 9

1 **a** $2x^2 - x - 6$ **b** $(2x+3)(x-2)(x+1)$

   c $x = 2, x = -1, x = -\frac{3}{2}$

2 $a = -3, a = -5$

3 **b** $(x-2)(x-3)(x-5)$

   c
$y = x^3 - 10x^2 + 31x - 30$

4 **b** $(x+4)(x-3)(2x-1)$

5 **a** $c = -60$ **b** $(x+3)(2x+5)(x-4)$ **c** -6

6 **b** $(x+2)(x+3)(x-1)$ **c** $x = -2, -3, 1$

7 **a** -6 **c** $(2x-1)(x+2)(x+3)$

8 **a** $a = -10, b = 21$ **b** -24

9 **b** $-1, -2, 4$

10 $(x-y)(x-2)(y-2)$

11 **a** $a = -12, b = 5, c = 6$ **b** $(x-2)(2x-3)(2x+1)$

12 $(a+b)(a-b)(2a+b)(2a-b)$

Before you start Answers

Chapter 10

1 **a** $y = 2x + 3$ **b** $7y + 4x = 13$

   c $3y = 10x + 21$ **d** $3y = 2x - 14$

   e $5y + 8x + 4 = 0$

2 **a** $(x+2)^2 - 4$ **b** $\left(x+\frac{5}{2}\right)^2 - \frac{25}{4}$

   c $\left(x-\frac{3}{2}\right)^2 - \frac{9}{4}$ **d** $\left(x-\frac{1}{2}\right)^2 - \frac{1}{4}$

   e $2(x-1)^2 - 2$

3 **a** two solutions   **b** two solutions

   c one solution   **d** no solution

   e two solutions

Exercise 10.1

1 **a** $(2, 3)$ **b** $\left(\frac{3}{2}, 6\right)$ **c** $\left(\frac{5}{2}, \frac{9}{2}\right)$

   d $\left(\frac{3}{2}, 4\right)$ **e** $\left(-3, \frac{1}{6}\right)$ **f** $\left(-\frac{5}{2}, -\frac{1}{2}\right)$

   g $(-0.55, 0.2)$ **h** $\left(3\sqrt{2}, -\frac{3}{2}\sqrt{3}\right)$

2 **a** 6.32   **b** 3.61   **c** 7.81   **d** 7.62

   e 2   **f** 5

3 **a** 1.41   **b** 3.91   **c** 3.35   **d** 10.3

   e 5.52   **f** 3.34

4 **a** $(5, 7)$ **b** $(-6, 3)$ **c** $(-10, -13)$

   d $(10, -10)$ **e** $\left(5\frac{1}{2}, -\frac{1}{2}\right)$ **f** $(-4, 9)$

5 **a** $3y + x = 22$ **b** $a = -2, b = 7$

7 1

8 **a** $x = -1, 4y + 10x = 1$ **b** centre $\left(-1, \frac{11}{4}\right)$

9 centre $\left(\frac{5}{2}, \frac{9}{2}\right)$, radius 2.92 units

10 **a** centre $\left(\frac{3}{2}, \frac{5}{2}\right)$ **b** radius 2.92 units

11 **a** centre $\left(\frac{3}{4}, \frac{3}{2}\right)$ **b** right-angle in a semi-circle

12 **a** $a = \frac{13}{2}$ **b** $2y = x + 6$

13 No

Exercise 10.2

1 **a** $(-1, 0), r = 3$ **b** $(-2, 1), r = 3$

   c $(3, 2), r = 4$ **d** $(\sqrt{2}, -\sqrt{3}), r = 2$

   e $(2\sqrt{3}, -\sqrt{3}), r = \sqrt{3}$ **f** $(1, -2), r = 2$

2 **a** $(x-1)^2 + (y-2)^2 = 4$

   b $(x+1)^2 + y^2 = 1$

   c $(x+2)^2 + (y-2)^2 = 9$

   d $(x-3)^2 + (y+4)^2 = 2$

   e $(x+\sqrt{2})^2 + (y+\sqrt{3})^2 = 7$

   f $\left(x-\frac{1}{2}\right)^2 + \left(y+\frac{1}{2}\right)^2 = \frac{1}{16}$

3 **a** centre $(2, 0); r = 1$ **b** $r = 2$

4 **b** point lies on the circumference   **c** $a = \sqrt{10}$

5 **a** $(x-3)^2 + (y-2)^2 = 8$

   b $(x-4)^2 + (y+1)^2 = 25$

   c outside the circle

7 **a** $(4, 7)$ **b** $(-1, 6)$

8 **a** $(2, 5), \left(-\frac{6}{5}, -\frac{7}{5}\right)$ **b** $(-1, -4)$

   c $(3, -2), (5, -4)$ **d** $P(-2, 0), Q(-3, -1)$

9 $A(5, 8), B(-1, 2)$

10 $a = -8.66$ or $a = 2.66$

11 **a** $AB = 2$

    b $(0, 0), (0, 9); (0, 0), (10, 0);$ centre $(5, 4.5)$

    c area 16 units^2

    e $P(-3, 0), Q(0, 3);$ area 4.5 units^2

12 **a** centres in order are $(3, 2), (3, -2), (2, -4), (-2, 4)$

    b any equation of the form
    $(x-2)^2 + (y-3)^2 = r^2$

Review 10

1 **a** $PQR = 90°;$ angle in a semi-circle

   b $PRQ = 56°;$ angles on same chord/segment

   c $POQ = 112°; POQ$ angle at centre = twice angle on circumference

2 $y + x = 8$

3 $r = 8.60, B(8, -9)$

4 $(x+2)^2 + (y-5)^2 = 25$

5 $(1, -1), (-3, -5)$

6 $x^2 + (y - 2\sqrt{3})^2 = 16, (0, 4 + 2\sqrt{3}), (0, -4 + 2\sqrt{3})$

7 **a** $A(4, 0)$ **b** radius 2   **d** $(0, 6), (0, 2)$

   e $2y = x + 8$

8 **a** $3y + x = 8$ **c** $(x-5)^2 + (y-1)^2 = 10$

9 **a** $2\sqrt{10}$ **b** $(2, 3)$

   c $(x-2)^2 + (y-3)^2 = 10$

10 $(x-4)^2 + (y-5)^2 = 40$

11 **a** $(6, 2)$ **b** $(x-6)^2 + (y-2)^2 = 25$

12 $p = -4, q = 3,$ radius 3; $x = -5.34, -2.66$

13 $r = \sqrt{(g^2 + f^2 - c)},$ centre $\left(-\frac{3}{2}, \frac{3}{4}\right),$ radius $\frac{1}{4}\sqrt{61}$

C2

Before you start Answers

Chapter 11

1 **a** $x = 0, x = \frac{1}{2}$ **b** $x = 2$ **c** $x = -\frac{1}{2}, x = 3$

   d $x = 1, x = -\frac{2}{3}$ **e** $x = -\frac{2}{5}, x = \frac{3}{2}$ **f** $x = 0, x = \frac{3}{2}$

2 **a** $192a^4$ **b** $\frac{7}{2}a^2$ **c** a^3

   d $\frac{8a}{9}$ **e** $4a^3$ **f** $\frac{2}{3}$

3 **a**

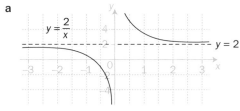

$y = \frac{2}{x}$ $y = 2$

   b

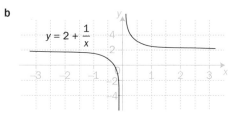

$y = 2 + \frac{1}{x}$

   c

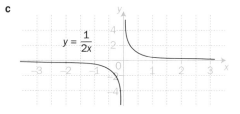

$y = \frac{1}{2x}$

   d

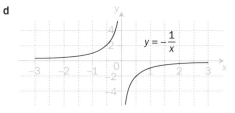

$y = -\frac{1}{x}$

Exercise 11.1

1

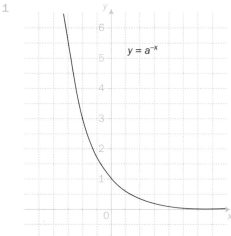

$y = a^{-x}$

2 **a**

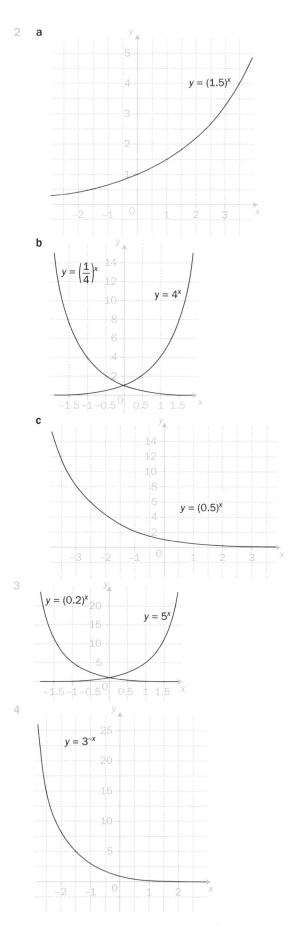

$y = (1.5)^x$

   b

$y = \left(\frac{1}{4}\right)^x$ $y = 4^x$

   c

$y = (0.5)^x$

3

$y = (0.2)^x$ $y = 5^x$

4

$y = 3^{-x}$

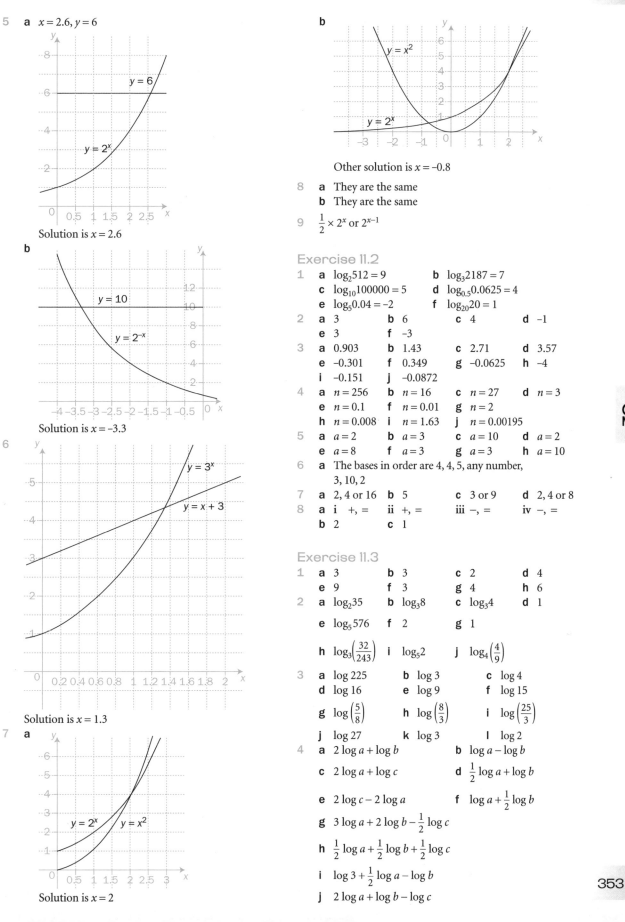

5 **a** $x = 2.6, y = 6$

Solution is $x = 2.6$

b

Solution is $x = -3.3$

6

Solution is $x = 1.3$

7 **a**

Solution is $x = 2$

b

Other solution is $x = -0.8$

8 **a** They are the same
  b They are the same

9   $\frac{1}{2} \times 2^x$ or 2^{x-1}

Exercise 11.2

1 **a** $\log_2 512 = 9$ **b** $\log_3 2187 = 7$
  c $\log_{10} 100000 = 5$ **d** $\log_{0.5} 0.0625 = 4$
  e $\log_5 0.04 = -2$ **f** $\log_{20} 20 = 1$

2 **a** 3   **b** 6   **c** 4   **d** −1
  e 3   **f** −3

3 **a** 0.903   **b** 1.43   **c** 2.71   **d** 3.57
  e −0.301   **f** 0.349   **g** −0.0625   **h** −4
  i −0.151   **j** −0.0872

4 **a** $n = 256$ **b** $n = 16$ **c** $n = 27$ **d** $n = 3$
  e $n = 0.1$ **f** $n = 0.01$ **g** $n = 2$
  h $n = 0.008$ **i** $n = 1.63$ **j** $n = 0.00195$

5 **a** $a = 2$ **b** $a = 3$ **c** $a = 10$ **d** $a = 2$
  e $a = 8$ **f** $a = 3$ **g** $a = 3$ **h** $a = 10$

6 **a** The bases in order are 4, 4, 5, any number,
    3, 10, 2

7 **a** 2, 4 or 16   **b** 5   **c** 3 or 9   **d** 2, 4 or 8

8 **a** **i** +, =   **ii** +, =   **iii** −, =   **iv** −, =
  b 2   **c** 1

Exercise 11.3

1 **a** 3   **b** 3   **c** 2   **d** 4
  e 9   **f** 3   **g** 4   **h** 6

2 **a** $\log_2 35$ **b** $\log_3 8$ **c** $\log_3 4$ **d** 1
  e $\log_5 576$ **f** 2   **g** 1
  h $\log_3\left(\frac{32}{243}\right)$ **i** $\log_5 2$ **j** $\log_4\left(\frac{4}{9}\right)$

3 **a** $\log 225$ **b** $\log 3$ **c** $\log 4$
  d $\log 16$ **e** $\log 9$ **f** $\log 15$
  g $\log\left(\frac{5}{8}\right)$ **h** $\log\left(\frac{8}{3}\right)$ **i** $\log\left(\frac{25}{3}\right)$
  j $\log 27$ **k** $\log 3$ **l** $\log 2$

4 **a** $2\log a + \log b$ **b** $\log a - \log b$
  c $2\log a + \log c$ **d** $\frac{1}{2}\log a + \log b$
  e $2\log c - 2\log a$ **f** $\log a + \frac{1}{2}\log b$
  g $3\log a + 2\log b - \frac{1}{2}\log c$
  h $\frac{1}{2}\log a + \frac{1}{2}\log b + \frac{1}{2}\log c$
  i $\log 3 + \frac{1}{2}\log a - \log b$
  j $2\log a + \log b - \log c$

C2

5   **a** 1.07918   **b** 1.25527   **c** 1.5563   **d** 0.17609

6   3 log 2 + log 3
    log 2 + log 6 + log 2
    log 2 + log 12
    4 log 2 + log 3 − log 2

7   $y = \log_{16} x$

8   **a** −2, −1, 0, 1, 2

Exercise 11.4

1   **a** 2.81   **b** 0.631   **c** 0.861   **d** 4.32
    e 4.74   **f** −1.74   **g** −2.86   **h** −0.969
    i 2.32   **j** 0.151

2   **a** 1.26   **b** 3.17   **c** 0.431   **d** 0
    e 1.66   **f** 1.40   **g** 1.20   **h** 2.10
    i 0.801   **j** −0.648

3   **a** 1.32   **b** 5.25   **c** 1.61   **d** 2.63
    e 0.870   **f** 0.461   **g** 0.730   **h** 2.21
    i 0.892   **j** −3.14

4   **a** 0   **b** 2   **c** 0   **d** 0.631
    e 1.58   **f** 0.861   **g** 0   **h** −0.631

5   **a** 0   **b** 0   **c** 1, 1.58
    d −0.631, 1.26   **e** 0.569   **f** 2, 1.32
    g 0.465, 0.771   **h** −1.32, −0.415   **i** 2, 1.32
    j 0.369

6   **a** 2.09   **b** 150   **c** 2.83   **d** 21.2
    e 15.9   **f** 246   **g** 1.90   **h** 6.43
    i 1.39   **j** 36.1

7   **a** 1.53   **b** 1.79   **c** 24.8   **d** 7.03×10^{16}
    e 1.52   **f** 8.34   **g** 3050 or 0.000328

8   **b** 4.72 or 0.211

9   **a** $x = \pm316, y = \pm3.16$ **c** 1, −2

10 **a i** 2   **ii** the first
    b The first method as no logs are involved, will
    give $x = −10$

Review 11

1   **a** 78100   **b** −32   **c** 0.00195
    d 0.00032   **e** 0.316   **f** 1.55
    g 14.0   **h** 0.000417   **i** 0.697

2   **a**

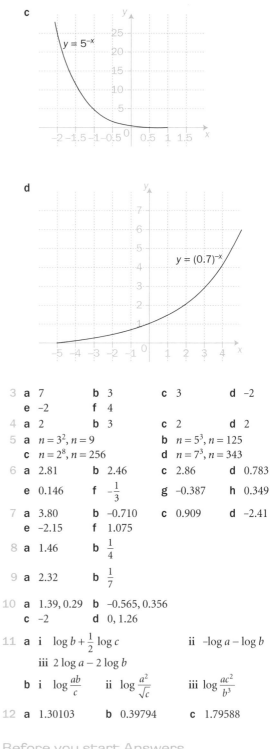

b

3   **a** 7   **b** 3   **c** 3   **d** −2
    e −2   **f** 4

4   **a** 2   **b** 3   **c** 2   **d** 2

5   **a** $n = 3^2, n = 9$ **b** $n = 5^3, n = 125$
    c $n = 2^8, n = 256$ **d** $n = 7^3, n = 343$

6   **a** 2.81   **b** 2.46   **c** 2.86   **d** 0.783
    e 0.146   **f** $-\dfrac{1}{3}$ **g** −0.387   **h** 0.349

7   **a** 3.80   **b** −0.710   **c** 0.909   **d** −2.41
    e −2.15   **f** 1.075

8   **a** 1.46   **b** $\dfrac{1}{4}$

9   **a** 2.32   **b** $\dfrac{1}{7}$

10 **a** 1.39, 0.29   **b** −0.565, 0.356
    c −2   **d** 0, 1.26

11 **a i** $\log b + \dfrac{1}{2} \log c$ **ii** $-\log a - \log b$
    iii $2 \log a - 2 \log b$

    b i $\log \dfrac{ab}{c}$ **ii** $\log \dfrac{a^2}{\sqrt{c}}$ **iii** $\log \dfrac{ac^2}{b^3}$

12 **a** 1.30103   **b** 0.39794   **c** 1.79588

Before you start Answers

Chapter 12

1   **a** $x = 3, x = -1$

    b $x = -2.3, x = 1.3$

    c $x = -\dfrac{1}{2}, x = 1$

    d $x = -3.7, x = -0.3$

    e $x = -1.4, x = -0.2$

2 bearings

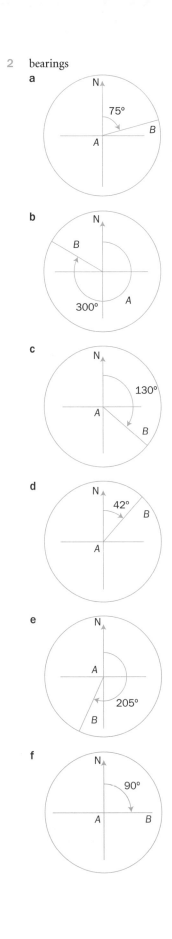

a

75°

b

300°

c

130°

d

42°

e

205°

f

90°

3   **a** $x = \dfrac{2b-a}{a-b}$ **b** $x = \dfrac{5a}{8}$

   c $x = a - b$ **d** $x = \dfrac{5}{a-b}$

Exercise 12.1

1   **a** $B = 37.1°$ **b** $b = 7.61$ cm   **c** $a = 8.67$ cm
   d $C = 56.3°$ **e** $C = 41.6°$ **f** $c = 13.0$ cm
2   **a** $C = 75°$, $a = 12.3$ cm, $b = 10.6$ cm
   b $T = 48°$, $s = 4.37$ cm, $t = 7.16$ cm
   c $Z = 68°$, $X = 59°$, $y = 22.4$ cm, $z = 26.0$ cm
3   **a** 45.5°, 103.5°, 24.5 cm; 134.5°, 14.5°, 6.32 cm
   b 84.3°, 25.7°, 15.7 cm; 95.7°, 14.3°, 8.94 cm
   c 30.5°, 124.5°, 29.3 cm; 149.5°, 5.5°, 3.40 cm
   d 75.2°, 39.8°, 5.30 cm; 104.8°, 10.2°, 1.47 cm
4   $x = 24.3°$, $y = 74.7°$
5   4.06 cm, 6.22 cm
6   13.7 km

Exercise 12.2

1   **a** $BC = 7$ cm   **b** $AB = 7.69$ cm
   c $BC = 14.4$ cm   **d** $A = 65.4°$
   e $B = 42.0°$ **f** $B = 49.4°$
2   **a** $A = 44.4°$, $B = 57.1°$, $C = 78.5°$
   b $b = 8.06$ cm, $C = 55.4°$, $A = 70.6°$
   c $C = 55°$, $a = 11.1$ cm, $b = 14.2$ cm
   d $c = 37.3$ cm, $C = 37.1°$, $B = 40.9°$
3   **a** $AC = 13.3$ cm, angle $ABC = 124°$ **b** 58°, 122°
   c 30.6°, 55.1°, 94.3°
4   263 m
5   14.3 km

Exercise 12.3

1   **a** 56.1 cm^2 **b** 99.1 cm^2 **c** 659 cm^2 or 221 cm^2
2   **a** 53.1° or 126.9°   **b** 23 cm
   c 103° or 36.4°   **d** 54.7° or 125.3°
3   **b** $x = 1$ **c** $x = \dfrac{1}{2}$
4   They are in the correct order based on area.

Exercise 12.4

1   **a** 0.349 radians   **b** 1.88 radians   **c** 9.16 radians
2   **a** 272°   **b** 286°   **c** 183°
3   **a** $\dfrac{2\pi}{9}$ **b** $\dfrac{3\pi}{2}$ **c** $\dfrac{5\pi}{36}$

   d $\dfrac{5\pi}{2}$ **e** $\dfrac{5\pi}{4}$ **f** $\dfrac{10\pi}{3}$

4   **a** 36°   **b** 1260°   **c** 157.5°
5   **a** 0.5   **b** 1   **c** 1
   d –1   **e** 0.5   **f** 1.732
6   **a** 31.7 cm   **b** 2.63 m   **c** 27.4 m
   d 0.0353 m
7   **a** 16 cm^2 **b** 8.04 cm^2 **c** 0.188 m^2
   d 14.5 cm^2 **e** 313 cm^2 **f** 0.00011 m^2
8   **a** 20.2°   **b** 23.9 cm   **c** 10.2 cm
9   **a** 6.77 cm   **b** 9.77 cm   **c** 78.0°
   d 33.5 cm   **e** 40.0 cm^2 **f** 3.82 cm^2
   g 10.9 cm
11   **b** 14.3 cm^2

C2

13 20.5 cm^2
14 79.1 cm^2

Exercise 12.5

1 Quadrants
   a III   **b** III   **c** III
   d IV   **e** IV   **f** IV
   g II   **h** I   **i** I

2 **a** 55°, IV   **b** 30°, II   **c** 60°, I
   d 40°, II   **e** $\frac{\pi}{4}$, II   **f** $\frac{\pi}{3}$, I
   g $\frac{\pi}{6}$, III   **h** $\frac{\pi}{5}$, II   **i** $\frac{\pi}{3}$, I

3 Quadrants
   a III, negative   **b** II, negative   **c** IV, negative
   d I, positive   **e** IV, negative   **f** IV, positive
   g I, positive   **h** II, positive   **i** III, negative

4 **a** $-\sin\theta$ **b** $-\cos\theta$ **c** $\tan\theta$
   d $\cos\theta$ **e** $\sin\theta$ **f** $\tan\theta$
   g $-\cos\theta$ **h** $\cos\theta$ **i** $\tan\theta$
   j $-\sin\theta$

5 **a** $-3\sin\theta$ **b** $-3\tan\theta+1$ **c** $6\cos\theta$
   d $-(\sin\theta)^2$ **e** $2\tan\theta$ **f** $5\sin\theta$
   g $5\tan\theta$ **h** $(\cos\theta)^2$ **i** $-\cos\theta\sin\theta$
   j $(\tan\theta)^2$

6 $\sin(360° + x) = \sin x$, $\sin(180° + x) = -\sin x$
   $\cos(360° + x) = \cos x$, $\cos(180° + x) = -\cos x$
   $\sin(180° - x) = \sin x$, $\cos(360° - x) = \cos x$
   $\cos(180° - x) = -\cos x$

7 First column: +, +, −, −
   Second column: −, +, +, −

8 **a** $\sin(180° - x)$
   b $\cos(360° - x)$; $\tan(180° + x)$
   c i 150°   **ii** 300°   **iii** 225°

Exercise 12.6

1 **a** $\sin 30°$ **b** $-\cos 30°$ **c** $-\tan 45°$
   d $-\sin 60°$ **e** $-\cos 45°$ **f** $\sin 60°$
   g $\cos 30°$ **h** $-\sin 60°$

2 **a** $\frac{(\sqrt{3})}{2}$ **b** 0   **c** $-\sqrt{3}$
   d $-\sqrt{3}$ **e** $-\frac{1}{2}$ **f** $\frac{(\sqrt{3})}{2}$
   g $-\frac{1}{2}$ **h** $-\sqrt{3}$

3 **a** 1   **b** 0   **c** 1
   d $-\sqrt{3}$ **e** $\frac{(\sqrt{3})}{2}$ **f** $-\infty$
   g $-\frac{1}{2}$ **h** $-\frac{(\sqrt{3})}{2}$

4 **a** $\frac{3}{5}$ **b** $\frac{3}{5}$ **c** $-\frac{3}{5}$ **d** $-\frac{4}{3}$
   e $-\frac{3}{5}$ **f** $-\frac{3}{5}$ **g** $-\frac{3}{4}$ **h** $-\frac{4}{5}$
   i $\frac{3}{5}$ **j** $\frac{3}{5}$

5 **a** $\cos A = \frac{2\sqrt{2}}{3}$; $\tan A = \frac{1}{2\sqrt{2}}$
   b $\cos A = -\frac{\sqrt{5}}{3}$; $\tan A = \frac{2}{\sqrt{5}}$
   c $\sin x = \frac{-1}{\sqrt{3}}$; $\cos x = \frac{-\sqrt{2}}{\sqrt{3}}$
   d $\sin B = \frac{\sqrt{3}}{2}$; $\tan B = -\sqrt{3}$
   e $\sin x = \frac{\sqrt{2}}{\sqrt{3}}$; $\cos x = \frac{-1}{\sqrt{3}}$
   f $\sin\theta = \frac{-5}{13}$; $\cos\theta = \frac{-12}{13}$

6 **a** 30°, 150°   **b** 30°   **c** 45°
   d no solution   **e** 225°, 315°   **f** 180°
   g 210°, 330°   **h** 150°

7 **a** $\frac{\pi}{6}, \frac{5\pi}{6}$ **b** $\frac{\pi}{2}, \frac{3\pi}{2}$ **c** no solution
   d $\frac{\pi}{3}, \frac{4\pi}{3}$ **e** $\frac{4\pi}{3}$ **f** $\frac{11\pi}{6}$
   g no solutions   **h** $\frac{\pi}{3}, \frac{5\pi}{3}, \frac{7\pi}{3}, \frac{11\pi}{3}$

8 **a** $\sqrt{3}$ **b** $\frac{1}{2}, \frac{\sqrt{3}}{2}, \frac{1}{\sqrt{3}}$

Exercise 12.7

1 **a**

$y = \cos x$

   b

$y = \sin\theta$

   c

$y = \tan x$

d

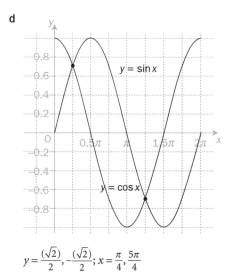

$$y = \frac{(\sqrt{2})}{2}, -\frac{(\sqrt{2})}{2}; x = \frac{\pi}{4}, \frac{5\pi}{4}$$

2   Values of sin and cos must be between −1 and 1.

Exercise 12.8

1   a

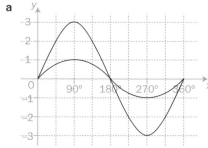

b

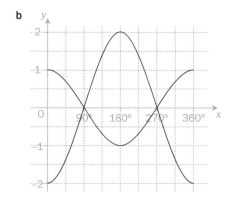

c

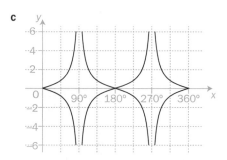

2   a

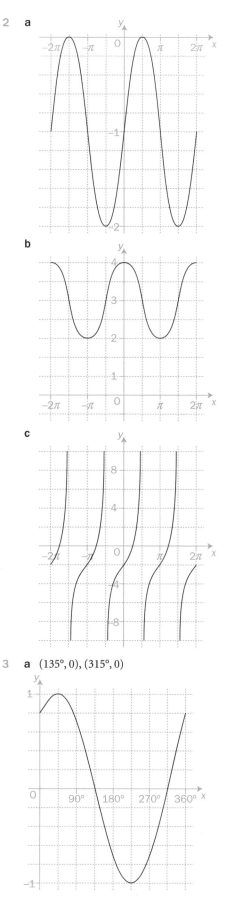

b

c

3   a $(135°, 0), (315°, 0)$

b $(0°, 0), (180°, 0), (360°, 0)$

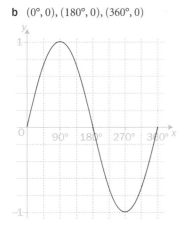

c $(45°, 0), (225°, 0)$

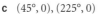
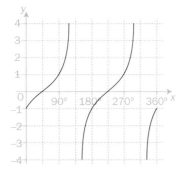

4 **a** $(0°, 0), (180°, 0), (360°, 0)$

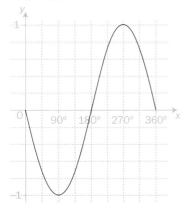

b $(45°, 0), (135°, 0), (225°, 0), (315°, 0)$

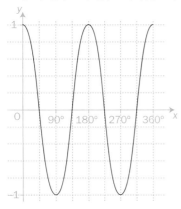

c $(0°, 0), (360°, 0)$

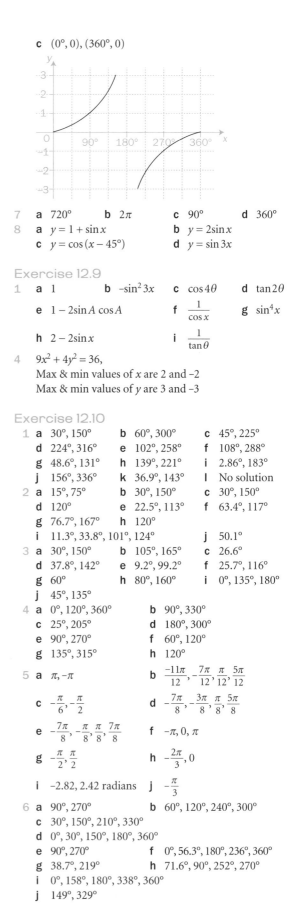

7 **a** $720°$ **b** 2π **c** $90°$ **d** $360°$

8 **a** $y = 1 + \sin x$ **b** $y = 2\sin x$
   c $y = \cos(x - 45°)$ **d** $y = \sin 3x$

Exercise 12.9

1 **a** 1 **b** $-\sin^2 3x$ **c** $\cos 4\theta$ **d** $\tan 2\theta$

   e $1 - 2\sin A \cos A$ **f** $\dfrac{1}{\cos x}$ **g** $\sin^4 x$

   h $2 - 2\sin x$ **i** $\dfrac{1}{\tan \theta}$

4   $9x^2 + 4y^2 = 36$,
   Max & min values of x are 2 and –2
   Max & min values of y are 3 and –3

Exercise 12.10

1 **a** $30°, 150°$ **b** $60°, 300°$ **c** $45°, 225°$
   d $224°, 316°$ **e** $102°, 258°$ **f** $108°, 288°$
   g $48.6°, 131°$ **h** $139°, 221°$ **i** $2.86°, 183°$
   j $156°, 336°$ **k** $36.9°, 143°$ **l** No solution

2 **a** $15°, 75°$ **b** $30°, 150°$ **c** $30°, 150°$
   d $120°$ **e** $22.5°, 113°$ **f** $63.4°, 117°$
   g $76.7°, 167°$ **h** $120°$
   i $11.3°, 33.8°, 101°, 124°$ **j** $50.1°$

3 **a** $30°, 150°$ **b** $105°, 165°$ **c** $26.6°$
   d $37.8°, 142°$ **e** $9.2°, 99.2°$ **f** $25.7°, 116°$
   g $60°$ **h** $80°, 160°$ **i** $0°, 135°, 180°$
   j $45°, 135°$

4 **a** $0°, 120°, 360°$ **b** $90°, 330°$
   c $25°, 205°$ **d** $180°, 300°$
   e $90°, 270°$ **f** $60°, 120°$
   g $135°, 315°$ **h** $120°$

5 **a** $\pi, -\pi$ **b** $\dfrac{-11\pi}{12}, -\dfrac{7\pi}{12}, \dfrac{\pi}{12}, \dfrac{5\pi}{12}$

   c $-\dfrac{\pi}{6}, -\dfrac{\pi}{2}$ **d** $-\dfrac{7\pi}{8}, -\dfrac{3\pi}{8}, \dfrac{\pi}{8}, \dfrac{5\pi}{8}$

   e $-\dfrac{7\pi}{8}, -\dfrac{\pi}{8}, \dfrac{\pi}{8}, \dfrac{7\pi}{8}$ **f** $-\pi, 0, \pi$

   g $-\dfrac{\pi}{2}, \dfrac{\pi}{2}$ **h** $-\dfrac{2\pi}{3}, 0$

   i $-2.82, 2.42$ radians   **j** $-\dfrac{\pi}{3}$

6 **a** $90°, 270°$ **b** $60°, 120°, 240°, 300°$
   c $30°, 150°, 210°, 330°$
   d $0°, 30°, 150°, 180°, 360°$
   e $90°, 270°$ **f** $0°, 56.3°, 180°, 236°, 360°$
   g $38.7°, 219°$ **h** $71.6°, 90°, 252°, 270°$
   i $0°, 158°, 180°, 338°, 360°$
   j $149°, 329°$

7 a −90°　　　　b −180°, −60°, 60°, 180°
  c −117°, −45°, 63.4°, 135°
  d −90°, 19.5°, 161°　e −60°, −48.2°, 48.2°, 60°
  f 38.2°, 142°　　　g −141°, 141°
  h −106°, 106°　　　i −144°, −69.9°, 36.2°, 110°

8 a $\dfrac{\pi}{12}, \dfrac{5\pi}{12}, \dfrac{7\pi}{12}, \dfrac{11\pi}{12}$　b $\dfrac{\pi}{12}, \dfrac{\pi}{4}, \dfrac{5\pi}{12}$

  c $\dfrac{\pi}{12}, \dfrac{5\pi}{12}, \dfrac{7\pi}{12}, \dfrac{11\pi}{12}$　d 0.945, 2.52, $\dfrac{3\pi}{8}, \dfrac{7\pi}{8}$

  e 0.252, 0.795, 2.35, 2.89
9 b 0.588, 3.73 radians

10 a $\sin 2\theta = \dfrac{2\tan\theta}{1 + \tan^2\theta}$, $\cos 2\theta = \dfrac{1 - \tan^2\theta}{1 + \tan^2\theta}$
11 $\sin x = 0$ also satisfied the equation
   Extra solutions are 0°, 180°, 360°
   plus 225° from $\tan x = 1$

Review 12

1 a 6.50 cm　　　　　　b 100°, 79.6°
2 angle $ACB = 49.3°$, area 63.7 cm²
3 a 0.954　　　　　　　b 1.27, 1.88 radians
4 a radius 9.27 cm　　　b area 40.1 cm²
5 perimeter 50.5 cm
6 b 1.287 radians　　c 16.1 m²　　d 4.1 m²
7 a $\sin\theta$　　　　　b $5\sin\theta$
8 −315°, −225°, 45°, 135°

9 $\cos x = \dfrac{(\sqrt{2})}{(\sqrt{3})}$, $\tan x = \dfrac{1}{\sqrt{2}}$

10 a $\dfrac{-(\sqrt{3})}{2}, \dfrac{1}{2}, -\sqrt{3}$　　b $\dfrac{2\pi}{3}, \dfrac{5\pi}{3}, -\dfrac{\pi}{3}, -\dfrac{4\pi}{3}$

11 maximum at $(0, 1)$ and $(2\pi, 1)$;
   minimum at $(\pi, -1)$

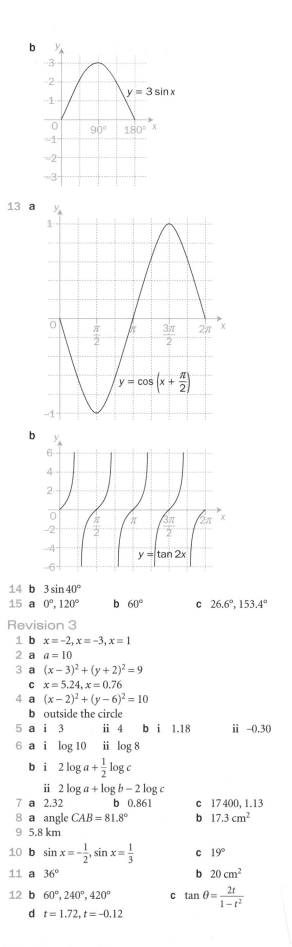

12 a

13 a

b

14 b 3 sin 40°
15 a 0°, 120°　　　b 60°　　　c 26.6°, 153.4°

Revision 3

1 b $x = -2, x = -3, x = 1$
2 a $a = 10$
3 a $(x − 3)^2 + (y + 2)^2 = 9$
  c $x = 5.24, x = 0.76$
4 a $(x − 2)^2 + (y − 6)^2 = 10$
  b outside the circle
5 a i 3　　　ii 4　　b i 1.18　　　ii −0.30
6 a i $\log 10$　　ii $\log 8$
  b i $2\log a + \dfrac{1}{2}\log c$
    ii $2\log a + \log b − 2\log c$
7 a 2.32　　　　　b 0.861　　　c 17 400, 1.13
8 a angle $CAB = 81.8°$　　b 17.3 cm²
9 5.8 km
10 b $\sin x = -\dfrac{1}{2}$, $\sin x = \dfrac{1}{3}$　　c 19°
11 a 36°　　　　　　　　　b 20 cm²
12 b 60°, 240°, 420°　　　c $\tan\theta = \dfrac{2t}{1 - t^2}$
   d $t = 1.72, t = -0.12$

$+ 17 + 26$

$5 + 14 + 27 + 44 + 65$

13   **c** $n = 5$ **d** $n = 7$

...ric series are **b**, **d**, **e** and **f**

...on ratios are 2, $\frac{1}{3}$, 2 and -2

2    $3, 6, 12, 24$ **b** $5, 15, 45, 135$

c $1\frac{1}{2}, 3, 6, 12$ **d** $2, 3, 4\frac{1}{2}, 6\frac{3}{4}$

e $-3, -1\frac{1}{2}, -\frac{3}{4}, -\frac{3}{8}$ **f** $5, -10, 20, -40$

g $\frac{1}{4}, -\frac{1}{8}, \frac{1}{16}, -\frac{1}{32}$ **h** $1, \frac{1}{4}, \frac{1}{16}, \frac{1}{64}$

3   **a** $(2)^{n-1}$ **b** $\frac{1}{2}\left(\frac{1}{2}\right)^{n-1}$ or $\left(\frac{1}{2}\right)^n$

c $4(2)^{n-1}$ or $(2)^{n+1}$ **d** $\frac{3}{4}(2)^{n-1}$ or $3(2)^{n-3}$

e $\frac{2}{5}\left(\frac{5}{2}\right)^{n-1}$ **f** $6(5)^{n-1}$

g $4(6)^{n-1}$ **h** $5\left(-\frac{1}{2}\right)^{n-1}$

i $-3\left(\frac{1}{4}\right)^{n-1}$

4   **a** $\frac{1}{8}, \frac{1}{128}$ **b** $\frac{3}{32}, \frac{3}{512}$ **c** $\frac{2}{81}, \frac{2}{6561}$

d $-\left(\frac{3}{4}\right)^5, -\left(\frac{3}{4}\right)^9$ or $-\frac{243}{1024}, -\frac{19683}{262144}$

5   **a** $12, 192$ **b** $\frac{5}{4}, \frac{5}{64}$ **c** $\frac{9}{4}, \frac{729}{4}$

d $\frac{2}{5}, \frac{32}{5}$

6   **a** $a = \pm12$ **b** $a = 2$ **c** $a = \pm4.5$

7   **a** $x = \frac{1}{3}, r = \frac{5}{2}$ **b** $a = \frac{1}{2}, r = 1$

8   **a** 14th term   **b** 22nd term   **c** 14th term

9   **a** 15 years   **b** 5 years   **c** 6 bounces

d i $8, 12, 18, 27, 40.5$

10   **a** $-1, 3, -9$ **b** $27, -81$

$\frac{1}{2}, 1, 2$ $4, 8$

$\frac{1}{3}, \frac{2}{3}, \frac{4}{3}$ $\frac{8}{3}, \frac{16}{3}$

Exercise 13.2

1   **a** $2^9 - 1$ or 511 **b** -170

c 0.9998 **d** 147.8 **e** 102.3 **f** 10.5

2   **a** $\frac{3}{2}(3^6 - 1)$ **b** $1 - \left(\frac{1}{2}\right)^8$ **c** $6(2^5 - 1)$

d $\frac{1}{3}(2^8 - 1)$ **e** $1 - \left(\frac{1}{3}\right)^{10}$ **f** $-\left(\frac{1}{2}\right)^{10} - \frac{1}{2}$

3   **a** $n = 12$ **b** $n = 18$

4   **a** $n = 10$ **b** $n = 11$

5   **a** $6, 3, 1.5, 0.75, 0.375; 11.625$

b first term 5, third term 11.25; 40.625

6   10

7    $\frac{192}{x + 1}$; $x = 3$ or 15

8   **a** 4th term $\frac{y^3}{x^2}$, n th term $\frac{y^{n-1}}{x^{n-2}}$, 19th term $\frac{y^{18}}{x^{17}}$

b $t = \pm\sqrt{2}$

9   **a** £1420.68   **b** £2645.70

c 14.69 km, 170.86 km

d below by 102 calories

10   Various possible answers

Exercise 13.3

1   **a** 4   **b** 14   **c** 10.286   **d** 8.1

e -10.667 **f** 0.625   **g** 4   **h** 6

i $\frac{a}{1-a}$ **j** $\frac{2a}{3-a}$

2   **a** 32 or $\frac{32}{3}$ **b** $p = \frac{4}{9}$

Exercise 13.4

1   **a** $1 + 5x + 10x^2 + 10x^3 + 5x^4 + x^5$

b $1 - 4x + 6x^2 - 4x^3 + x^4$

c $1 + 6x + 12x^2 + 8x^3$

d $1 - 12x + 54x^2 - 108x^3 + 81x^4$

e $1 + \frac{3}{2}x + \frac{3}{4}x^2 + \frac{x^3}{8}$

f $1 - 10x + 40x^2 - 80x^3 + 80x^4 - 32x^5$

g $1 + 12x + 48x^2 + 64x^3$

h $1 + 14x + 84x^2 + 280x^3 + 560x^4 + 672x^5 + 448x^6 + 128x^7$

2   **a** $16 + 32x + 24x^2 + 8x^3 + x^4$

b $81 - 108x + 54x^2 - 12x^3 + x^4$

c $8 + 36x + 54x^2 + 27x^3$

d $243 - 810x + 1080x^2 - 720x^3 + 240x^4 - 32x^5$

e $27x^3 - 108x^2 + 144x - 64$

f $64x^6 - 192x^5 + 240x^4 - 160x^3 + 60x^2 - 12x + 1$

g $\frac{x^4}{16} - \frac{x^3}{2} + \frac{3}{2}x^2 - 2x + 1$

h $x^6 + 3x^4y^2 + 3x^2 y^4 + y^6$

3   **a** $1 - 3x + 2x^2 + 2x^3 - 3x^4 + x^5$

b $2 + 7x + 8x^2 + 2x^3 - 2x^4 - x^5$

c $1 + 2x - 2x^3 - x^4$

d $x^5 + 3x^4 - 6x^3 - 10x^2 + 21x - 9$

4   **a** $1 + 3x + 6x^2 + 7x^3 + 6x^4 + 3x^5 + x^6$

b $8 - 24x + 36x^2 - 32x^3 + 18x^4 - 6x^5 + x^6$

c $x^6 + 3x^5 - 3x^4 - 11x^3 + 6x^2 + 12x - 8$

d $a^3 + 3a^2b + 3a^2c + 3ab^2 + 6abc + 3ac^2 + b^3 + 3b^2c + 3bc^2 + c^3$

5   **a** -3 **b** -1 **c** $-3x^3$ **d** 0

6   **a** $a = 3$ **b** $a = 2, b = -1$; 2

7    $\frac{3}{2}$

8   **a** $a : b = 3 : 2$ **b** $k = 18$ **c** $a = 1$ or -3

9   **a i** $x^3 + 3x + \frac{3}{x} + \frac{1}{x^3}$ **ii** $x^4 + 4x^2 + 6 + \frac{4}{x^2} + \frac{1}{x^4}$

b n is even

Exercise 13.5

1 **a** 120 **b** 5040 **c** 504 **d** $\frac{1}{20}$

   e 144 **f** 34560 **g** 480 **h** 32

2 **a** 6 **b** 10 **c** 20 **d** 6

   e 35 **f** 28 **g** 126 **h** 36

3 **a** $1 + 9x + 36x^2 + 84x^3$

   b $1 + 16x + 112x^2 + 448x^3$

   c $1 - 10x + 45x^2 - 120x^3$

   d $1 + 18x + 135x^2 + 540x^3$

   e $1 - 21x + 189x^2 - 945x^3$

   f $1 + 4x + 7x^2 + 7x^3$

4 **a** $128 + 448x + 672x^2$

   b $6561 - 17496x + 20412x^2$

   c $1024 + 2560x + 2880x^2$

   d $\frac{1}{256} - \frac{x}{16} + \frac{7x^2}{16}$

   e $64 + 576x + 2160x^2$

   f $x^7 - 28x^6 + 336x^5$

5 **a** $a = 2$ **b** $a = 2, b = 0, c = 80$ **c** 112

   d $n = 4$ **e** 70

7 **a** $8064\, y^5 x^5$ **b** $1 + 7x + 28x^2 + 77x^3$

   c $n = 0, -1, -2$ **d** 0.33; 5.36%

Review 13

1 **a** $r = \pm 3$ **b** $a = \pm \frac{4}{3}$ **c** $x = \pm 12$

2 **a** $r = 0.9$ **b** $a = 8$ **c** 79.588 **d** 0.412

3 **b** 0.03 **c** 3.996

4 **b** 51150 **c** 6.25

5 **b** $r = \frac{4}{5}, r = \frac{1}{5}$ **c** $a = 5, a = 20$ **e** $n = 15$

6 $a = 2, 1 + 16x + 112x^2 + 448x^3$

7 $729 - 1458x + 1215x^2$

8 **a** $1 + 8ax + 28ax^2$ **b** $a = -2, b = 112$

9 $a = 1, b = -3, c = 0$

10 **a** $1 - \frac{7}{2}x + \frac{21}{4}x^2$

11 $a = 2, b = 4, n = 6$

Before you start Answers

Chapter 14

1 **a** $\frac{dy}{dx} = 12x - 2$ **b** $\frac{dy}{dx} = 2x - 3$

   c $\frac{dy}{dx} = 2x - 4x^3$ **d** $\frac{dy}{dx} = 1 + \frac{4}{x^2}$

   e $\frac{dy}{dx} = 8x - 12$

2 **a**

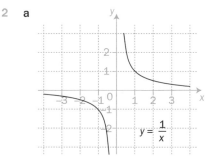

$y = \frac{1}{x}$

b

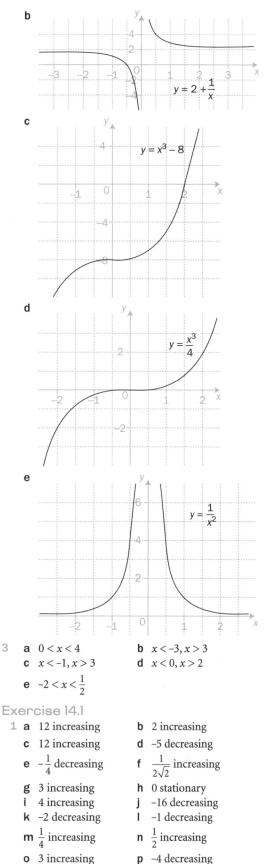

$y = 2 + \frac{1}{x}$

c $y = x^3 - 8$

d $y = \frac{x^3}{4}$

e $y = \frac{1}{x^2}$

3 **a** $0 < x < 4$ **b** $x < -3, x > 3$

   c $x < -1, x > 3$ **d** $x < 0, x > 2$

   e $-2 < x < \frac{1}{2}$

Exercise 14.1

1 **a** 12 increasing **b** 2 increasing

   c 12 increasing **d** –5 decreasing

   e $-\frac{1}{4}$ decreasing **f** $\frac{1}{2\sqrt{2}}$ increasing

   g 3 increasing **h** 0 stationary

   i 4 increasing **j** –16 decreasing

   k –2 decreasing **l** –1 decreasing

   m $\frac{1}{4}$ increasing **n** $\frac{1}{2}$ increasing

   o 3 increasing **p** –4 decreasing

2 a $x > 3$, increasing; $x < 3$, decreasing

b $x > -\frac{1}{4}$, increasing; $x < -\frac{1}{4}$, decreasing

c $x < 0$, increasing; $0 < x < 4$, decreasing; $x > 4$ increasing

d $x > \frac{1}{6}$, decreasing; $x < \frac{1}{6}$, increasing

e $x < 0$, decreasing; $0 < x < \frac{2}{3}$, increasing; $x > \frac{2}{3}$, decreasing

f $x < -2$, increasing; $-2 < x < 3$, decreasing; $x > 3$, increasing

g always decreasing

h $x < -2$, increasing; $-2 < x < 2$, decreasing; $x > 2$, increasing

i $x < \frac{11}{4}$, decreasing; $x > \frac{11}{4}$, increasing

j $x < \frac{1}{3}$, decreasing; $x > \frac{1}{3}$, increasing

k $x < 3$, increasing; $3 < x < 5$, decreasing; $x > 5$, increasing

l $x < 0$, decreasing; $0 < x < \frac{4}{3}$, increasing; $x > \frac{4}{3}$, decreasing

3 a 4 **b** $f'(x) = 4 - \frac{1}{x^2}$, $x < -\frac{1}{2}$, $x > \frac{1}{2}$, increasing

4 $0 < x < 2$, decreasing

5 a $x = -1$ **b** $x = -1, x = 1$ **c** $x = -2$
d $x = 4$ **e** $x = 2$ **f** $x = 0$
g $x = 2$ **h** $x = 0, x = \frac{4}{3}$

6 a minimum point $(1, -2)$

b maximum point $\left(\frac{2}{3}, \frac{4}{3}\right)$

c inflection $(0, 0)$
d minimum point $(-2, -1)$
e minimum point $(3, 0)$

f maximum point $\left(-\frac{1}{2}, \frac{49}{4}\right)$

g minimum point $(0, 0)$, maximum point $\left(\frac{2}{3}, \frac{4}{27}\right)$

h minimum point $(0, -16)$

7 a maximum point $(-3, 18)$, minimum point $(3, -18)$

b minimum point $(3, 27)$

c minimum point $(2, -44)$, maximum point $(-3, 81)$

d minimum point $(-2, -20)$, maximum point $(1, 7)$

e minimum point $\left(\frac{1}{2}, -\frac{17}{4}\right)$, maximum point $(3, 27)$

f maximum point $(0, 3)$, minimum points $\left(\pm\frac{3}{2}, -\frac{33}{16}\right)$

8 $s = 0$

9 maximum $(-1, 0)$, minimum $(1, -4)$

10 a $(1, 2)$ Minimum point, $(-1, -2)$ Maximum point

b The curve approaches the line $y = x$

c

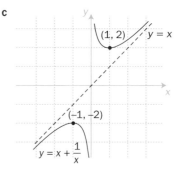

d $y = x$ and $x = 0$

11 a The suspension wire will form a parabola such as $y = x(x - 4)$.

b $(2, -4)$

Exercise 14.2

1 a $36, 36$ **b** $6, 2$ **c** $-\frac{1}{4}, \frac{1}{4}$ **d** $\frac{1}{2\sqrt{2}}, \frac{-1}{8\sqrt{2}}$

e $10, 2$ **f** $\frac{1}{4}, -\frac{1}{4}$ **g** $-4, 24$ **h** $4\frac{1}{4}, 1\frac{3}{4}$

2 a minimum, $x = -1$ **b** maximum, $x = 0$

c maximum, $x = 2$ **d** minimum, $x = -\frac{2}{3}$

e minimum, $x = \frac{13}{12}$ **f** maximum, $x = \frac{1}{2}$

g maximum, $x = \frac{1}{2}$ **h** minimum, $x = \frac{3}{2}$

3 a minimum $(2, -32)$; maximum $(-2, 32)$

b maximum $(3, 54)$; minimum $(-3, -54)$

c minimum $\left(\frac{5}{2}, -\frac{25}{4}\right)$

d minimum $\left(\frac{1}{3}, 8\right)$; maximum $\left(-\frac{1}{3}, -4\right)$

e minimum $(0, 0)$; maximum $\left(\frac{2}{3}, \frac{4}{27}\right)$

f minimum $\left(\frac{3}{2}, -\frac{45}{8}\right)$; maximum $\left(-2, \frac{26}{3}\right)$

g minimum $(4, -304)$; maximum $(-5, 425)$

h no stationary points; $x = \sqrt{(-1)}$ has no real solutions

4 a maximum at $(3, 1)$

C2

b minimum at $(-1.75, -10.125)$

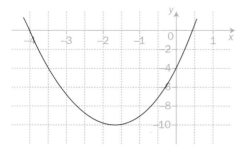

c maximum at $(-0.5, 6.25)$

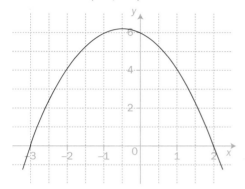

d maximum at $(0.5, 2.25)$

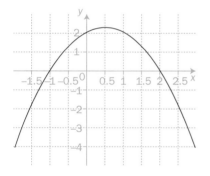

5 **a** maximum $(0.67, 1.19)$,
minimum $(2, 0)$

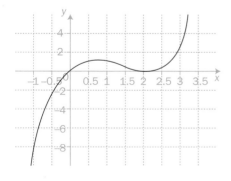

b minimum $(0, 0)$, maximum $(-2, 4)$

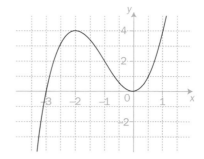

c minimum $(1.73, -10.39)$,
maximum $(-1.73, 10.39)$

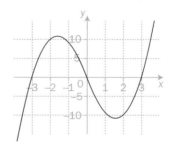

d maximum $(-1, 7)$, minimum $(2, -20)$

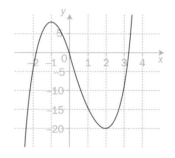

e minimum $(2.12, -4.06)$,
maximum $(-0.79, 8.21)$

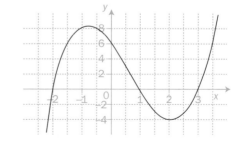

6 **a i** $(-3, 0)$ **ii** $(-3, 0)$

7 **c** Maximum turning point at $(1, 5)$,
point of inflexion at $(2, 3)$,
minimum turning point at $(3, 1)$

C2

Exercise 14.3

1 a $t = 5, s = 125$

   b $t = \frac{1}{2}, a = -1$ (a retardation)

2 a $x = 10, A = 200$

   b $V = 5(4 - x)(3 + x), x = \frac{1}{2}, V = 61.25$

3 $x = 1$

4 a $A = x(150 - 2x)$

   b $x = 37.5$ (or 75), $A = 2812.5 \text{ m}^2$

5 $x = 0.196, V = 0.132 \text{ m}^3$

6 $r = 4, A = 301 \text{ cm}^2$

7 c $V = 269\pi$

8 c $A = 192 \text{ cm}^2$, 8 cm by 8 cm by 4 cm

9 $V = \frac{32\pi r^3}{81}$

10 b 50 when number of predators is 10

Review 14

1 a $6x - 12$ b decreasing   c $x = 2$

2 $x < 0, x > \frac{1}{4}$

3 $(0, 0)$ and $\left(\frac{4}{3}, -\frac{32}{27}\right)$

4 1960 metres, 20 seconds

5 maximum $(0, 0)$, minimum $(1.33, -5.93)$

6 area 50 cm^2

7 a $v = 70$ kph   b $\frac{2800}{v^3}$ c £40

8 a $3x^2 - 18x + 24$

   b $(2, 4), (4, 0)$

   c $6x - 18$

   d Maximum $(2, 4)$

     Minimum $(4, 0)$

9 b $x = \frac{80}{4 + \pi}$ d 448 m^2

10 $\left(\frac{2}{3}, 0\right), (-4\ 0), (0, -8)$; minimum $\left(-\frac{5}{3}, -\frac{49}{3}\right)$

11 a $x = -4.41, x = 3.41$ b $(-0.5, -15.25)$

   c

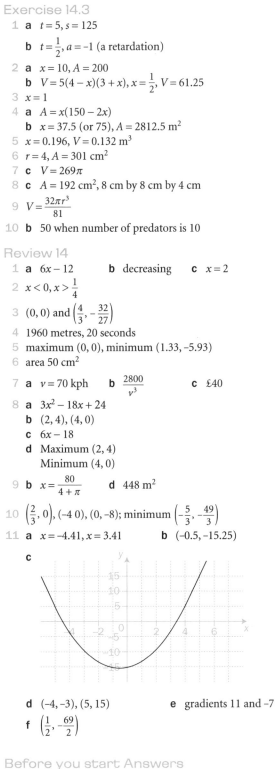

   d $(-4, -3), (5, 15)$ e gradients 11 and -7

   f $\left(\frac{1}{2}, -\frac{69}{2}\right)$

Before you start Answers

Chapter 15

1 a $y = -\frac{2}{9}$ b $y = \frac{43}{6}$ c $y = \frac{25}{4}$ d $y = \frac{1}{4}$

2 a 39 cm^2 b 16.5 cm^2 c 42.5 cm^2

   d $10\frac{3}{4}$ cm^2

3 a $\frac{x^2}{2} - 2x + c$ b $\frac{x^3}{3} - x^2 + c$

   c $\frac{x^3}{3} - 2x^2 + 4x + c$ d $\frac{x^4}{4} - \frac{4x^3}{3} + 2x^2 + c$

Exercise 15.1

1 a $\frac{1}{3}$ b 9   c 14   d 4

   e $12\frac{1}{3}$ f 65

2 a 4.67   b -3.67   c 8   d -12

   e 6.5   f 0.67   g 5.28   h 9.33

   i 1.25

3 $n = 3$

4 a $8\frac{2}{3}$ b $2 \int_0^1 (x^2 + 4)\, \mathrm{d}x$

Exercise 15.2

1 a 80   b 4   c 24   d 4.67

   e 82.14   f 6.67   g 18.67   h 4

2 a 1.33   b 4.5   c 1.33   d 0.17

   e 0.13   f 4.5   g 1.33   h 36

3 a 0.5   b 40.5   c 0.5   d 3.08

   e 11.83

4 a 9.83   b 2   c 4.92   d 8

   e 3.08   f 1.50   g 10.25   h 1.50

5 a 1.33   b 10.67

6 a 1.33   b 0.17   c 1.69   d 1.78

7 a 4.5 m^2 b 2250 m^3

8 b $\int_{-1}^{0}$ and $-\int_{0}^{3}$

Exercise 15.3

1 a 5.56   b 9.33   c 5.24   d 3.73

   e 13.2   f 43.1

2 a 6.73   b 9.21   c 51.9   d 5.35

   e 12700   f 2.93

3 a 17.5   b 17.4

4 a 9.33   b 8.83

5 a 18.1   b 18

6 19.18; underestimate (convex curve); 19.20

7 b 0.55   c overestimate (concave curve)

8 a underestimate   b overestimate

   c exact

9

No. of strips	Estimate	% error
1	1.5	3.97
2	1.46	1.20
3	1.45	0.51

Review 15

1 a 69.3   b 2   c 0.833   d 44

   e 4.67

2 a 12.43, 67.07, 155.56   b 4840 m

3 **a** $\frac{1}{2}, 2$ **b** $\frac{9}{8}$

4 **a** 6.75

5 **a** 1.6(00), 3.394, 3.2(00)   **b** 43.86 m²
   c 5260 m³

6 3.5

7 **a** $(-1, 0), (0, 0), (1, 0)$ **b** 0.5
   c 0.234, 0.468

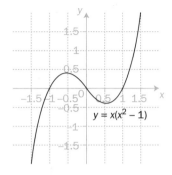

$y = x(x^2 - 1)$

8 0.34

$y = \sin x$

$y = 0.5$

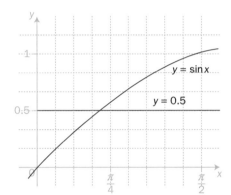

Revision 4

1 **a** 5, 10, 20 40   **b** 5115   **c** $n = 12$

2 **a** $1 + 24x + 264x^2 + 1760x^3$
   b $a = 1, b = 23, c = 240$

3 **a** $a = 2$ **b** $64 - 192x + 240x^2$

4 **a** $a = -\frac{7}{4}$ **b** maximum point at $(-1.75, 21.125)$

5 $h = \dfrac{2r}{\sqrt{3}}$

6 **a** maximum point at (3.75, 3.125)
   b

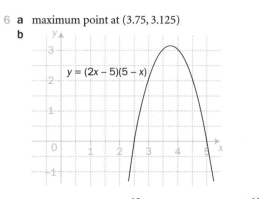

$y = (2x - 5)(5 - x)$

   c **i** increasing for $x < \frac{15}{4}$ **ii** decreasing for $x > \frac{15}{4}$

7 maximum at $(1, 4)$; minimum at $(3, 0)$

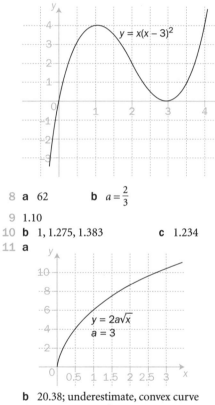

$y = x(x - 3)^2$

8 **a** 62   **b** $a = \frac{2}{3}$

9 1.10

10 **b** 1, 1.275, 1.383   **c** 1.234

11 **a**

$y = 2a\sqrt{x}$
$a = 3$

   b 20.38; underestimate, convex curve
   c 20.78   **d** 1.92%

C2

These formulae relate to the Core modules C1 and C2. You need to learn them; they are **not** given in the Edexcel formula booklet. You may need to use formulae from C1 in the C2 examination.

C1

Algebra and Functions

Difference of two squares		$A^2 - B^2 = (A - B)(A + B)$
Roots of a Quadratic Equation	$ax^2 + bx + c = 0$	$x = \dfrac{-b \pm \sqrt{b^2 - 4ac}}{2a}$
Disciminant	$b^2 - 4ac$	> 0 two real roots
		$= 0$ two equal roots
		< 0 no real (imaginary) roots

Transformation of functions f(x)

Translation	a units in the positive direction of the x-axis	$f(x - a)$
	a units in the positive direction of the y-axis	$f(x) + a$
Stretch	Parallel to the x-axis	$f(ax)$ scale factor $\dfrac{1}{a}$
	Parallel to the y-axis	$af(x)$ scale factor a

Coordinate Geometry

Equation of a straight line

General Equation	$ax + by + c = 0$
Gradient /y intersect form	$y = mx + c$
Gradient/one point on line form	$y - y_1 = m(x - x_1)$
Two points	$\dfrac{y - y_1}{y_2 - y_1} = \dfrac{x - x_1}{x_2 - x_1}$

General

Gradient (m)	$\dfrac{y_2 - y_1}{x_2 - x_1}$
Parallel gradients	$m_1 = m_2 \quad m_1 \neq 0, \quad m_2 \neq 0$
Perpendicular gradients	$m_1 m_2 = -1$
Coordinates of the mid point	$\left(\dfrac{x_1 + x_2}{2}, \dfrac{y_1 + y_2}{2} \right)$
Distance between two points	$\sqrt{(x_2 - x_1)^2 + (y_2 - y_1)^2}$

Differentiation

Function	derivative
x^n	nx^{n-1}
$f(x) + g(x)$	$f'(x) + g'(x)$

Integration

function   integral

x^n $\dfrac{1}{n+1}x^{n+1} + c,\ n \neq -1$

$\int \{f(x) + g(x)\}dx$ $\int f(x)dx + \int g(x)dx$

Algebra and Functions

Remainder Theorem

If $f(x)$ is divided by $(x-a)$ the remainder is $f(a)$

If $f(x)$ is divided by $(ax-b)$ the remainder is $f\left(\dfrac{b}{a}\right)$

Factor Theorem

If $(x-a)$ is a factor of $f(x)$ then $f(a) = 0$

Co-ordinate Geometry

Equation of a circle, centre the origin $x^2 + y^2 = r^2$

Equation of a circle, centre (a, b) $(x-a)^2 + (y-b)^2 = r^2$

Trigonometry

For the triangle ABC   Sine rule $\dfrac{a}{\sin A} = \dfrac{b}{\sin B} = \dfrac{c}{\sin C}$

Area of triangle $\dfrac{1}{2}ab\sin C$

$\tan\theta = \dfrac{\sin\theta}{\cos\theta}$

$\sin^2\theta + \cos^2\theta = 1$

π radians $= 180°$

Length of an arc $s = r\theta$ θ in radians   Area of a sector $A = \dfrac{1}{2}r^2\theta$ θ in radians

Exponential and Logarithms

$x = a^y \Leftrightarrow y = \log_a b$

$\log_a x + \log_a y = \log(xy)$ $\log_a x - \log_a y = \log\left(\dfrac{x}{y}\right)$ $k\log_a x + \log_a(x^k)$

$\log_a a = 1$

Differentiation

For a stationary point $f'(x) = 0$

Integration

Area under a curve $= \displaystyle\int_a^b y\,dx \quad (y \geqslant 0)$

Formulae given in examination

Mensuration

Surface area of sphere $= 4\pi r^2$

Area of curved surface of cone $= \pi r \times$ slant height

Arithmetic series

$$u_n = a + (n-1)d$$

$$S_n = \tfrac{1}{2}n(a+l) = \tfrac{1}{2}n[2a + (n-1)d]$$

Candidates sitting C2 may also require those formulae listed under C1.

Cosine rule

$$a^2 = b^2 + c^2 - 2bc \cos A$$

Binomial series

$$(a+b)^n = a^n + \binom{n}{1}a^{n-1}b + \binom{n}{2}a^{n-r}b^2 + \ldots + \binom{n}{r}a^{n-r}b^r + \ldots + b^n \qquad (n \in \mathbb{N})$$

$$\text{where } \binom{n}{r} = {}^nC_r = \frac{n!}{r!(n-r)!}$$

$$(1+x)^n = 1 + nx + \frac{n(n-1)}{1 \times 2}x^2 + \ldots + \frac{n(n-1)\ldots(n-r+1)}{1 \times 2 \times \ldots \times r}x^r + \ldots \quad (|x| < 1, n \in \mathbb{R})$$

Logarithms and exponentials

$$\log_a x = \frac{\log_b x}{\log_b a}$$

Geometric series

$$u_n = ar^{n-1}$$

$$S_n = \frac{a(1-r^n)}{1-r}$$

$$S_\infty = \frac{a}{1-r} \quad \text{for } |r| < 1$$

Numerical integration

The trapezium rule: $\displaystyle\int_a^b y\,dx \approx \tfrac{1}{2}h\{(y_0 + y_n) + 2(y_1 + y_2) + \ldots + y_{n-1})\}, \quad$ where $h = \dfrac{b-a}{n}$

CI/C2

Glossary

Absolute value The positive value of a function or number. The negative sign is ignored.
Notation: $|k|$ is the absolute value of k.
e.g. $|-2| = 2$ and $|2| = 2$

Acute angle An angle between $0°$ and $90°$.

Ambiguous case Given the size of one angle and the lengths of two sides a unique triangle can not be drawn.

Angle in a semi circle An angle formed by two lines drawn from either side of a diameter and joining on the circumference.

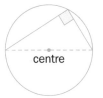

centre

Angle of depression The angle formed below the horizontal to an object.

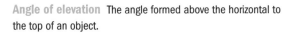

Angle of elevation The angle formed above the horizontal to the top of an object.

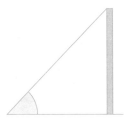

Angle subtended by a chord The angle formed between two lines drawn from each end of a chord intersecting on the circumference.

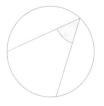

Arc The arc of a circle is part of the circumference of a circle.

Arithmetic Progression (AP) Another name for an arithmetic series.

Arithmetic series A series generated by the same constant, or common difference, being added onto the previous term.
e.g. $2, 5, 8, \ldots\ldots$

Associated acute angle The acute angle solution when solving a trigonometric equation in a given interval.
e.g. If $\sin x = \frac{1}{2}$ then $x = 30°$ is the associate acute angle and also a solution; but if $\sin x = -\frac{1}{2}$ then $x = 30°$ is the associate acute angle but not a solution.

Asymptote A straight line which a curve gets nearer and nearer to but never actually touches or crosses.

Base of a logarithm In $\log_a x$, a is the base of the logarithm.

Base A number associated with a power.
e.g. In 5^6, 5 is the base.

Bidmas A mnemonic to help you to remember the order of mathematical operations: Brackets Indices Division Multiplication Addition Subtraction.

Change the subject Rearrange a formula to express one of the unknowns in terms of the others.
e.g. To make b the subject of $a = b + 2$ you rewrite as $b = a - 2$

Chord A straight line joining two points on the circumference of a circle.

Coefficient The constant used as a multiplier of a term including a variable.
e.g. 3 is the coefficient of x in the term $3x$ and 7 the coefficient of x^2y in the term $7x^2y$.

Combinations Choices. The number of possible arrangements when order is not important.

CI/C2

Common difference (d) The constant difference between consecutive terms in an arithmetic progression.

Common factor A factor which is common to all terms under consideration.

Common ratio (r) The constant multiplier used to form each consecutive term in a geometric sequence.

Completing the square Rearranging a function into the form $(ax + b)^2 + c$ where c is a constant.

Constant A quantity with a fixed value.
e.g. 8, π

Constant of integration When a constant is differentiated it goes to zero. When integrating you need to assume that there was a constant in the original function and add this onto the result.

Convergent series The sum of the series tends towards a specific value as the number of terms in the series increases.

Cubic equation An equation in which the highest power of the variable is 3.
e.g. $x^3 - 2x + 1$

Cyclic quadrilateral A quadrilateral with its four vertices lying on the circumference of a circle.

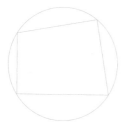

Decreasing function A function f(x) is decreasing for $a < x < b$ if the graph of $y =$ f(x) has a negative gradient, or f′(x) < 0, for all values of x in the interval $a < x < b$.

Definite integral Integration between given limits, a and b,
written $\int_a^b$ f(x)dx.

Denominator The 'bottom' of a fraction.
e.g. the 4 in $\frac{3}{4}$ or the ($x - 3$) in $\frac{x}{x-3}$

Derivative The result when a function has been differentiated. The derivative with respect to x is denoted by $\frac{dy}{dx}$ or f′(x).

Difference of two squares (DOTS) Expressions in the form of a square term minus another square term, $A^2 - B^2$. They can be factorised into $(A - B)(A + B)$.

Differentiate from first principles Use small increments, ∂x, to find the results of differentiation.

Differentiate To find the gradient of the tangent to a curve at a particular point.

Discriminant In a quadratic equation $ax^2 + bx + c = 0$ the discriminant is $b^2 - 4ac$

Displacement The distance of a moving body from the original point after time t. This is a vector quantity.

Divergent series The sum of a divergent series has no limit, it changes value as the number of terms increase.

Divisor In division the term which is divided into the other.
e.g. In 6 ÷ 5, 5 is the divisor, or in $\frac{x^2 + 6}{x - 3}$, ($x - 3$) is the divisor.

Ellipse A closed curve with an equation $\frac{x^2}{a^2} + \frac{y^2}{b^2} = 1$ where a and b are constants.

Equilateral triangle A triangle with all sides equal.

Estimate An informed guess, given certain information, to find an approximate solution, which is correct to a given place value.

Evaluate Review Work out the sum and give a single numeric answer.

Expand Multiply out the bracket(s).

Exponential function A function of the form a^x where a is a positive constant.

Expression A collection of algebraic terms.
e.g. $4x - 5$

Factor theorem If ($x - a$) is a factor of the function f(x) there is no remainder when f(x) is divided by ($x - a$) and hence f(a) = 0

Factorial of a number The product of all integers up to and including that number.
e.g. factorial 4, 4! = 4 × 3 × 2 × 1

Factorising/Factorise The reverse of 'expand'.

Family of curves Curves which are parallel to each other. Their equations differ by a constant only.

Finite series A series which has a finite number of terms.

First derivative A function differentiated once. If the function is differentiated with respect to x the first derivative is denoted $\frac{dy}{dx}$ or $f'(x)$.

First term of a series Denoted by a in an arithmetic and geometric progression.

Formula (Plural formulae) A formula is used to express the relationship between two or more variables.
e.g. $C = 2\pi r$ expresses the relationship between the circumference C of a circle and its radius r.

General form of a straight line $ax + by + c = 0$ where a, b, and c are constants.

General term of a series/sequence Denoted by U_n. By substituting values for n the general term becomes a specific term.

Geometric Sequence A sequence in which the next term is always formed by multiplying the previous term by the same constant (r). Sometimes called a Geometric Progression or GP.

Geometric Series The sum of the terms of a geometric sequence.

Gradient The slope of a straight line which includes its direction or sign. Positive gradient is and negative gradient is.

Highest Common Factor (HCF) The largest factor common to the terms being considered.

Hyperbola A curve with an equation $ax^2 - by^2 = c^2$ where a, b, c are constant.

Hypotenuse The side opposite the right-angle in a right-angled triangle.

Increasing function A function f(x) is increasing for $a < x < b$ if the graph of $y = f(x)$ has a positive gradient, or $f'(x) > 0$, for all values of x in the interval $a < x < b$.

Independent of x A term independent of x does not include x or a power of x.

Index The power to which a number or variable is raised.
e.g. 3 is the index in 2^3.

Indices The plural of index.

Infinite series A series with an infinite number of terms.

Integer A whole number. It can be positive, negative or zero.

Integrand The function to be integrated.

Integration The opposite of differentiation.

Intercept The y-intercept is the y-coordinate of the point where a graph cuts the y-axis.

Like terms Terms which include exactly the same letters or variables, including their powers.
e.g. $3x$ and $4x$ are like terms, as are $3x^2y$ and $4x^2y$. $3x$ and $3y$ are not like terms.

Limit of the sum The sum to infinity of a convergent series.

Line produced A line, say AB, extended beyond the point B.

Linear equations An equation which involves no powers greater than 1 of the variables.
e.g. $3x + 4 = 5$ is a linear equation. $3xy + 4 = 5$ and $3x^2 + 4 = 9$ are not.

Linear functions A function given in terms of a linear expression.

Logarithm ($\log_a x$) The logarithm of a number is the power to which the base, a, must be raised to give that number, x.

Magnitude Size.

Maximum point The point at which the gradient of the curve changes from positive to negative giving a $\cap$ shape.

Local maximum point The name given to a maximum point of a curve which has more than one of these points.

Minimum point The point at which the gradient of the curve changes from negative to positive giving a $\cup$ shape.

Local minimum point The name given to a minimum point of a curve which has more than one of these points.

Natural logarithm A logarithm to base e. This is covered in C3.

Natural numbers Whole positive numbers. Zero is not included.

Neighbouring point Another point on the same curve which is near to the point being considered.

Normal The normal to a point on a curve is the straight line perpendicular to the tangent at that point.

Numerator The 'top' of a fraction.
e.g. the 3 in $\frac{3}{4}$

Obtuse angle An angle whose size is between 90° and 180°.

Parabola A smooth $\cup$ or $\cap$ shaped curve. The corresponding function is quadratic.

Parallel Two lines which do not meet or intersect.

Perfect square A function which can be written exactly in the form $(ax + b)^2$.

Period The interval in which a periodic function repeats itself.
e.g. the period of $y = \sin x$ is π (180°).

Periodic function A function which repeats itself after a given interval.

Permutation An arrangement in which the order of items is important.

Perpendicular bisector A line which intersects another line at its mid point and is also perpendicular to that line.

Perpendicular lines Lines which are at right angles to each other.

Point of inflexion At this point the gradient $[f'(x)]$ is zero and the gradient of the curve has the same sign on both sides of the point.

Polynomial A function which includes positive powers on a variable and a constant.
e.g. $a_0 + a_1x + a_2x^2 + \ldots\ldots + a_nx^n$

Power The same as index.

Product The result of a multiplication.

Quadrant of a circle A quarter of a circle. First, second, third and fourth quadrants of the coordinate axes are used in trigomometry.

Quadratic Equation An equation in which the highest power of the variable is 2. A quadratic in the variable x has the general form $ax^2 + bx + c = 0$ where a, b, and c are constant and $a \neq 0$.
e.g. $x^2 + x + 1$

Quadratic formula The formula used to solve a quadratic equation if the equation does not factorise easily.
For the equation $ax^2 + bx + c = 0$, the formula is
$$x = \frac{-b \pm \sqrt{b^2 - 4ac}}{2a}$$

Quadratic function A function given in terms of a quadratic expression.

Quadratic Inequality A quadratic expression given in term of an inequality.

Quotient The answer when an expression is divided by another.

Radians A unit of angle measurement. π radians = 180°

Rate of change $\frac{dy}{dx}$ is the rate of change of y with respect to x.

Rationalising the denominator Removing a surd (defined later) from the denominator of a fraction to give an integral denominator. You do this by multiplying both top and bottom of the fraction by the same quantity.

Reciprocal curve A reciprocal curve has a function in the form
$$y = \frac{1}{(x - a)}$$

Recurrence formula A rule, or formula, which generates the next term in a sequence.

Reflex angle An angle whose size is between 180° and 360°.

Remainder theorem When $f(x)$ is divided by $(x - a)$ the remainder is given by $f(a)$.

When $f(x)$ is divided by $(ax - b)$ the remainder is given by $f\left(\frac{b}{a}\right)$.

Roots The roots of an equation $f(x) = 0$ are the values of x which satisfy the equation. In other words when a root is substituted for x in $f(x)$ the answer is zero.

Satisfies A value of x satisfies an equation if it is a solution of the equation.

Second derivative The result when a function has been differentiated twice.

Second derivative The result when a function $f(x)$ has been differentiated twice. If the function is differentiated with respect to x the

Second order derivative second derivative is denoted f"(x) or $\frac{d^2y}{dx^2}$.

Sector The area of a portion of a circle bounded by two radii. There is a major and a minor sector.

Segment of a circle The area of a circle formed when a circle is divided into two parts by a chord. There is a major and a minor segment.

Sequence A set of terms which are derived using a general rule.

Series The sum of the terms in a sequence.

Simultaneous equations Several equations in several variables which you can solve to give a common solution.

Sketch A freehand drawing of a curve showing the shape of the curve and the important features of that curve such as the points where the curve cuts the axes.

Small increments (method of) Increasing the x coordinates by very small amounts and considering the points generated on a particular curve.

Specific term of a series The general term when evaluated for a specific value, r, denoted U_r. This is the term used when expressing the series in sigma notation $\sum_{r=a}^{r=b} u_r$

Stationary point At this point the gradient of the function is zero. It can be a maximum or minimum point or a point of inflexion.

Stretch of a function/graph A transformation where shape and position are changed.

Stretch parallel to the x axis All points on the curve are stretched with the same scale factor in the x direction. Points on the y-axis remain in the same position.

Stretch parallel to the y axis All points on the curve are stretched with the same scale factor in the y direction. Points on the x-axis remain in the same position.

Substitution
Formulae Replace a variable in a formula by a particular value.

Simultaneous equations You use this method when solving simultaneous equations.

Sum to infinity of a series The sum of a convergent series.

Supplementary angles Angles whose sum is 180°.

Surd The positive root of a number written with a root sign. A surd is an exact value.
e.g. $\sqrt{7}$

Tangent A line which touches a curve and is parallel to the curve at this point of contact.

Translation A transformation which moves an object or curve without changing its size or shape.

Trapezium A quadrilateral with one pair or opposite sides parallel.

Trial and improvement method A method involving trying different values in order to improve your solution.

Trigonometric identity A relationship between trigonometric functions which is true for **all** values of the angle.

Turning point The point at which the gradient of a curve changes direction. It can be a maximum or minimum point.

Variable A letter which can take various numerical values. i.e. Not a constant.

C1/C2

CI/C2

C1/C2